No. 2950
$21.95

THE CET

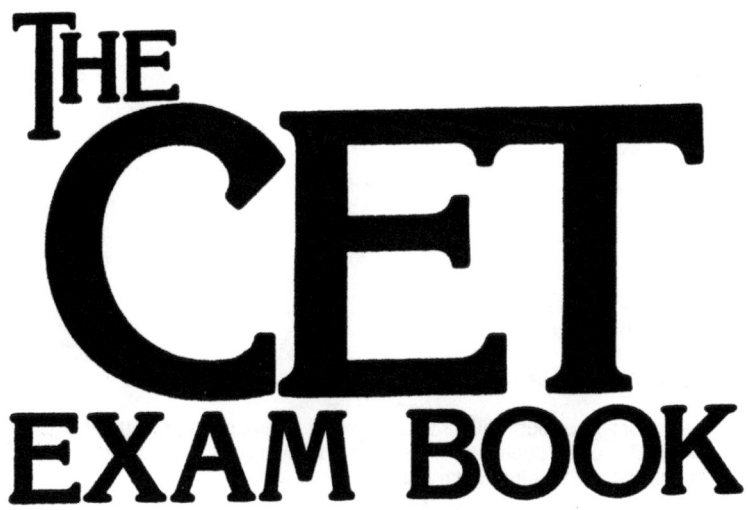

EXAM BOOK

2nd Edition

BY RON CROW & DICK GLASS

The Professional Electronics Technicians Association

 TAB BOOKS Inc.

Blue Ridge Summit, PA

This book is written for electronics technicians in training. It was requested by instructors in electronics curriculums. It is dedicated to the volunteer Certification Administrators who help make it all work.

SECOND EDITION
THIRD PRINTING

Printed in the United States of America

Library of Congress Cataloging in Publication Data

Crow, Ron
      The CET exam book.
      Glass's name appears first on the earlier edition.

      Includes index.
      1. Electronics—Examinations, questions, etc.
2. Electronic technicians—Certification—United States.
I. Glass, Dick. II. Title.
TK7863.C76 1987   621.381′076   87-10193
ISBN 0-8306-1950-X
ISBN 0-8306-2950-5 (pbk.)

TAB BOOKS Inc. offers software for sale. For information and a catalog, please contact TAB Software Department, Blue Ridge Summit, PA 17294-0850.

Questions regarding the content of this book should be addressed to:

      Reader Inquiry Branch
      TAB BOOKS Inc.
      Blue Ridge Summit, PA 17294-0214

Contents

Introduction

In this revised edition of *The CET Exam Book*, the authors have added information on some electronics topics that were not covered in the original work, primarily because the thrust of industry was not strong in those directions. For example, some basics of satellite communications are contained in this revision. Also, additional information is included on test equipment for computer trouble-shooting as that industry has seen tremendous growth in recent years.

THE CET EXAM

While the program of certification of electronics technicians is never a static program and is constantly changing as the industry changes, it is still important to know what the program is at the present time in order that you might know where you fit in.

There are four levels of certification at the present time in the ETAI program:

■ Associate
■ Journeyman
■ Senior
■ Master

The Associate level consists of questions on basic electronic principles that pertain to all areas of electronics. This level is intended for student or apprentice technicians with less than four years of experience or schooling in electronics. A passing grade is 75 percent correct. The Associate certificate expires four years after instatement.

The Journeyman level is for technicians and others with four or more years of experience or schooling in electronics. This test consists of some basic electronics questions and some questions in a specific area of electronics. The choices for Journeyman level are:

- Consumer Electronics
- Commercial Electronics
- Communications Electronics
- Industrial Electronics
- Computer Electronics
- Biomedical Electronics

Three of the above options are subdivided into specialty areas, any one of which can be chosen for the Journeyman option. The specialties, as subdivided, are:

- Consumer Electronics:
  —Radio and TV
  —Audio-Hi Fi
  —TVRO (satellite)
- Commercial Electronics:
  —MATV
  —VCR
- Communications Electronics:
  —Two-Way
  —Avionics

An Associate CET (a person who holds a valid current certificate) may elect to skip the basic questions in the Journeyman's test but all others take the complete exam. Previously paid Associate level test fees are also applied toward the Journeyman option test fees at the time of exam for qualified CETs. Likewise, a passing score of 75 percent is required on the Journeyman exam.

The Senior level is the same exam as taken for the Journeyman exam, but the technician or testee must have eight years experience or schooling in electronics and they must pass the exam in the option of their choice with an 85 percent correct response, or better. For an extra fee, a brass certificate is presented with the successful completion of this examination.

The Master level certification exam may be written by a technician, electronics instructor, etc., with eight or more years experience or schooling. It requires the taking and passing of all options of the CET exams, or the taking of an equivalent exam. A brass certificate is awarded, without extra fee, upon the successful completion of this exam, which requires 75 percent correct response for a passing score.

The authors would like to encourage you to use this book as a guide in your study for undertaking the certification examination. We further would like to extend our personal encouragement to you. Good luck.

C E T
ASSOCIATE
1

What the Associate
CET Must Know

The Associate Level technician typically is a graduate of a vocational electronics course in a commercial or public school. Upon completion of the technical course a technician should have the basic knowledge needed to enter any of the present fields of electronics technology. This doesn't mean an Associate CET is ready to work at troubleshooting costly electronics products or work on worldwide communications equipment. It does mean that he or she has the basic training needed to understand electronic circuitry. With the knowledge of basic circuitry the technician is then able to apply that understanding to his work in specialized fields. Often the specialized circuitry in one field may appear to be unrelated to that in another. An example might be a technician working on communications radio equipment that involves tuning coils and capacitors, antennas, audio circuitry, squelch and automatic gain controls, etc. Another technician may find himself working on computers such as process-control manufacturers produce, numerical-control machine tool equipment, or video game units. The latter technician finds himself using different test equipment such as logic probes, pulsers, and built-in diagnostic programs. He may never run into the need for a plastic tuning tool or rf signal generator. The two jobs seem nearly unrelated.

In truth all electronics jobs are related. The well trained technician can easily change from one electronics position to another—if they have a sound understanding of basic electronics.

If you are weak in basics, you will not only be unable to pass the examinations produced by the Electronics Technicians Association International (ETAI) but may find that you have difficulty understanding electronic products and how the circuitry is supposed to operate. You may be able to work in one field, if you learn the routines for that particular product, but other fields may be impossible to grasp.

So the "complete" electronics technician should realize that it is as important to have a sound basics understanding and to be able to utilize the tools and equipment all technicians must use to complete their work as it is to be knowledgeable about an existing product such as a TV set or a computer. The *Associate Level Exam* will test for an understanding of these basics, rather than testing for your knowledge of any of the products that are presently being manufactured, sold, and serviced by today's technicians. The *Journeyman Certification Exams* will test for understanding of individual fields of electronics, such as Industrial, Consumer Products, Communications, and so forth. The certificate is in Fig. 1-1.

ASSOCIATE LEVEL TOPICS

Each of the chapters of this book deals with important topics needed by all technicians. Because electronics is a subject that is

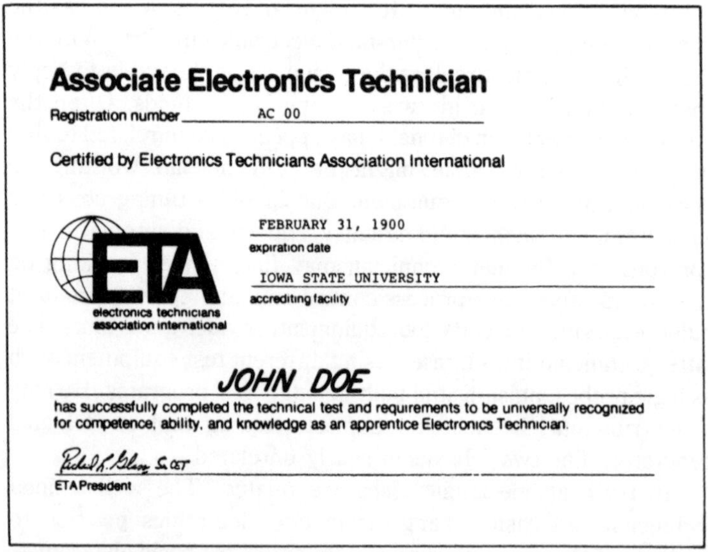

Associate Electronics Technician

Registration number _____ AC 00 _____

Certified by Electronics Technicians Association International

FEBRUARY 31, 1900
expiration date

IOWA STATE UNIVERSITY
accrediting facility

electronics technicians
association international

JOHN DOE
_____

has successfully completed the technical test and requirements to be universally recognized for competence, ability, and knowledge as an apprentice Electronics Technician.

ETA President

Fig. 1-1. Associate CET certificate.

difficult to comprehend, the components, circuitry, and theory of operation are broken down into their simplest forms. Once you know how electric current affects resistors, capacitors, and inductors you start getting a 'feel' for its nature. In addition to the basic volts, amps, and ohms you will work with, you need to understand how dc and ac acts in series and parallel circuits. You have to know how transistors and diodes work and how they are put together in IC chips. All technicians must be able to logically break a product down into sections in order to localize a trouble. Block diagrams help you do this. After localizing the trouble to a block or smaller circuit you may be able to solve the immediate problem by switching an entire circuit board. Much of today's complex equipment servicing is made easier to service in this manner.

But eventually a technician must be able to troubleshoot to the 'component level'. And that takes an understanding of how each component reacts; how you turn it on, or off; and how you can prove which part is bad. Even with the fundamentals, a technician has to know how to work safely, for his own good, and that of his co-workers. Also he must be familiar with component nomenclature. It does no good to locate a bad part and then find you can't identify it in order to obtain a replacement. So with these basic tools an Associate technician is ready to enter any of the fascinating fields of electronics and to perform a valuable service in a safe manner.

MATHEMATICS

Because electronics is an 'inhuman' science and therefore difficult to gain a thorough understanding of, the learning process involves many comparisons with things we do understand. An example might be comparing electric voltage with that of water 'pressure' in a garden hose. Or we try to understand oscillators by comparing them with a 'swing' such as we played on in grade school. Much of your understanding of electronics must come through the use of mathematics. Many people dislike math and would rather work with their hands. So many of the concepts of electronics can only be understood by using arithmetic, algebraic formulas, ratios, and just plain addition, subtraction, division, and multiplication. A technician needs to accept it and to let math become his 'friend'. That's the bad news.

The good news is that much of the match is used in learning electronics but often thereafter may be encountered only rarely. Most electronics work is a hands-on job. But by working problems out mathematically the math will be teaching you the relationships you must know to get the feel of electronics circuitry. You will find math used on nearly every page of the exam. Included here is a math quiz that contains problems similar to those on the exam.

BASIC MATH QUIZ

Q1. The most basic electronics formula is: $I = E/R$. If $E = 40$ V and $R = 10$ ohms, what is I?

    a. 4 amps
    b. 4 milliamps
    c. 40 amps

Q2. $I = 0.01$ amps, $R = 1000$ ohms, what is the value of E?

    a. 10 V
    b. 0.00001 V
    c. 100 V

Q3. One of the power formulas is: $P = EI$. If $R = 20$ and $I = 0.001$ amps, what is the value of P?

    a. 0.0002 watts
    b. 0.002 watts
    c. 0.00002 watts

Q4. The formula for inductive reactance is: $X_L = 2\pi fL$. If the frequency (f) goes up what happens to the inductive reactance?

    a. it goes up
    b. it goes down
    c. it does not change

Q5. $X_c = \dfrac{1}{2\pi fC}$, $C = .01$ farad, $f = 1000$ Hz. What is X_c?

    a. 159.2 ohms
    b. 0.01592 ohms
    c. 15923 ohms

Q6. If the formula for wavelength is $\lambda = 984,000$ ft/f(kHz) then what is the wavelength of a 1500 kHz radio wave?

a. 0.0656 ft
b. 6560 ft
c. 656 ft

Q7. Parallel impedance totals are calculated using the formula

$$Z = \frac{Z_1 Z_2}{Z_1} + Z_2.$$ If Z_1 = 684 and Z_2 = 1000 ohms

what is the total impedance?

a. 406 ohms
b. 4060 ohms
c. 40.6 ohms

Q8. A capacitor charged to 100 V discharges in 14 milliseconds to 37 V through a 4700-ohm resistor. Since T = RC the capacitance is:

a. 336 farads
b. 2.98 μF
c. 5000 μF

Q9. The formula for resonance is: $f_o = \dfrac{1}{2\pi\sqrt{LC}}$ L = 0.01 henrys and C = 1.0 μF. What is f_o?

a. 15.924 MHz
b. 1590 Hz
c. 31 MHz

Q10. A meter movement to be used for 5 V full-scale deflection requires 50 μA. The internal resistance of the movement is 5 kΩ. What must be used to measure the 5 V?

a. a 95 kΩ resistance in parallel
b. a 105 kΩ resistance in parallel
c. a 95 kΩ resistance in series
d. a 105 kΩ resistance in series

If you did well on this exam you should find the math in the remainder of the book easy. If not, then you should go back and work on those questions that bothered you until that type of math starts to come easy for you. If you have trouble transposing a formula, work out some similar formula problems until you find them easy and until you know that they are correct. Part of the problem with electronics math is that you are dealing in extremely small amounts such as 0.01 μF, and in extremely large amounts such as 2.8 gigahertz. Not only do you have need to know how to work the math equations, but you need to be able to convert the maxi and mini quantities to figures that are easier to handle in your mind. In addition you need to know several electronics formulas—starting with Ohm's law. If you make up your mind to master the math so that it doesn't bother you on the exam, then your problem will only be to recall the applicable formula or relationship of the electronic components.

The mathematical relationships in electronics are seemingly endless. To try to remember them all is impossible. The trick is to sort out those that are commonly used and not to cloud your mind with those that should be obtained from a reference book if, and when, needed. In this book we will be using those that are commonly needed. Be sure you firmly implant them in your mind prior to actually sitting for the exam.

QUIZ REVIEW

As in each chapter in this book, we will review each quiz question so that you understand them. However, be sure that you take the quiz and answer each question prior to reading the review. To merely view the quiz and look at the review will gain you little. Take the quiz and review each explanation, even if you obtained the correct answer.

In *Question 1*, the basic formula is simple. All you need do is divide E (40) by R (10) to get the answer 4. And unlike many electronics formulas this one is straightforward: I is in amps, E in volts, and R in ohms.

Question 2 is a little tougher. Now we have to deal with decimals rather than integer numbers. In addition we have to figure out how to transpose the equation, $0.01 = E/1000$. One way is to cross-multiply: $\frac{I}{I} = E/R'$; E times 1 = E; R times I = RI; E = IR or E = 0.01 times 1000 or 10 V. Of course it's a lot easier to simply remember the Ohm's law formula that E = IR.

The concepts in *Question 3* seem simple enough. The only problem is that the P = EI power formula has no R in it. Instead it has an E. The easy way is to simply remember that P also = I^2R. Or, you could change the P = EI formula to P = IR times I (remember that E equals IR as in *Q2*) or, P = I^2R. I^2 is I times I, or 0.001 × 0.001 (0.001 × 0.001 is 0.000001). Therefore, 0.000001 times R (20) then equals 0.00002 or answer *c*. Maybe you like to work math problems using powers of 10. In that case you multiply (0.001) or 1 × 10^{-3} by (0.001) or 1 × 10^{-3} which gives you 1 × 10^{-6} times 2 times 10^{+1} = 2 × 10^{-5}, or 0.00002.

Does *Question 4* seem too simple? Some technicians have trouble with this relationship. Anything on the right side of the formula that increases has to increase the value of X_L. After all, if X_L is truly *equal* to the right side of the formula, then if the right side gets bigger, the left side has to also. What confuses some of us is that we see this formula and confuse it with its sister formula, the formula for capacitive reactance (X_C = $1/2\pi fC$). Or, we first encounter pi (π) and our minds quit! The quantity π is simply a quantity: 3.14, and 2 pi is 6.28. The formula is easy and X_L goes up if f (frequency) goes up. The remaining confusing thing about this simple formula is that you may get it tangled up with *inductance*, or L. Inductive *reactance* is not inductance. Keep the two separated in your mind and you will have little trouble with this problem.

Question 5 is opposite of the previous question and formula, capacitive reactance gets smaller if f or C get larger. (1/10 is smaller than 1/2, isn't it?). The problem here is to find $2\pi fC$ so we can get rid of that awful fraction by dividing $2\pi fC$ into 1. To do so we can use our calculator (they are allowed) and multiply 6.28 (that's 2 pi) times 0.01 times 1000. The answer is 62.80. Divide 1 by 62.80 and the answer is 0.01592 ohms for X_C. Notice there is no way you could merely guess at the correct answer.

While the big numbers in *Question 6* concerning wavelength are difficult, the real problem is that few of us remember the formula for wavelength. And even if you know the formula you can't easily know that our forefathers decided that f, or frequency, should be in kilohertz! So, you can easily get the wrong answer even if your math is right. In addition, around the world a more common formula for wavelength is 300,000/f (kHz) which gives you the same answer, but in meters rather than feet. There is no easy answer. Just put this formula into a separate brain cell and never forget it.

The formula in *Question 7* can be used to figure impedances or resistances in parallel. If you have more than 2 parallel paths you can figure two of them, then use that answer to work out the next, or third leg, in combination with 1 and 2, and so forth.

The concepts needed in *Question 8* concern the time constant formula, or RC time. You can't figure it out, it must be memorized. One RC time is R times C, or in this case we don't know, because the C is what the question asks for. So with more than one problem here we have the likelihood that we must guess at the answer, or know all about RC time. First we need the formula; T, (time in *seconds*) = RC (R is in ohms and capacitance in *farads*.) That is: T = RC.

The second thing we need to know about RC time is that the capacitor will charge to 63 percent of its full value (or discharge to 37 percent *from* its full value) in just 1 RC time (or time constant). It takes 5 RC times for it to charge to nearly 100 percent (actually 99.3 percent). Since *Q 8* tells us it takes 14 milliseconds to discharge from 100 V to 37 V, we know then that one RC time is 14 milliseconds. If you have all the above now firmly implanted in your memory cells, then, all you have to do is work the math to get the answer to this question: T = RC; 0.014 = 4700 × C; 0.014 = 4700 C; C = 0.014 ÷ 4700; C = 0.000002978, or 2.98μF.

The only thing tough about *Question 9*, since the formulas is given is that you end up with 0.00000001 under the radical!. The rest is merely math.

The first thing to realize in *Question 10* is that you will need a resistance in series with the meter movement. If you try a parallel resistance you will see that applying the 5 volts will result in 5 V / 5 kΩ (meter resistance) amps, or 1 mA through the 50 μA meter movement. That would no doubt cause damage to the meter coil. With a series circuit required then, the current through the circuit at the applied 5 V must be the 50 μA needed for full scale deflection. The total resistance needed then, is 5 V / 50 μA, or 100 kΩ. This leads to the series resistance being 100 kΩ − 5 kΩ or 95 kΩ. Another way to solve this problem is to use Ohm's law to find that the meter movement will need 0.25 V across its 5 kΩ resistance to provide 50 μA of current at full scale, 0.25 V is 1/20th of 5 V, so 1/20th, or 5 percent of the total resistance must be the meter movement. If that is true, then 95 percent is the series resistance that is needed—in this case 95 kΩ.

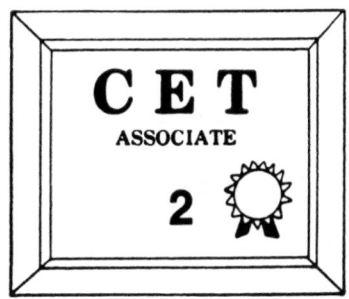

Mathematics

As stated in Chapter 1, mathematics is fundamental to a thorough understanding of electronics. In this chapter some more mathematical concepts are explored. Some of these equations are more complex than those expected on the Associate Exam. If you feel comfortable with these you should have little problem with the mathematics on the Associate Certification Exam.

QUIZ

Q1. When the frequency is increased in an inductive circuit the inductive reactance:

    a. increases   c. remains the same
    b. decreases

Q2. In the circuit shown in Fig. 2-1, R equals:

    a. 20 kΩ   c. 5 Ω
    b. 5 kΩ   d. 20 MΩ

Q3. In the circuit shown in Fig. 2-2, V_{R2} (voltage across R_2) equals:

    a. 10 V   c. 5 V
    b. 6.67 V   d. 4 V

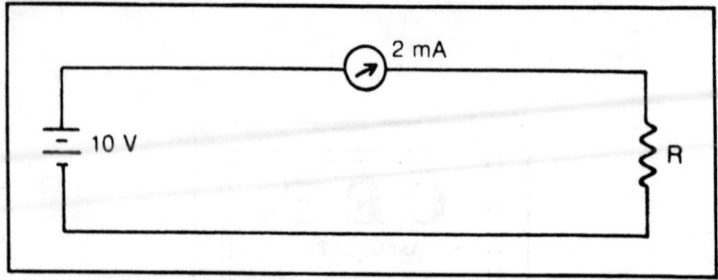

Fig. 2-1. Circuit for Ohm's law problem in Q2.

Q4. $C = \dfrac{KA}{d}$. As this formula explains, the capacitance of a parallel plate capacitor is proportional to the area of the facing plate and the dielectric coefficient K, and inversely proportional to the distance, d, between plates. Solving this formula for d gives d equal to:

a. C/KA

c. CKA

b. CK/A

d. none of these

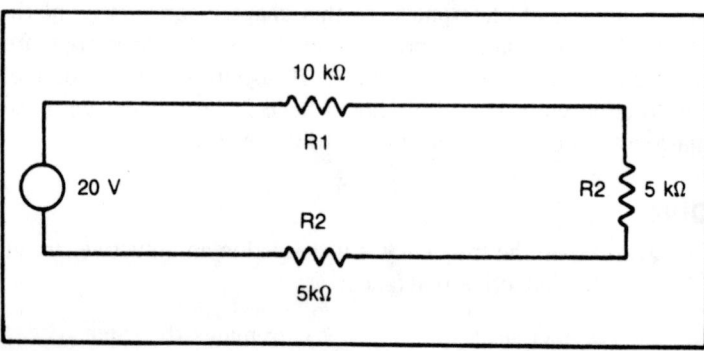

Fig. 2-2. Series resistor circuit for Q3.

Q5. In a certain transmission line the wave front travels at a velocity, v, 65 percent of the speed of light. If the speed of light is 186×10^3 miles/second and a 50 MHz signal is sent down the line, one wavelength, λ will be:

$$\lambda = \% \left[5280 \left(\frac{V}{f} \right) \right]$$

a. $\dfrac{50 \times 10^6}{(186 \times 10^3)\,(.65)\,5280}$ feet

b. $\dfrac{(186 \times 10^3)\,(.65)\,5280}{50 \times 10^6}$ feet

c. $\dfrac{50\,(5280)}{(186 \times 10^3)\,300}$ feet

d. none of these

Q6. If in the power formula $P = EI \cos \theta$ for ac circuits, θ can vary from 0 to 90°, $\cos \theta$ varies from:

a. 1 to ∞   c. 0 to ∞
b. 1 to 0   d. none of these

Q7. If the phase angle in *Question 6* in 90° this means that the circuit would have no power dissipation. In other words it would be purely:

a. reactive
b. resistive

Q8. The number 1101 in binary is equivalent to a decimal number of:

a. 13   c. 25
b. 11   d. none of these

Q9. Add the binary numbers: 101101 + 110100:

a. 1100001   c. 111001
b. 1011001   d. none of these

Q10. In counting numbers in a system with a base (or radix) of 8, the next three numbers after 7 will be:

a. 8, 9, 10   c. 10, 11, 12
b. 8, 10, 11   d. none of these

Q11. The binary number 110101 is equivalent to an octal number of:

a. 35   c. 53
b. 65   d. none of these

11

Q.12 The hexadecimal number 2E is equivalent to the decimal number of:

a. 46
b. 37

c. 16
d. none of these

Q13. The hexadecimal number C4 is equivalent to a binary number of:

a. 11110100
b. 10100010

c. 01110111
d. none of these

Q14. The Boolean statement, A AND B equals Q may be written:

a. AB = Q
b. A • B = Q

c. (A) (B) = Q
d. all of the above

Q15. The Boolean statement A • $\overline{A}$ is the same as:

a. 1
b. 0

c. A
d. $\overline{A}$

Q16. Reduce the following Boolean expressions to a simpler form:

a. ABC + AB$\overline{C}$ = _____
b. X(X + Y)   = _____
c. (G + H) (G + K)   = _____
d. $\overline{A}$C + $\overline{A}$C + BC   = _____
e. $\overline{A}$B + $\overline{A}\overline{B}$ + A   = _____
f. $\overline{A}\overline{B}$ (A + B)   = _____

Q.17. If the three inputs to an OR gate are "1", "0", "0" respectively the output will be:

a. 1 V
b. 0 V

c. "1"
d. "0"

Q18. $\overline{A • B}$ describes:

a. a NOR gate
b. a flip-flop

c. an AND gate
d. a NAND gate

Q19. An exclusive OR may be represented as $A \oplus B = F$, or it may be written as:

a. $A\overline{B} + \overline{A}B = F$ c. $(A + \overline{B})(\overline{A} + B) = F$
b. $AB + \overline{A}\overline{B} = F$ d. none of these

FORMULAS

Several of the quiz questions deal with the manipulation of formulas. *Question 1* requires that the formula for inductive reactance be recalled and that the relationships be understood in an algebraic equation. In this case $X_L = 2\pi fL$ is the formula you should remember. Increasing f will increase the product of $2\pi fL$, hence X_L will increase. The companion formula for X_C is $X_C = 1/2\pi f_C$. Here if frequency is increased the product $2\pi fc$ again increases; but, since the product is in the denominator the quotient $1/2\pi fC$ decreases.

Question 2 requires some manipulation of Ohm's law. Since we are looking for R, the formula $E = IR$ can be changed to $R = E/I$ by proper algebraic procedures. Substituting $E = 10$ V and $I = 2$ mA give

$$R = \frac{10 \text{ V}}{2 \text{ mA}} = \frac{10}{2 \times 10^{-3}} = 5 \times 10^3 = 5 \text{ k}\Omega$$

Question 3 is more manipulation of Ohm's law. To find the voltage across R2 first find the series current flow. $I = E/R_T$ where R_T is the total series resistance $R_1 + R_2 + R_3$

$$I = \frac{20}{10 \text{ k} + 5 \text{ k} + 5 \text{ k}}$$

$$= \frac{20}{20 \times 10^3}$$

$$= 1 \text{ mA}$$

The voltage drop $V_{R2} = I R_2$
$= (1 \text{ mA})(5 \text{ k})$
$= 5 \text{ V}$

You can expect any kind of question dealing with the manipulation of formulas. You may be expected to recall from memory the more important formulas such as Ohm's law and the reactance formulas.

Question 4 contains a formula and you are expected to manipulate the algebraic terms and solve for one term (d). Remember that an equation remains equal if we do the same thing to both sides of the equation:

$$C = K\frac{A}{d}$$

$$(d)\ C = K\frac{A}{d}\ (d) \quad \text{multiply both sides by d}$$

$$\frac{dC}{(C)} = \frac{KA}{(C)} \quad \text{divide both sides by C}$$

$$d = KA/C \quad \text{answer d, ''none of these,'' is therefore correct}$$

In *Question 5* a formula is again given but some conversions and substitutions are necessary. The formula to determine wavelength in a cable is $\lambda = v/f$ where v is the velocity of propagation and f is the frequency. But (v = .65c where c is the speed of light ($\approx$ 186,000 miles/sec.)

$$\text{hence } \lambda = \frac{0.65\ (186,000)}{50 \times 10^6}\ \text{miles}$$

but to convert to feet, 1 mile = 5280 feet.

$$\lambda = \frac{0.65\ (186,000)}{50 \times 10^6} \times 5280\ \text{feet}$$

$$\text{therefore } \lambda = \frac{186 \times 10^3\ (0.65)\ 5280}{50 \times 10^6}\ \text{feet}$$

Question 6 requires knowledge of the relationships in a right triangle. These are defined as shown in Fig. 2-3.

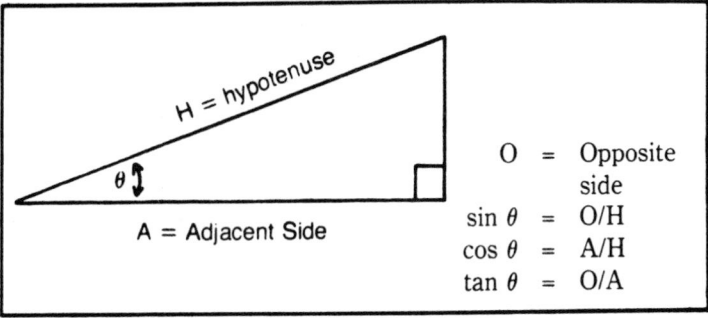

Fig. 2-3. Trigonometric functions of a right triangle.

θ varies from $0°$ to $90°$ as stated in *Question 6.* At $0°$ the opposite side is 0 and $A = H$ hence:

$$\cos\theta = \frac{A}{H} = \frac{A}{A}$$

$$= 1$$

At $90°$ the adjacent side equals 0 and $O = H$ hence:

$$\cos\theta = \frac{0}{1}$$

therefore $\cos\theta$ varies from 1 to 0.

Some meanings of the power formula $P = EI\cos\theta$, for the relationships in the formula, are covered in *Question 7.* Since the $\cos\theta$ at $90°$ is equal to zero the power dissipated in the circuit must be zero since $EI(0) = 0$. The only way for this to occur is to have no resistance in the circuit. Hence the circuit is entirely reactive. To say it another way if the circuit has any resistances the phase angle θ cannot be $90°$. Also note that if the circuit is resistive $\theta = 0$, $\cos\theta = 1$ and the formula reduces to the familiar $P = EI$.

BINARY MATHEMATICS

Binary mathematics is really no different than mathematics in our more commonly used decimal system. All the rules are the same. The problem is that most of us forgot the rules a long time ago. We are so used to numbers with place values that we give little thought to the structure of our decimal system. In binary math only two digits are available for counting. The symbols for these two digits were chosen as 0 and 1, the same symbols used for two of the digits used in the decimal system. 0 is used to designate the nothing situation and 1 to designate a single unit.

In the decimal system we have ten digits: 0, 1, 2, 3, 4, 5, 6, 7, 8, 9. These are symbols used to designate these digits and their meanings are familiar to us all. If we desire a quantity of items designated as 5 we all know how many items to expect. If we desire to designate a quantity of items more than 9 then we use a system of numbering that gives value to the position of the digits with respect to each other. The digits arranged as "21" means that we have 1 "unit" plus 2 "tens." The number 5941 means we have 1 "unit," 4 "tens", 9 "hundreds", and 5 "thousands." We even give the numbers names to help us keep track. This last number, for example is named five thousand nine hundred forty one. Our naming system takes into account the place value. In the binary system all the same rules apply. Table 2-1 shows a comparison of a few numbers in decimal and binary.

It will be noticed that in binary "place" also has value just as it does in a decimal system. The place value is different however. In decimal the place values are units, tens, hundreds, thousands, and so forth. Each place named, to indicate the value that a digit in that place is multiplied by to obtain the total place value. For example in 3406 the fourth place indicates that there are 3 times 1000 counts in this number. The third place indicates there are 4 times 100 counts in this number. No tens (0×10) are indicated by the second place and 6 units (6×1). In binary the place names are units, twos, fours, eights, sixteens, and so forth with each place value double the last.

Question 8 concerns changing a binary number to a decimal number. The number given is 1101 in binary. In this number there

	Binary Number	Decimal Number Equivalent
	0	0
Table 2-1. Counting with Only Two Symbols, 0 and 1.	1	1
	10	2
	11	3
	100	4
	101	5
	110	6
	111	7
	1000	8
	1001	9

is one unit, no twos, one four, and one eight. $8 + 4 + 1 = 13$. If this is unclear, practice counting in binary. Other examples using base 10 and base 2: $1_{(10)} = 1_{(2)}$, $2_{(10)} = 10_{(2)}$, $3_{(10)} = 11_{(2)}$, $4_{(10)} = 100_{(2)}$, $5_{(10)} = 101_{(2)}$, etc.

Decimal #	Binary #
1	1
2	10
3	11
4	100
.	.
.	.
.	.
16	10000
17	10001
18	10010
.	.
.	.

Question 9 is on adding two binary numbers. In addition the following must be true $0 + 0 = 0$, $1 + 0 = 1$, and $1 + 1 = 10$ (one, zero) and $1 + 1 + 1 = 11$ (one, one). As in decimal, addition of larger numbers can be accomplished by "lining up" the places and successively applying the addition rules from right to left. Thus:

$$
\begin{array}{r}
1111 \longleftarrow \text{Carries} \\
101101 \\
+ \quad 110100 \\
\hline
1100001 \quad \text{Answer } (a) \text{ in Question 9}
\end{array}
$$

When writing about more than one system of numbering it is often convenient to designate which system we are using. This is done normally by designating the base or radix of the system. The base is the amount of symbols used in a particular system. The decimal system has a base of 10 (ten) since there are ten symbols. The binary system has two symbols therefore the base or radix is 2 (two). To designate the base when systems are mixed is done as follows:

$$101_{(2)} = 5_{(10)}$$

This is read "one zero one to the base two is equal to five to the base ten."

A numbering system with a base of radix of 8 is called an octal system. In counting in this system the digits used are 0, 1, 2, 3, 4, 5, 6, and 7. Hence counting in the base 8 would proceed as follows: 0, 1, 2, 3, 4, 5, 6, 7, 10, 11, 12, and so forth. The answer to *Question 10* is C. The place values in this system (proceeding from the right, least significant digit) are units, eights, sixty fours, five hundred twelves, etc. The base eight number 523 means there are five 64s, two eights, and three units. Or the decimal value is $(5 \times 64) + (2 \times 8) + (3 \times 1) = 339$.

$$523_{(8)} = 339_{(10)}$$

One of the reasons octal numbering is popular in the computer world is because of the ease of converting binary numbers to octal numbers. If a binary number's digits are arranged in groups of threes, and each "triad" is converted to an octal number the result is an octal equivalent of the binary number. An example should help illustrate this point.

For example: Let us suppose the binary number 1101110110 is to be converted to an octal number. First group the numbers in "triads" thusly:

$$(00)1 \ 101 \ 110 \ 110$$

Note that the extra zeros added to the left really won't change the value, they are there only for grouping purposes. Now convert each group of three to an equivalent octal value (same as converting to decimal since three binary digits can only count as high as 7) as shown here:

$$(00)1 \quad 101 \quad 110 \quad 110$$
$$\downarrow \qquad \downarrow \qquad \downarrow \qquad \downarrow$$
$$1 \qquad 5 \qquad 6 \qquad 6$$

If this procedure is correct then:

$$1101110110_{(2)} = 1566_{(8)}$$

To check it let's convert each number to its decimal equivalent and compare the results. To make the problem consume less space first write the binary number. Next jot the binary place value above each single digit in the binary number, as follows:

(512)	(256)	(128)	(64)	(32)	(16)	(8)	(4)	(2)	(1)
1	1	0	1	1	1	0	1	1	0

Multiply the place value by the digit in that place (either 1 or 0) and add the results:

$$(512 \times 1) + (256 \times 1) + (128 \times 0) + (64 \times 1) + (32 \times 1)$$
$$+ (16 \times 1) + (8 \times 0) + (4 \times 1) + (2 \times 1) + (1 \times 0) =$$
$$512 + 256 + 64 + 32 + 16 + 4 + 2 = 886$$

Therefore: $1101110110_{(2)} = 886_{(10)}$.

Now do the same for the octal number, as follows:

(512)	(64)	(8)	(1)
1	5	6	6

Again multiplying the place value by the digit in the places you obtain the decimal equivalents:

$$(512 \times 1) + (64 \times 5) + (8 \times 6) + (1 \times 6) =$$
$$512 + 320 + 48 + 6 \qquad = 886$$

Therefore: $1566_{(8)} = 886_{(10)}$.

From the above example you can see that the following is proven:

$$886_{(10)} = 1566_{(8)} = 1101110110_{(2)}$$

Again the reason this notation is used is the ease of converting to a number more easily read and written. By arranging a group of LEDs (corresponding to the binary information of interest in a computer) into groups of threes, the octal number can be easily read with a little practice, and written down with much more ease and accuracy than the binary number.

Hexadecimal is of interest for the same reason. If the binary groups are in fours instead of threes, four bits can be read as a hexadecimal number quite easily. Let's try the same binary number but group it in fours. First, however, let's count in hexadecimal or base 16. In hexadecimal there are 16 symbols which range from 0 through F as shown in Table 2-2.

Table 2-2. Comparison of Decimal, Hexadecimal, and Binary.

Base 10 Decimal	Base 16 Hexadecimal	Base 2 Binary
0	0	0
1	1	1
2	2	10
3	3	11
4	4	100
5	5	101
6	6	110
7	7	111
8	8	1000
9	9	1001
10	A	1010
11	B	1011
12	C	1100
13	D	1101
14	E	1110
15	F	1111
16	10	10000
17	11	10001

Note that four binary digits take you through a count of F in hexadecimal or 15 in decimal.

Now getting back to our binary number that we converted to octal. It was $1101110110_{(2)}$. Let's arrange this number in groups of four and convert each "quatro" into its equivalent hexadecimal number.

$$\underset{3}{(00)11} \qquad \underset{7}{0111} \qquad \underset{6}{0110}$$

If this really works, then:

$$1101110110_{(2)} = 1566_{(8)} = 376_{(16)} = 886_{(10)}$$

Having already checked binary and octal, let's use the same check on the hexadecimal number, as shown below:

$$\begin{array}{ccc} (256) & (16) & (1) \\ 3 & 7 & 6 \end{array}$$

Multiply the place value by the digit as before prior to adding the results:

$$(256 \times 3) + (16 \times 7) + (1 \times 6) =$$

$$768 + 112 + 6 = 886$$

Therefore: $376_{(16)} = 886_{(10)}$.

In *Question 11* the question asks for the octal equivalent of the binary number 110101. Arranging it in groups of three you should be able to easily convert to 65 (answer *b*).

By knowing the place value, the decimal equivalent of $2E_{(16)}$ in *Question 12* can be found.

$$(16 \times 2) + (E \times 1) =$$

$$32 + 14 = 46$$

Grouping each binary number into "quads" in *Question 13* shows the following:

$$\text{Answer a was } 1111\ 0100_{(2)} = F4_{(16)}$$
$$\text{Answer b was } 1010\ 0010_{(2)} = A2_{(16)}$$
$$\text{Answer c was } 0111\ 0111_{(2)} = 77_{(16)}$$

Therefore answer *d* is correct as there was no correct number.

BOOLEAN ALGEBRA

In Boolean algebra mathematical notation is different than in regular algebra. In regular algebra AB, or A • B or (A) (B), all mean the quantity A times the quantity B. In Boolean algebra these sequences mean the *logical operation*, AND. Thus AB, or A • B, or (A) (B) means the quantity A *AND* the quantity B. The answer to *Question 14* is therefore "*d,* all of the above."

It is also true in Boolean algebra that all quantities are limited to only two states. When using Boolean algebra, the number of quantities a function can possess is limited. Normally in computers these values are a logic "1" state or a logic "0" state. Therefore a function can only be a "1" or a "0" at any one time.

A bar or vinculum is used in Boolean algebra to indicate an inversion, or NOT, function. Thus $\overline{A}$ is read "not A." If a function is designated as B on the input to an inverter the output is $\overline{B}$, as in Fig. 2-4.

In *Question 15* the statement $A \cdot \overline{A}$ could be represented by a logic diagram as shown in Fig. 2-5.

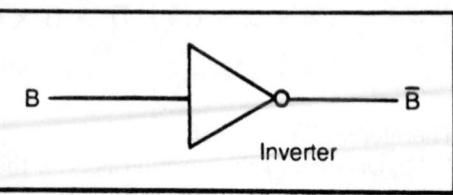

Fig. 2-4. The NOT gate or inverter.

B ——— $\overline{B}$

Inverter

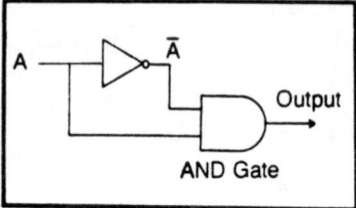

A ——— $\overline{A}$

Output

AND Gate

Fig. 2-5. Logic diagram of the logic function A • $\overline{A}$.

Fig. 2-6. Truth table of the AND logic function.

A	B	A•B
0	0	0
0	1	0
1	0	0
1	1	1

A	B	A+B
0	0	0
0	1	1
1	0	1
1	1	1

Fig. 2-7. Truth table of the OR logic function.

The output $\overline{A}$ will be ANDed with A. An AND gate has the truth table of Fig. 2-6. (A truth table is a table showing an output behavior for all possible combinations of input quantities.)

In other words an AND function will be "1" only when all inputs are "1."

Now getting back to *Q15* the inputs to the AND gate can never be "1" at the same time since if A is "1", $\overline{A}$ is "0", and if A is "0", $\overline{A}$ is "1." Therefore the output must be "0" at all times. We can therefore write A • $\overline{A}$ = "0." The answer to *Q15* is *b*, "0."

The regular algebraic symbol for addition was chosen in Boolean algebra to represent the logical OR function. Hence A + B is read "the quantity A or the quantity B", or simply "A or B." A truth table for an OR function is shown in Fig. 2-7.

Reduction of Boolean expressions is not covered on the Associate Certification Exam as the subject is not much needed in technical work. A few items for reduction are shown in *Question 16* for practice. All technicians should be aware of the methods used for reduction even if they are not required often.

With a few axioms of Boolean algebra, and some practice, the equation in *Q16* should be easy to reduce. Some Boolean algebra axoms are shown in Table 2-3.

Using these rules reduce $AB + AC + A\overline{C}$, as follows:

From (14) ⟶ $AB + AC + A\overline{C} = A(B + C + \overline{C})$
From (11) ⟶ $\phantom{AB + AC + A\overline{C}} = A(B + 1)$
From (9) ⟶ $\phantom{AB + AC + A\overline{C}} = A(1)$
From (7) ⟶ $\phantom{AB + AC + A\overline{C}} = A$

(1)	$1 \bullet 1$	=	1
(2)	$1 \bullet 0$	=	0
(3)	$1 + 0$	=	1
(4)	$1 + 1$	=	1
(5)	$A \bullet A$	=	A
(6)	$A + A$	=	A
(7)	$1 \bullet A$	=	A
(8)	$0 \bullet A$	=	0
(9)	$A + 1$	=	1
(10)	$\underline{A} + 0$	=	A
(11)	$\overline{A} + A$	=	1
(12)	$\overline{A} \bullet A$	=	0
(13)	$\overline{\overline{A}}$	=	A
(14)	$AB + AC$	=	$A(B + C)$
(15)	$\overline{A} \bullet \overline{B}$	=	$\overline{A + B}$
(16)	$\overline{A} + \overline{B}$	=	$\overline{A \bullet B}$

Table 2-3. Axioms of Boolean Algebra.

Just for a check let's construct a truth table for this expression to see if $AB + AC + A\overline{C}$ can actually be replaced by the single variable, A (Fig. 2-8).

Note that the column for A is identical to the last column. This means that $A = AB + AC + A\overline{C}$ and that our reduction was correct.

Now let's find the answers for *Q16*:

Q16 a. is $ ABC + AB\overline{C} =$
From (14) ⟶ $ AB\ (C + \overline{C}) =$
From (11) ⟶ $ AB(1) =$
From (7) ⟶ $ AB =$
Q16 b. is $ X(X + Y) =$
From (14) (backwards) ⟶ $XX + XY =$
From (5) ⟶ $X + XY =$

23

A	B	C	$\overline{C}$	AB	AC	A$\overline{C}$	AB+AC+A$\overline{C}$
0	0	0	1	0	0	0	0
0	0	1	0	0	0	0	0
0	1	0	1	0	0	0	0
0	1	1	0	0	0	0	0
1	0	0	1	0	0	1	1
1	0	1	0	0	1	0	1
1	1	0	1	1	0	1	1
1	1	1	0	1	1	0	1

Fig. 2-8. Truth table for the logic function AB + AC + A$\overline{C}$.

From (14) and (7) $\longrightarrow$ X(1 + Y) =
From (9) $\longrightarrow$ X(1) =
From (7) $\longrightarrow$ X

Q16 c. is (G + H) (G + K) =

To simplify this one we need to show that the AND works like multiplication in algebra—that is that each term in the left parentheses is ANDed into each term in the right parentheses. To do this let's first let A = G + H, then:

(G + H)(G + K) =
A(G + K)   =
From (14) $\longrightarrow$ AG + AK

Putting G + H back in, for A, results in:

(G + H)G + (G + H)K =
From (14) $\longrightarrow$ GG + GH + GK + HK =
From (5) $\longrightarrow$ G + GH + GK + HK =
From (14) $\longrightarrow$ G(1 + GH + GK) + HK =
From (9) $\longrightarrow$ G(1) + HK =
From (7) $\longrightarrow$ G + HK

Q16 d. is $\overline{A}\overline{C}$ + $\overline{A}$C + BC =
From (14) $\longrightarrow$ $\overline{A}(\overline{C}$ + C) + BC =
From (11) $\longrightarrow$ $\overline{A}$(1) + BC =
From (9) $\longrightarrow$ $\overline{A}$ + BC

Q16 e. is $\overline{A}$B + $\overline{A}\overline{B}$ + A =
From (14) $\longrightarrow$ $\overline{A}$(B + $\overline{B}$) + A =
From (11) $\longrightarrow$ $\overline{A}$ + A = 1

Q16 f. is $\overline{A}\overline{B}(A + B)$ =
From (14) $\longrightarrow \overline{A}\overline{B}A + \overline{A}\overline{B}B$ =
rearranging
$(\overline{A}A)\overline{B} + \overline{A}(\overline{B}B)$ =
From (12) $\longrightarrow 0 \bullet \overline{B} + \overline{A} \bullet 0$ =
From (2) $\longrightarrow 0 + 0$ = 0

Any time any OR input is "1" the output will be "1." *Question 17* asks what an OR gate output will be with three inputs at "1," "0," and "0" respectively. The truth table shows that the output will be "1" hence answer *c* is correct.

In logic several combination gates are popular because of the physical structure. OR gates followed by inverting amplifiers were quite popular and when they were incorporated in one package it became convenient to describe the package in terms of its total logical function, that is, the OR followed by a NOT (inverter) function became a NOT-OR shortened to NOR. A NOR truth table is shown here in Fig. 2-9.

A	B	A+B	$\overline{A+B}$ = NOR
0	0	0	1
0	1	1	0
1	0	1	0
1	1	1	0

Fig. 2-9. Truth table for NOR function.

A NAND is a NOT AND functionally, The truth table appears in Fig. 2-10.

This gives the answer to *Question 18.*

When using the bar over the letters care should be taken. Notice that $\overline{A}\overline{B}$ does not equal $\overline{AB}$. This can be shown by comparing the Fig. 2-11 circuits that give these two functions.

For ease of comparison a truth table Fig. 2-12 can be used to keep track of what each output is for various combinations of inputs.

Fig. 2-10. Truth table for NAND function.

A	B	A•B	$\overline{A•B}$ = NAND
0	0	0	1
0	1	0	1
1	0	0	1
1	1	1	0

25

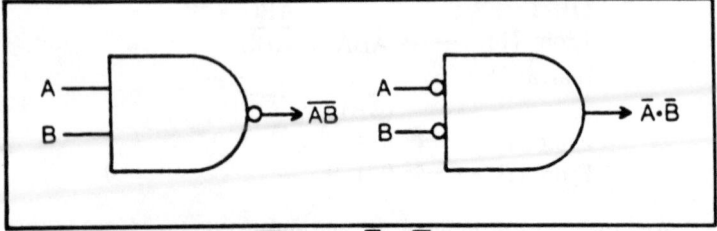

Fig. 2-11. Logic circuit for $\overline{AB}$ and for $\overline{A} \cdot \overline{B}$.

Column 3 simply shows the AND function and A ANDed with B. Column 4 is found by inverting column 3. Column 4 is the output of the first circuit above. Columns 5 and 6 are simply inverses of A and B respectively. Column 7 is 5 and 6 ANDed together, or in other words $\overline{A} \cdot \overline{B}$. Column 4 and column 7 are not the same for every combination of inputs therefore $\overline{A \cdot B} \neq \overline{A} \cdot \overline{B}$.

The answer to *Question 19* is *a*. An exclusive OR is similar to a regular OR except the output is excluded when both A and B are "1" at the same time. A truth table is shown here in Fig. 2-13.

Checking each answer in problem 15 against the truth table is one way to solve this problem. This can be done by substituting a circuit for each equation. Answer *a* is $A\overline{B} + \overline{A}B = F$. A circuit to represent this is shown in Fig. 2-14.

In the circuit of Fig. 2-14 when A = 0 and B = 0 then G = 0 and H = 0. G OR H then equals 0, which is F. If A = 0 and B = 1 then G = 0 and H = 1 and G + H = 1. If A = 1 and B = 0 then G = 1 and H = 0, therefore, G + H = 1 again. But, if A = 1 and B = 1 then G = 0 and H = 0, making G + H = 0. Answer *a* for *Q15*, therefore, is correct. Answers *b* and *c* can be checked in a similar manner just to make sure they are wrong. A circuit for b is shown in Fig. 2-15.

The circuit for answer c would be as in Fig. 2-16.

1.	2.	3.	4.	5.	6.	7.
A	B	A•B	$\overline{A \cdot B}$	$\overline{A}$	$\overline{B}$	$\overline{A} \cdot \overline{B}$
0	0	0	1	1	1	1
0	1	0	1	1	0	0
1	0	0	1	0	1	0
1	1	1	0	0	0	0

Fig. 2-12. Truth table showing that $\overline{AB}$ does not equal $\overline{A} \cdot \overline{B}$.

A	B	A⊕B
0	0	0
0	1	1
1	0	1
1	1	0

Fig. 2-13. Exclusive OR truth table.

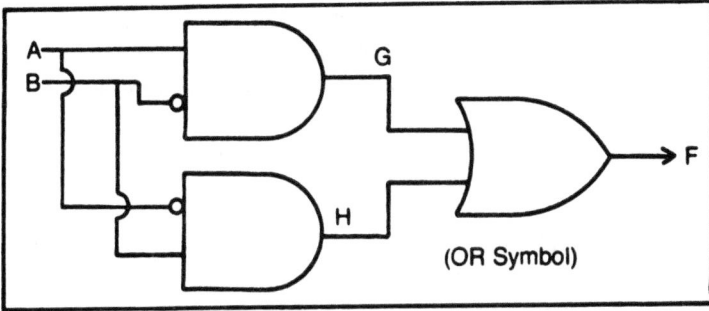

Fig. 2-14. Logic diagram for $A\overline{B} + \overline{A}B = F$.

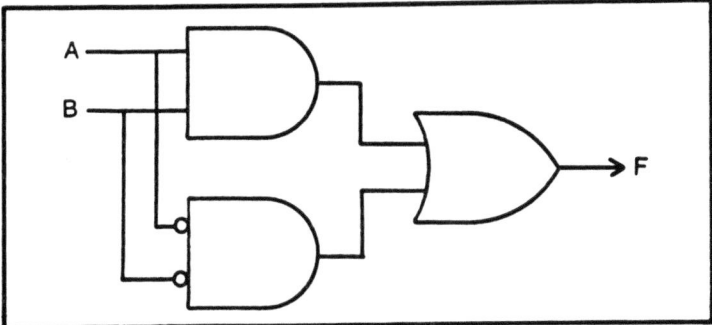

Fig. 2-15. Logic diagram for incorrect answer b.

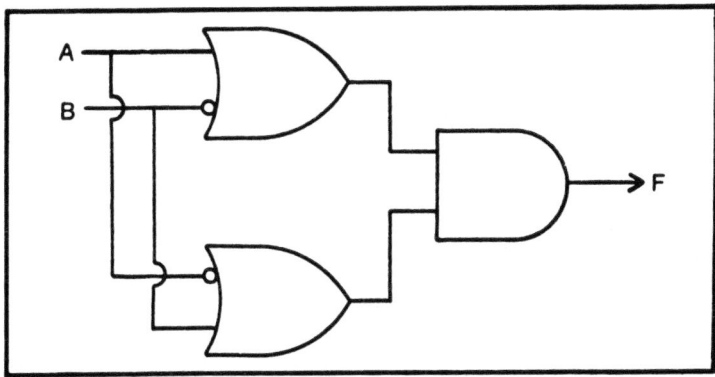

Fig. 2-16. Logic diagram for incorrect answer c.

ADDITIONAL READING

Chinn, William G., et al: *Arithmetic and Calculators,* Walt Freeman and Company, 1978.

Cooke, Nelson M. and Herbert F. R. Adams: *Basic Mathematics for Electronics,* McGraw-Hill, 1970.

Osborne, Adam: *An Introduction to Microcomputers, Volume 0: The Beginner's Book,* Osborne and Associates, Inc., 1977.

Ward, Brice: *Boolean Algebra,* Howard W. Sams, 1971.

Warring, R. H.: *Understanding Electronics—2nd Edition,* TAB BOOKS, Inc., 1984.

Electrical

The most exotic video games, computers, military fire control units, and satellite earth stations work with the same basic elements that have been used since the first radios initiated us into the science of electronics. Every technician must be familiar with these elements. Becoming familiar with the basic electronic components is necessary in order to understand how an electronic product works, and what if anything might be malfunctioning. Below is a quiz relating to these basic elements.

QUIZ

Ql. How much current is flowing in the circuit of Fig. 3-1?

a. 1 amp   c. <u>10 amps</u>
b. 0.1 amp   d. 100 amps

$I = E.R = 10 \times 1 = 10A$
$P = I.E = 10 \times 10 = 100w$

Fig. 3-1. Circuit for problems in Q1 and Q2.

Q2. In the circuit of Fig. 3-1, how much power will be dissipated by the resistance?

a. 1 watt   c. 100 watts
b. 10 watts   d. 1000 watts

Q3. The pi-type filter in Fig. 3-2, C1, L1, and C2 will change the pulsating ripple voltage at A to _____at B?

a. a 10 V P-P waveform   c. a 0.1 V waveform
b. the same level waveform

Q4. The voltage across R1 in Fig. 3-3 is:

a. 25 V   c. 37.5 V
b. 75 V

Q5. The effective total capacitance across R_L in the circuit of Fig. 3-4 is:

a. 4 μF   c. 8 μF
b. 6 μF   d. 12 μF

Q6. If the circuit in Fig. 3-4 operates near 150 Vdc then what minimum voltage ratings should C1 and C2 have?

a. 75 V   c. 300 V
b. 150 V

Q7. A resistor which changes value greatly with small changes in voltage across it is:

a. a thermistor   c. a thyristor
b. a varistor

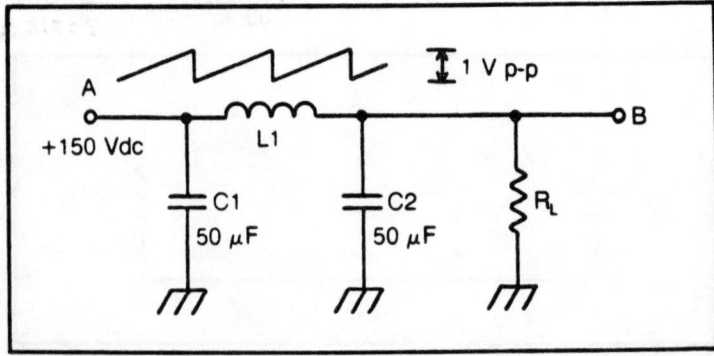

Fig. 3-2. Pi-type filter for Q3, Q14, and Q15.

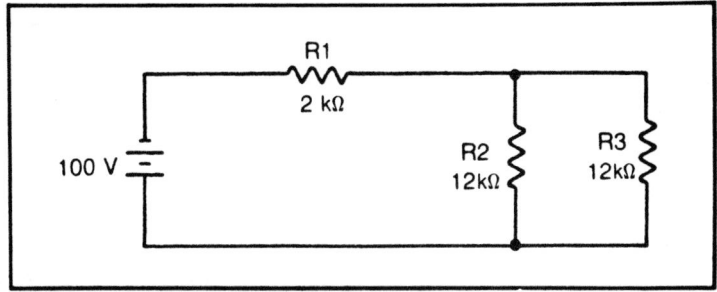

Fig. 3-3. Series parallel circuit for Q4.

Q8. The values of two or more inductors in series or parallel combine like:

a. capacitors   c. neither
b. resistors

Q9. A coil with the same length of wire but whose coils are spaced further apart will have:

a. less inductance
b. more inductance

Q10. Match the following:

a. inductor   x. current lags voltage
b. capacitor   y. current and voltage are in phase
c. resistor   z. current leads voltage

Q11. If the LC circuit in Fig. 3-5 is resonant at 500 kHz, how will it affect the incoming 500 kHz signal?

a. it will allow 500 kHz to pass through to the output but will resist or oppose lower or higher frequencies

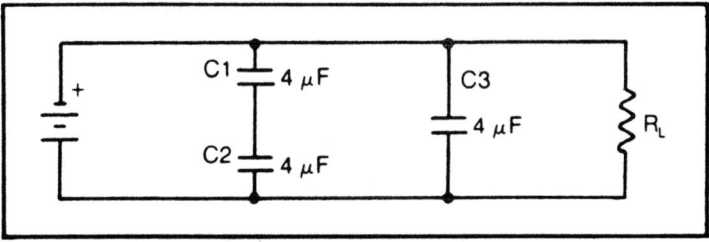

Fig. 3-4. Series parallel circuit for Q5 and Q6.

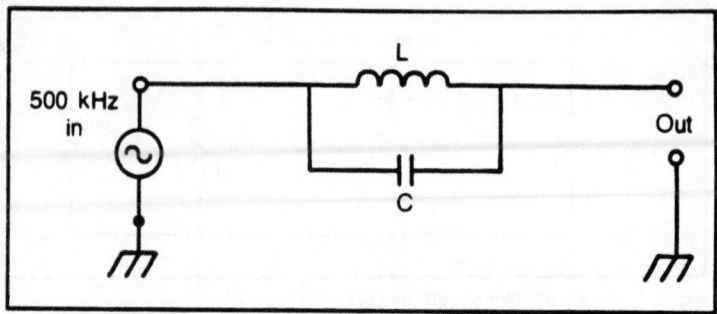

Fig. 3-5. LC circuits for Q11, Q12, and Q13.

b. it will present a high impedance to 500 kHz but will allow higher or lower frequencies to pass to the output

Q12. Calculate the capacitive reactance presented to 500 kHz in the circuit of Fig. 3-5.

a. if C = 0.001 μF   a. _____
b. if C = 0.000001 μF   b. _____
c. if C = 1000 μF   c. _____
d. if C = 0.00001 μF   d. _____

Q13. Figure the inductive reactance in Fig. 3-5:

a. if L = 1 henry   c. if L = 50 μH
b. if L = 50 mH

Q14. Looking back to Fig. 3-2, what is the capacitive reactance of C1 to 120 Hz?

a. 0.00265 ohms
b. 26.5 ohms

Q15. If, in Fig. 3-2, L1 is 2.6 H, what is its inductive reactance at 120 Hz?

a. 1.959 ohms
b. 1959. ohms

Q16. A resistor color-coded yellow, violet, silver is:

a. 0.47 ohms   c. 470 ohms
b. 4.7 ohms

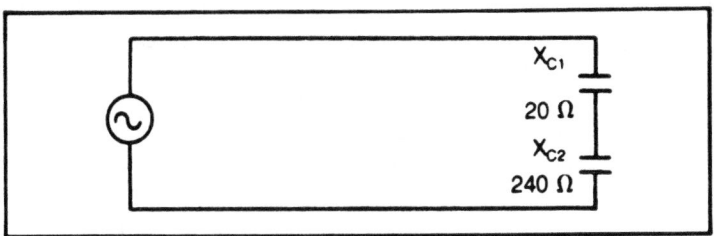

Fig. 3-6. Series capacitive reactance circuit for Q17.

Q17. What is the total reactance in the circuit of Fig. 3-6?

    a. 16.3 ohms   c. 260 ohms
    b. 12 ohms

Q18. With an ac waveform of 100 V on the primary and a turns ratio of 10 to 1, the secondary in Fig. 3-7 will have:

    a. 10 V and half the current of the primary
    b. 10 V and 10 times the current of the primary
    c. 10000 V and 1/10000 of the current in the primary

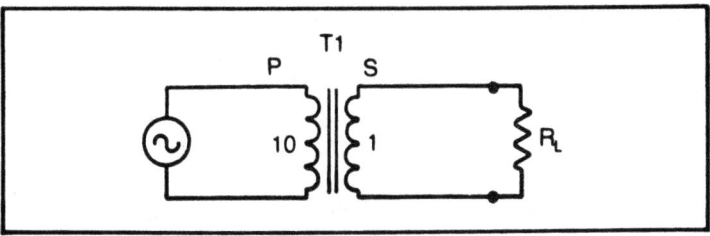

Fig. 3-7. Transformer circuit for Q18.

Q19. If the waveform on the primary in Fig. 3-8 is 500 V, what should you expect at A and B?

    a. over 5000 V at A, over 500 V at B
    b. over 5000 V at A, under 10 V at B

Q20. What is the RC time of the circuit in Fig. 3-9?

    a. 0.47 seconds   c. 47 microseconds
    b. 0.0047 seconds

Now that you have taken the quiz regarding basic electricity and the basic elements of electronic circuits, ask yourself if any

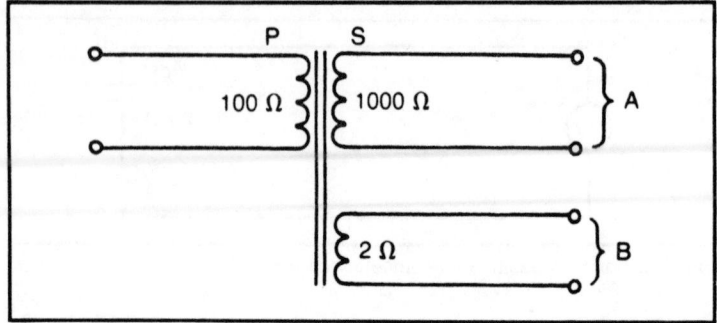

Fig. 3-8. Partial transformer circuit for Q19.

of the questions were difficult. If you were not able to systematically work out the answers, or the answers weren't quickly evident, then you need to do further study before attempting the Certification Exam.

ELECTRICAL UNITS

Several questions on the ETAI Certification Exams deal with basic electricity. They aren't all as simple as *Question 1* but they still test your understanding of current flow and the relationships between voltage, current, and resistance.

One ampere of electrical current is 6.25×10^{18} electrons flowing past a given point, per second. One volt is the practical unit we use to identify the electromotive force needed to move 6.25×10^{18} electrons between two points. Instead of referring to that large number, we refer to that quantity as a *coulomb.* To put into perspective the amount of work done by a one volt charge in moving a coulomb of electrons past a given point in one second, it is about 3/4 of a foot-pound of work, or one joule of work.

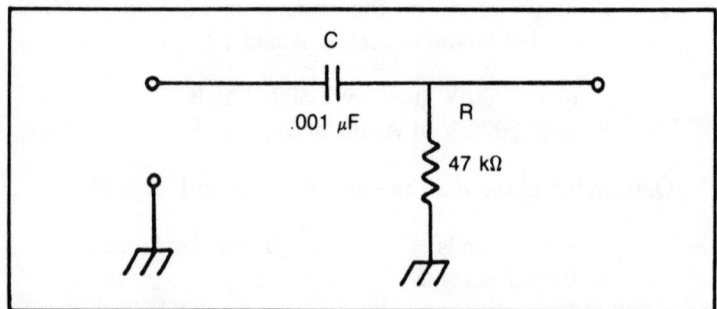

Fig. 3-9. C and R in series for Q20.

34

One *ohm* of resistance is the unit of opposition to current flow that allows only 1 amp of current to flow when moved by a 1 volt charge. (As a side note, a resistance of one ohm will develop 0.24 calories of heat in one second.) Thus the formula I = E/R: The amount of current in an electrical circuit equals the voltage divided by the resistance.

Some of the relationships you are introduced to in school never (or at least rarely) will be referred to after graduation. That's not true about Ohm's law. Especially the power calculations. You will need to, on occasion, calculate the wattage of a resistor you intend to place in a circuit, or you will want to estimate the amount of excess current that may be the fault symptom in a circuit you are troubleshooting. The power formulas are:

$$P = E \times I; \quad P = \frac{E^2}{R}; \quad P = I^2R$$

Or, you can transpose in problems where you have the amount of current, resistance, or voltage, when you know the amount of power:

$$E = \frac{P}{I}; \quad I = \sqrt{\frac{P}{R}}; \quad E = \sqrt{PR}$$

$$\text{or: } I = \frac{P}{E}; \quad R = \frac{P}{I^2}; \quad R = \frac{E^2}{P}$$

Some technicians have difficulty remembering Ohm's law unless their job calls for its constant use. One helpful method is to name the elements: "Eagle," "Rabbit," and "Indian." In the basic Ohm's law formulas and power formulas (excepting the easiest one: P = EI) the Eagle is always in the air, the rabbit and Indian on the ground:

$$I = \frac{E}{R}; \quad R = \frac{E}{I}; \quad E = IR; \quad P = \frac{E^2}{R}; \quad P = I^2 R.$$

In calculating I, E, and R, when given the other two factors, most technicians have little difficulty with simple problems as in *Q1* and *Q2*. When the circuit becomes complex and divides into multiple paths the solutions become more difficult. However, by dividing the circuit into subcircuits and working out the paths one portion at a time, and by knowing how to work Ohm's law formulas you should have no difficulty with these questions.

Wattage problems seem to confuse some technicians. The question of how to add power dissipations in series and parallel gets mixed up with resistance or capacitance in series or parallel. Remember that wattages add, whether in parallel or in series.

CAPACITORS

In *Question 3* you are introduced to the most common power supply filter arrangement used in electronics. If we use an oscilloscope we should see some small ripple voltage floating atop the + 150 Vdc (which was rectified from the 117 Vac line). The filter combination will reduce the ripple. C1 attempts to smooth out the rectified pulsating dc that is produced by the rectifier. It does this by acting as a giant reservoir for electrons. Any increase in voltage at "A" must first push a lot of electrons into C1 before the voltage can build to its full potential. Likewise, when the voltage attempts to decrease at "A" any change will immediately be opposed by C1, as it contains a vast reservoir of electrons. C1 can't do it all, though, so C2 is added as insurance and acts in the same manner as C1.

In between C1 and C2 is L1, a coil that also acts as a "shock absorber." The coil, by nature, works on the ripple in an opposite manner as the filter capacitors: where current *leads* the voltage in the capacitors (current flows in until the voltage is at its high point), the current *lags* the voltage in the inductor coil. Before any increase in voltage is impressed through L1, the current must trickle through the windings. As the current attempts to increase or decrease through the coil windings it produces a back-emf that opposes that change, thus slowing the current. The current then lags the voltage across the coil. With the capacitors opposing change in one manner (current leading voltage) and the coil opposing change in an opposite manner (current lagging voltage) yet both opposing any changes, the ripple is smoothed to a very low level, (dc).

COMBINATION CIRCUITS

Question 4 can be solved by calculating the combined resistances of R2 and R3 prior to trying to determine what portion of the 100 V supply is dropped across R1. The formula for parallel resistance is: $R_T = \dfrac{R1 \times R2}{R1 + R2}$. However, where equal resistors are in parallel it is easier and faster to divide one of the equal resistors in half, in this case 6 k. Then you can figure out the current flow using Ohm's law:

$$I = \frac{100}{6\ k + 2\ k}; \ I = \frac{100}{8\ k}; I = 12.5 \text{ mA}; E = IR;$$

$$E = .125 \times 2000; E = 25 \text{ V}$$

It is easier to see that R2 and R3, totaling 6 k, are equal to 75% of the total resistance. Since that is true then 75% of the voltage will be dropped across R2 and R3, leaving 25%, or 25 V to be dropped across R1.

Series and parallel capacitors are combined in *Question 5*. In parallel capacitors the available plate area is increased and thus the electrostatic field area is increased. In series the opposite occurs. The electrostatic field must divide itself and attempt to attract or repel electrons on two "fronts." It is the same as increasing the thickness of the dielectric between the plates. As such the total capacitance will be less than the smallest capacitor, or if two equal capacitors, it will be 1/2 that of one of them. Don't get this confused with capacitive reactance. X_c and C are two different things.

The working voltage of combined capacitors is of concern in *Question 6*. Since connecting two capacitors in series is, in effect, increasing the thickness of the dielectric, and the dielectric determines the working voltage the capacitor is able to withstand, then putting two capacitors in series allows you to add the maximum voltage ratings, two 75 V rated capacitors serving in place of a single 150 V capacitor.

INDUCTORS AND OTHER COMPONENTS

Many terms used in electronics simply must be remembered. The name for various types of parts must be fixed in your mind. In *Question 7* you should eliminate answer *a* since that resistor, a thermistor, by its name, is affected by temperature. A *thy*ristor (answer c) is a semiconductor, like an SCR, that functions similarly to a *thy*ratron tube, turning on after a certain level of trigger voltage is reached, then not turning off until the power source is removed.

L = L1 + L2 + L3. Inductors in series add like resistors in series. Two coils in series act as one, with the combined inductance of both. Inductors in parallel combine the same as resistors in parallel. Two equal inductances in parallel equal only 1/2 the value of each one of them. Inductive reactances also combine like resistors. The answer to *Question 8* is therefore *b*.

It is the interaction of the magnetic fields surrounding the coil wire that produces the inductance. If you move magnetic fields away from each other the attraction or repulsion is less between adjacent windings, thus putting wider spacing between the wire of a coil reduces the inductance; answer *a* in *Question 9*.

In an inductor, a voltage pulse is impressed across the coils due to the back-emf caused by the interaction of the magnetic fields surrounding each turn of the wire, the current is opposed, or slowed, thus the current lags the voltage. *A* therefore matches *x* in *Question 10*.

For *b*, the current fills the capacitor's reservoir—its wide plates—before the capacitor's electrostatic field reaches its maximum level, thus the current leads the voltage in a capacitor. *b* matches *z*.

For *c*, current and voltage are in phase in a resistor—there is no lead or lag, so *c* matches *y*.

Figure 3-10 gives comparative voltage, current, and power waveforms for inductors, capacitors, and resistors.

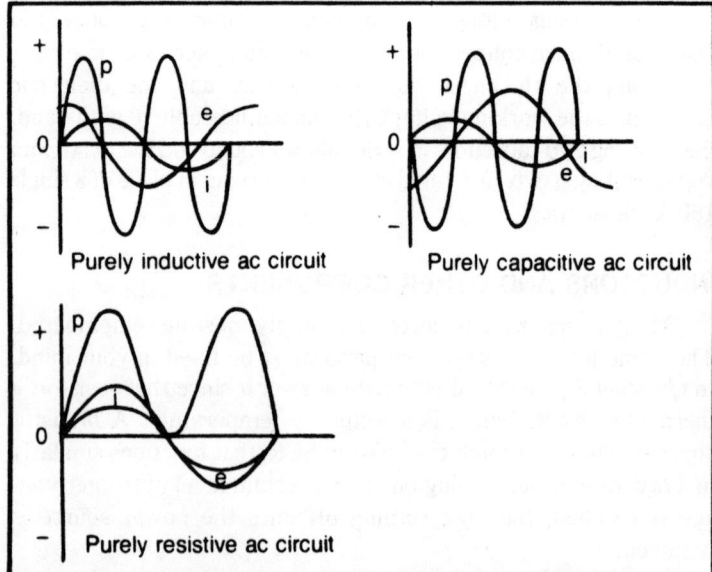

Fig. 3-10. Sine wave for pure L, C, or R circuits.

Many incorrect answers on Certification Exams have been associated with circuits such as the LC circuit in *Question 11*. If the circuit is resonant at 500 kHz then the inductive and capacitive reactance are equal at that frequency. Above 500 kHz the capacitor will have less reactance and will tend to allow higher frequencies to pass through. The X_C will be greater at frequencies lower than 500 kHz. Note that as f gets smaller, X_C gets larger:

$$X_C = \frac{1}{2\pi FC}$$

The capacitor will tend to retard or limit frequencies below 500 kHz. The coil acts in an opposite manner allowing anything lower than 500 kHz to pass easily but opposing any frequencies above 500 kHz. As a result the circuit acts to impede frequencies in the 500 kHz range only. It could be classified as a 500 kHz trap.

To better understand how the combination works let's hook it up parallel to the signal or across the line, rather than in series with the signal, as in Fig. 3-11.

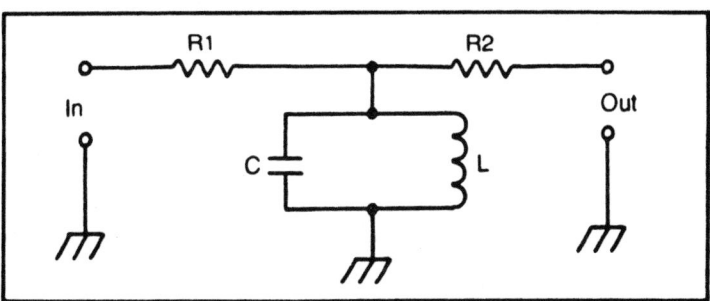

Fig. 3-11. LC tuned circuit.

The circuit still presents an impedance to frequencies near 500 kHz, but instead of impeding them it presents a barrier which keeps the 500 kHz signals from being passed to ground. Highs are passed through the capacitor to ground, and lower frequencies pass through the coil to ground. Those near 500 kHz can be passed right on through R2 and to the output.

REACTANCES

If the working of the formula for X_C in *Question 12* is difficult for you, the best way to solve the problem is for you to set up a

39

dozen or more hypothetical equations using some different values and to work them until you have made 'friends' with it. It is unnatural to deal with such small and large numbers, but with a little practice you can master them. As you see, after you work one, you then change only one number in your calculator to get the answers to the others.

The same necessity to discipline yourself to work such equations until you have mastered them is needed in solving the inductive reactance problems of *Question 13*. The relationship of a large coil and a small coil to the lower end of the radio-band frequencies (500 kHz) is important also.

You need to actually work out the answer for *Question 14* to get the right one. There is no way to guess it correctly. Some people attempt to pass the Certification Exams by guessing, but it is virtually impossible. You must "know" how to solve the problems.

Question 15 more firmly implants the effect of a coil on the circuit at different frequencies. It shows why a large choke coil is necessary at ac line frequencies.

MISCELLANEOUS PROBLEMS

Don't forget the color codes that indicate tolerances, and the below-10-ohm band indicators. Don't take the exam until you have the color codes down pat. In the third, or multiplier band, if the color is silver multiply by 0.01, and if it is gold multiply by 0.1 for the correct value.

Reactance of capacitors adds like resistance—therefore 240 ohms and 20 ohms = 260 ohms in *Question 17*. The question doesn't ask about the combined capacitances, which would be less than the value of the smaller capacitor.

Transformers inductively couple power from the primary to the secondary. The voltage coupled is directly proportional to the turns ratios. The current transferred is inversely proportional. *Question 18's* correct answer is therefore *b*.

The resistance of the wire in separate windings of a transformer is not directly related to the turns and thus the voltage. However, if the wire sizes are relatively close and the resistances are not close, as in *Question 19*, the expected voltages can be approximated.

RC time is used in *Question 20* and on all Certification Exams. One RC time is simply R × C, R is in ohms and C in farads. The decimal point and large number of zeros makes the math tough, but you must be able to work this type of problem. Also you need to know that in 1 RC time, the capacitor charges to 63 percent of the applied voltage and that it takes 5 RC times to charge to 99 percent, and 10 RC times to be considered fully charged. Discharging takes the same time, 1 RC time to discharge to 37 percent of the applied voltage. (Note we did not say ''1 RC time to discharge *to* 63 percent''.)

ADDITIONAL READING

Basic Electricity, Bureau of Naval Personnel, Dover Publishers, 1962.

Faber, Rodney B.: *Applied Electricity and Electronics for Technology*, John Wiley and Sons, 1978.

Horn, Delton T.: *Basic Electronics Theory—with projects & experiments*, TAB BOOKS Inc., 1981.

Kaufman, Milton and J.A. Wilson: *Basic Electricity: Theory and Practice*, McGraw-Hill, 1973.

Mandl, Matthew: *Fundamentals of Electric and Electronic Circuits*, Prentice-Hall, 1964.

Series and Parallel Circuits

This chapter provides a review of the concepts of series and parallel circuits. As before, the quiz at the beginning covers circuit concepts important to these subjects. If you have trouble with any of these questions, review material is presented after the quiz.

QUIZ

Q1. The equivalent resistance of these three resistors (Fig. 4-1) is:

a. 50 Ω
b. 15 Ω
c. nearly 5 Ω
d. none of these

Q2. In Fig. 4-2 the resistance R equals

a. 15 k ohms
b. 50 k ohms
c. 150 k ohms
d. 35 k ohms

Q3. The equivalent capacitance of this group of capacitors (Fig. 4-3) is:

a. 125 picofarads
b. 1250 picofarads
c. 750 picofarads
d. 5 microfarads

Q4. If, at some frequency, the capacitive reactances of C1, C2, and C3 in Question 3 are as shown in Fig. 4-4, then the equivalent capacitive reactance is:

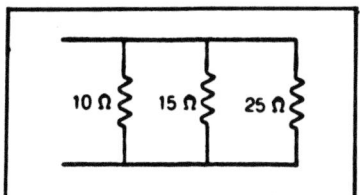

Fig. 4-1. Parallel resistor circuit for Q1.

Fig. 4-2. Series resistors for Q2.

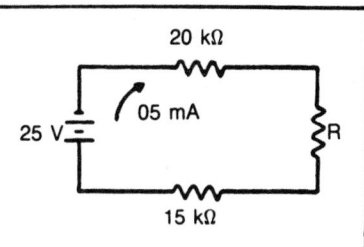

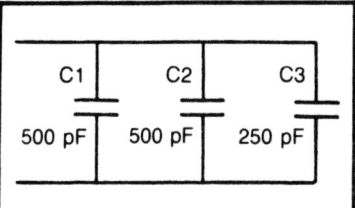

Fig. 4-3. Parallel capacitor circuit for Q3.

Fig. 4-4. Capacitance in parallel for Q4.

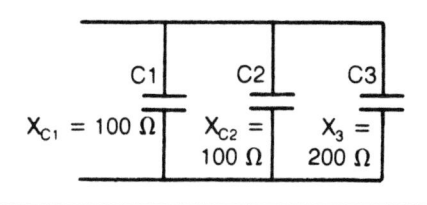

a. 350 ohms   c. 400 ohms
b. 100 ohms   d. 40 ohms

Q5. In Fig. 4-5, what capacitance does the generator "see"?

a. 0.055 microfarads   c. 0.5 microfarads
b. 5 nanofarads   d. None of these

Q6. In this circuit (Fig. 4-6) the voltage across C2 will be:

a. 0 Vdc   c. 20 Vdc
b. 120 Vdc   d. 100 Vdc

43

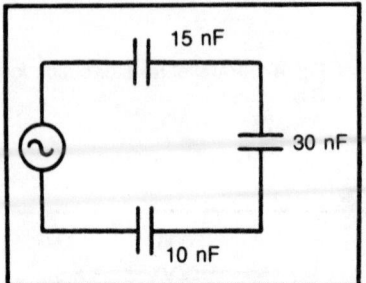

Fig. 4-5. Series capacitors for problem in Q5.

Q7. The formula for finding inductance of three parallel inductances is:

a. $L_T = L1 + L2 + L3$

b. $L_T = \dfrac{1}{L1} + \dfrac{1}{L2} + \dfrac{1}{L3}$

c. $L_T = \dfrac{1}{\dfrac{1}{L1} + \dfrac{1}{L2} + \dfrac{1}{L3}}$

d. none of these

Q8. In this circuit of Fig. 4-7 find the ac voltage drop across L2:

a. 2.5 Vac   c. 0 volts at this frequency
b. 7.5 Vac   d. 10 volts at this frequency

Q9. In the circuit of Fig. 4-8 the combination of impedances (Zin) is:

a. 40 ohms   c. 10 ohms
b. 20 ohms   d. 28.3 ohms

Fig. 4-6. Dc voltage on capacitors for Q6.

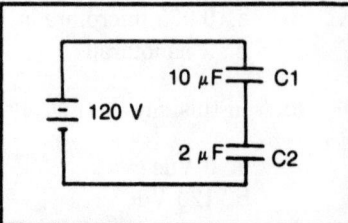

44

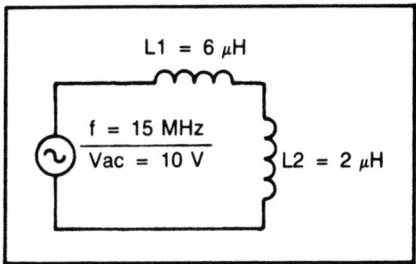

Fig. 4-7. Series inductors for problem in Q8.

L1 = 6 µH

f = 15 MHz
Vac = 10 V

L2 = 2 µH

Q10. Find the impedance of the parallel combination of R and C in the circuit of Fig. 4-9:

a. 240 ohms   c. 700 ohms
b. 350 ohms   d. 500 ohms

Q11. In the circuit of Fig. 4-10 find the voltage drop across the resistor:

a. 35   c. 10 V
b. 30 V   d. 22 V

Q12. The output of the circuit in Fig. 4-11 will respond to an input step voltage in the following fashion:

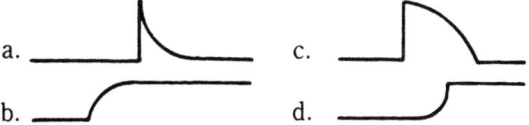

a.   c.

b.   d.

Q13. In the circuit of Fig. 4-12 the output voltage will reduce to 7.4 volts after a rise of 20 V at the occurrence of the input step voltage. It will take how much time to do this?

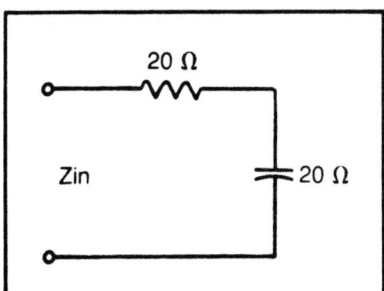

20 Ω

Zin   20 Ω

Fig. 4-8. R and C in series, Q9.

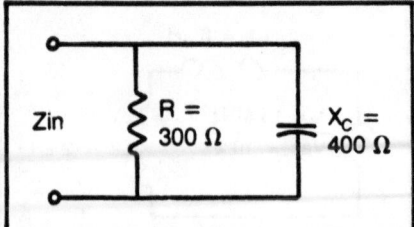

Fig. 4-9. R and C in parallel for problem in Q10.

Zin
R = 300 Ω
X_C = 400 Ω

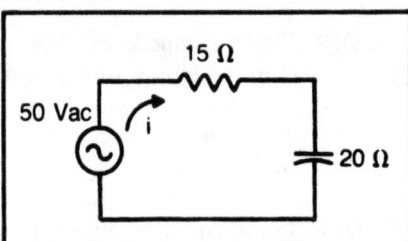

Fig. 4-10. Series RC circuit for Q11.

50 Vac
i
15 Ω
20 Ω

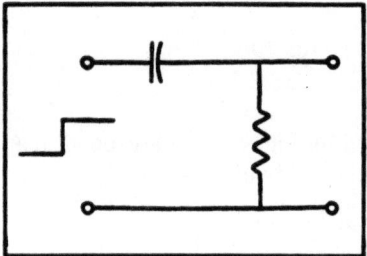

Fig. 4-11. Input and circuit for problem in Q12.

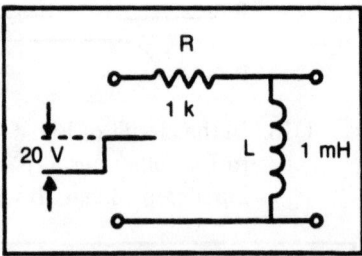

Fig. 4-12. Input and circuit for problem in Q13.

R
1 k
20 V
L
1 mH

    a. 1 milli second   c. 1 second
    b. 1 micro second   d. none of these

Q14. In a parallel LC tank circuit like Fig. 4-13 if the frequency of the applied voltage is less or lower than the resonant frequency the circuit will appear:

    a. capacitive   c. inductive
    b. resistive   d. none of these

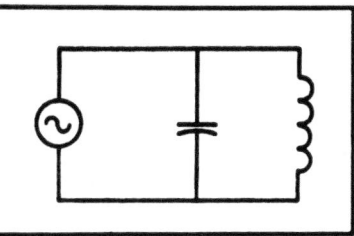

Fig. 4-13. Tuned circuit for Q14 and Q15.

Q15. If X_L = 30 ohms and X_C = 40 ohms in the circuit of Fig. 4-13, what combined impedance will the generator see?

a. 120 ohms   c. 10 ohms
b. 70 ohms   d. none of these

Q16. A parallel resonant circuit connected as shown in Fig. 4-14 would be:

a. a trap at f_0 c. a high-pass filter
b. a low-pass filter   d. a bandpass filter

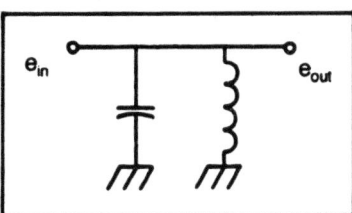

Fig. 4-14. Resonant circuit for Q16.

Q17. In the circuit of Fig. 4-15 what is the voltage at A with respect to B?

a. −8 V   c. +10 V
b. +8 V   d. +4 V

Q18. In the circuit of Fig. 4-16 R1 is a brown, green, red 20% resistor but its actual resistance is:

a. 1500   c. out of tolerance
b. 1.67 k   d. b and c are correct

PARALLEL CIRCUITS (RESISTIVE)

The *first question (Q1)* in the quiz deals with resistors in parallel. Parallel resistances each draw current from the external circuit;

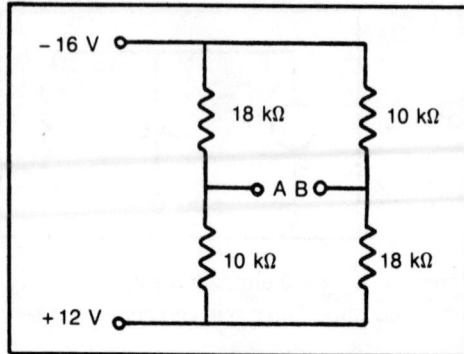

Fig. 4-15. Resistor circuit problem, Q17.

therefore, the external circuit "sees" a total of the three currents. This total is larger than any individual current. If this current were supplied to an equivalent resistance, the equivalent resistance would be smaller than any one of the three. Also:

$$R_{eq} = \cfrac{1}{\cfrac{1}{R1} + \cfrac{1}{R2} + \cfrac{1}{R3}} = \cfrac{1}{\cfrac{1}{10} + \cfrac{1}{15} + \cfrac{1}{25}}$$

$$= \frac{10(15)25}{15(10) + 15(25) + 10(25)}$$

$$= \frac{10(15)(25)}{150 + 375 + 250}$$

$$= \frac{(10)(15)(25)}{775}$$

$$= 4.84 \ \Omega$$

$$= \text{Nearly 5}$$

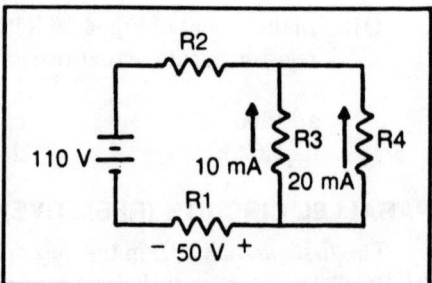

Fig. 4-16. Series parallel resistance circuit for problem in Q18.

Hence the correct answer to *Q1* was "c, nearly 5 ohms."

Another way to solve this problem is to assume some convenient voltage and then calculate individual currents. Summing the individual currents and dividing into the assumed voltage will result in the equivalent resistance. For example, assume for question one a voltage of 150 volts. The three currents would then be:

$$\frac{150 \text{ V}}{10} \ = \ 15 \text{ A}$$

$$\frac{150 \text{ V}}{15} \ = \ 10 \text{ A}$$

$$\frac{150 \text{ V}}{25} \ = \ 6 \text{ A}$$

The total current is then 15 A + 10 A + 6 A = 31 A; and the equivalent resistance is 150 V/31 A which equals a little less than 5 ohms.

SERIES CIRCUITS (RESISTIVE)

In series circuits, each circuit element has the entire current flowing through it. And also of importance is that the voltage drop around a closed loop must equal zero. In *Question 2* since we are dealing with a circuit in which all the current goes through each element, it is a series circuit. For this problem we are already given the value of the current. Since we also know the source voltage, we can easily calculate the resistance the source "sees." Let's call it R_T.

Then R_T = 25 V ÷ 0.5 mA = 50 k
and since R_T also = R + 20 k + 15 k
then R + 20 k + 15 k = 50 k
R = 50 k – 35 k
= 15 k

Therefore, the correct answer to problem 2 is answer *a*. 15 k.

Just for review let's use this same circuit to calculate the voltage drops around this loop to make sure they total zero. Since each voltage drop across a resistor is the current (0.5 mA) multiplied by the resistance then the three resistance voltage drops are:

$$(0.5 \text{ mA}) (20 \text{ k}) \ = \ 10 \text{ V}$$

49

$$(0.5 \text{ mA}) (15k) = 7.5 \text{ V}$$
$$\text{and } (0.5 \text{ mA}) (15 \text{ k}) = 7.5 \text{ V}$$

Now, remembering that in going around a loop it is conventional to assign minuses to voltage drops and pluses to voltage rises we have:

$$+25 \text{ V} - 10 \text{ V} - 7.5 \text{ V} - 7.5 \text{ V} = 0$$

CAPACITORS IN PARALLEL

The capacitance of capacitors in parallel adds. Hence, a 1000 picofarad capacitor in parallel with a 500 picofarad capacitor would be 1500 picofarads. Or, as in *Question 3*, a 500 picofarad capacitor in parallel with a 500 picofarad capacitor and also in parallel with a 250 picofarad capacitor would be:

$$500 \text{ pF} + 500 \text{ pF} + 250 \text{ pF} = 1250 \text{ pF}$$

But, the capacitive reactances of capacitors in parallel act like the resistances of resistors in parallel. That is:

$$\frac{1}{X_{CT}} = \frac{1}{X_{C1}} + \frac{1}{X_{C2}} + \frac{1}{X_{C3}}$$

$$\text{or } X_{CT} = \frac{1}{\dfrac{1}{X_{C1}} + \dfrac{1}{X_{C2}} + \dfrac{1}{X_{C3}}}$$

Therefore, to find the equivalent reactance in *Question 4:*

$$X_{CT} = \frac{1}{\dfrac{1}{100} + \dfrac{1}{100} + \dfrac{1}{200}}$$

$$= \frac{1}{\dfrac{2 + 2 + 1}{200}}$$

$$= \frac{200}{2 + 2 + 1}$$

$$= 40 \ \Omega$$

If it is difficult to remember this, it might help to approach it in this way. Since C_T = C1 + C2 + C3 (three capacitors in parallel) and

$$\text{since } X_C \ = \ \frac{1}{2\pi fC} \ : \ \text{or} \quad C = \frac{1}{2\pi fX_c}$$

$$\text{then} \quad \frac{1}{\pi 2 fX_{CT}} \ = \ \frac{1}{2\pi fX_{C1}} \ + \ \frac{1}{2\pi fX_{C2}} \ + \ \frac{1}{2\pi fX_{C3}}$$

then multiplying both sides of this equation by $2 \ \pi \ f$ gives

$$\frac{1}{X_{CT}} \ = \ \frac{1}{X_{C1}} + \frac{1}{X_{C2}} + \frac{1}{X_{C3}}$$

Another memory aide would be to replace the capacitors in the circuit with their capacitive reactances, as in Fig. 4-17. You can then work the problem like a resistor problem.

CAPACITORS IN SERIES

The capacitance of capacitors in series is combined in a similar fashion to resistances in parallel, that is:

$$\frac{1}{C_T} \ = \ \frac{1}{C_1} \ + \ \frac{1}{C_2} \ + \ \frac{1}{C_3}$$

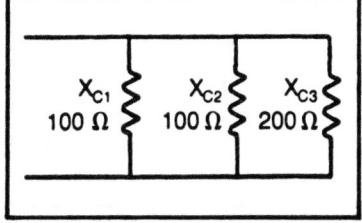

Fig. 4-17. Equivalent circuit for capacitive reactance.

Then to solve *Question 5:*

$$\frac{1}{C_T} = \frac{1}{15 \text{ nF}} + \frac{1}{30 \text{ nF}} + \frac{1}{10 \text{ nF}}$$

$$= \frac{2}{30 \text{ nF}} + \frac{1}{30 \text{ nF}} + \frac{3}{30 \text{ nF}}$$

$$= \frac{2 + 1 + 3}{30 \text{ nF}}$$

$$= \frac{6}{30 \text{ nF}}$$

Taking the reciprocal of both sides gives:

$$C_T = \frac{30 \text{ nF}}{6}$$

$$= 5 \text{ nF}$$

Suppose the circuit was the same but input frequency and current were given. The voltage drops around the circuit could be calculated by finding capacitive reactances. For example: To find voltage drop across C2 in Fig. 4-18:

Since we know $C2 = 30$ nF

$$X_{C2} = \frac{1}{2\pi f C_2}$$

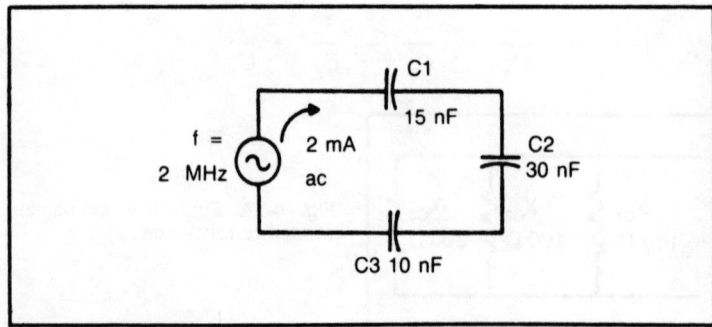

Fig. 4-18. Series capacitor circuit.

$$= \frac{1}{2\pi(2 \times 10^6)(30 \times 10^{-9})}$$

$$= 26.7 \text{ ohms}$$

$$V_{C2} = IX_{C2}$$

$$= 2 \text{ mA } (26.7)$$

$$= 53.4 \text{ mV}$$

If this is giving you trouble, practice by finding voltages for C1 and C3 and for C_T. If calculations are correct $V_{CT} = V_{C1} + V_{C2} + V_{C3}$. Do they?

It should be no surprise to notice that the voltage drop is largest across the largest capacitive reactance. But also notice that the *smallest* capacitor has the largest reactance. Also notice that when a technician wants a small capacitor, reference is to the capacitance. A 100 picofarad is much *smaller* than a one microfarad capacitor, even though the physical size may be the opposite.

Voltage across capacitors in a dc circuit also distribute in an inverse relationship. That is the smaller capacitor will have the largest voltage drop. This is a tough one to get in mind, partly because some of the things studied about capacitors seem to contradict this. We all learned that "capacitors block dc." With that in mind, looking at the circuit in *Question 6* might lead to the conclusion that since C1 "can't pass dc" then the voltage across C2 ought to be zero volts. But if that were true then the voltage across C1 ought likewise to be zero, and then Kirchhoff's voltage law wouldn't hold up. In actuality in this circuit each capacitor charges initially as the electrons flow around the circuit when it is first connected up. Each has the same charge of electrons (careful here, charge is not the same as voltage), but because the capacitors have different capacitances—in different sizes—the electrons per square inch are different. That is, the voltage across one is different than the voltage across the other. The relationship is shown mathematically as:

$$Q = CE$$
$$\text{where } Q = \text{charge}$$

Apply this to the circuit in Q6

$$Q1 = Q2$$
$$\text{and } Q1 = C1 \, E_{C1}$$

where E_{C1} = the voltage across C1

and $\quad Q2 = C2\ E_{C2}$

which gives $C1\ E_{C1} = C2\ E_{C2}$

$$\text{or}\quad \frac{E_{C1}}{E_{C2}} = \frac{C_2}{C_1}$$

This equation says that the voltage drops are inversely proportional to the capacitances. And Kirchhoff's laws tell us that:

$E_{C1} + E_{C2} = 120$ V in this circuit and substituting C1 and C2 values in the ratio equation gives:

$$\frac{E_{C1}}{E_{C2}} = \frac{10\mu F}{2\ \mu F}$$

Hence: $\quad E_{C1} = E_{C2} \bullet 5$

Substituting this in Kirchhoff's equation and solving for E_{C2} gives:

$$5E_{C2} + E_{C2} = 120$$
$$E_{C2}(5+1) = 120$$
$$E_{C2} = 20\ V$$

Occasionally technicians need to substitute or try a capacitor in a circuit and they find that to obtain the capacitance they desire they have to put two capacitors in series. The above distribution of voltages needs to be kept in mind when selecting working voltages if dc voltage is involved in the circuitry.

Let's look at a circuit just to examine a hypothetical use. Suppose that in the circuit of Fig. 4-19 you suspect the bypass capacitor C2 and don't have the exact value, but you do have a 200 μF@10 WV and a 300 μF@ 50 WV. If you make the substitution, the emitter circuit will look like the circuit in Fig. 4-20.

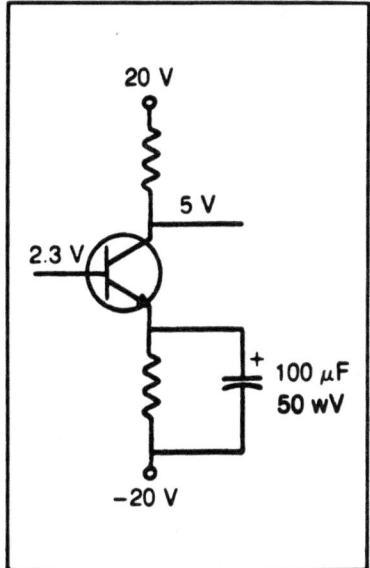

Fig. 4-19. Emitter bypass capacitor.

Will C_{S1} and C_{S2} be OK? You can expect in excess of 20 V drop across the emitter resistor. This voltage will divide 2/5 across C_{S2} and 3/5 across C_{S1}, or C_{S2} will drop in excess of 2/5 (20) = 8 V and C_{S1} will drop in excess of 3/5 (20) = 12 V.

Chances are that C_{S1} will not last long since its rated working voltage is less than the dc drop it will encounter used in this way. The capacitance will be close to the right value.

$$\frac{1}{C_T} = \frac{1}{C_{S1}} + \frac{1}{C_{S2}}$$

$$\frac{1}{C_T} = \frac{1}{200} + \frac{1}{300}$$

$$\frac{1}{C_T} = \frac{3 + 2}{600 \ \mu F}$$

$$\frac{1}{C_T} = \frac{5}{600 \ \mu F}$$

$$C_T = \frac{600 \ \mu F}{5}$$

$$= 120 \ \mu F$$

55

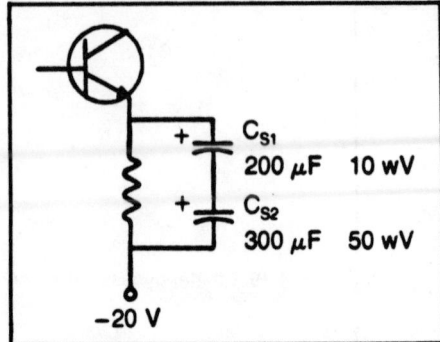

Fig. 4-20. Substitution of capacitor may give voltage breakdown problem.

INDUCTANCES IN PARALLEL AND SERIES

Inductors in parallel add like resistances in parallel. That is, each inductance in parallel reduces the effective parallel inductance.

Hence: $\dfrac{1}{L_T} = \dfrac{1}{L_1} + \dfrac{1}{L_2} + \dfrac{1}{L_3}$

or $L_T = \dfrac{1}{\dfrac{1}{L_1} + \dfrac{1}{L_2} + \cdot\dfrac{1}{L_3}}$ (Answer to Q7)

There are several ways to solve *Question 8*. One way is to use Ohm's law and the inductive reactances to find the circuit's current. Then multiply that current by the X_L (inductive reactance) of L2 to find the voltage. Another way is to do those exact steps but not solve for the numerical value until the end. If we do it this way we won't actually ever have to solve for the value of the current.

$$i_T = \frac{10 \text{ V}}{X_{LT}}$$

where X_{LT} = total inductive reactance

$\qquad = X_{L1} + X_{L2}$ (X_{L1} = reactance of L_1; X_{L2} = reactance of L2)

$\qquad = 2\,\pi\,f\,L_1 + 2\,\pi\,f\,L_2$

But the voltage across L_2 is $i_T\,(X_{L2})$

Therefore:

$$V_{L2} = i_T (X_{L2}) = \frac{10 \text{ V}}{X_{CT}} (X_{L2})$$

$$= \frac{10 \text{ V} (2\pi fL_2)}{2\pi fL_1 + 2\pi fL_2} = \frac{10 \text{ V} (2\pi f) L_2}{(2\pi f)(L_1 + L_2)}$$

$$= 10 \text{ V} \left(\frac{L_2}{L_1 + L_2} \right)$$

now substituting values:

$$V_{L2} = 10 \text{ V} \left(\frac{2 \text{ h}}{6 \text{ h} + 2 \text{ h}} \right)$$

$$= 10 \text{ V } 2/8$$

$$= 2.5 \text{ Vac}$$

RL AND RC CIRCUITS

Series and parallel RC and RL circuits are a little more complicated because the current and voltage may not be in phase with each other. This necessitates addition or combinations by vectors. For example, in the series RC circuit of *Question 9*, the voltages are 90° out of phase. If we use the voltage across the resistor as our reference and remember that current leads voltage in a capacitor, then we can make a vector drawing to represent the relationships (Fig. 4-21).

The reactance relationships have the same phase relationship (Fig. 4-22).

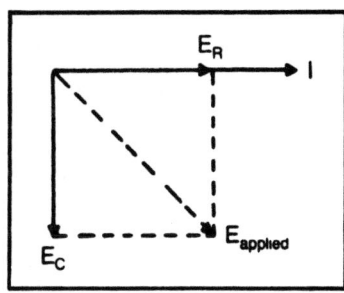

Fig. 4-21. Vector drawing.

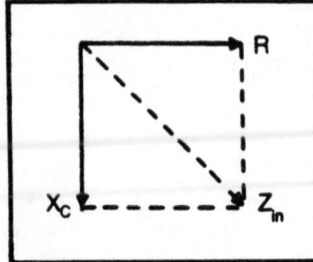

Fig. 4-22. Vector drawing of reactance.

Since X_c = 20 Ω in this problem and since R = 20 Ω, we could estimate Z_{in} by constructing our vector diagram carefully on a graph where the lengths are proportional to the ohmic values as in Fig. 4-23. Even a rough graph like this shows that the length (value) of Z_{in} is between 25 and 30 ohms. Thus, if there is to be a correct answer in *Q9*, it must be *d*, 28.3 ohms.

Of course, the problem can also be solved using the Pythagorean theorem or by the trigonometric functions. We'll solve the next problem by Pythagorean's theorem and the next with trigonometry.

In *Question 10*, the vector drawing shown in Fig. 4-24 could be constructed. Notice that the voltage is used as reference since E is the same on the parallel components; but again, I_C leads the voltage in the capacitor and I_R is in phase with the voltage in the resistor. Again, the applied voltage will lag the resultant circuit current (Fig. 4-25).

Pythagoras discovered that in right triangles the hypotenuse squared was equal to the sum of the square of the two sides. The

Fig. 4-23. Graphic solution of vectors.

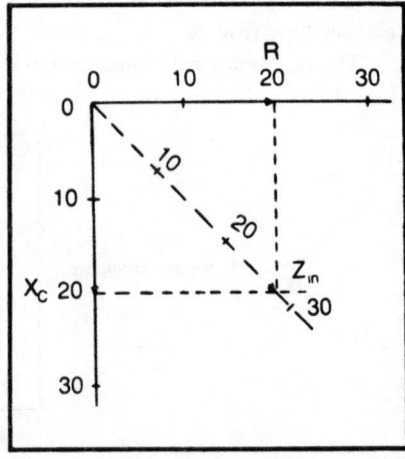

I_C
$I_{Resultant}$
E
I_R

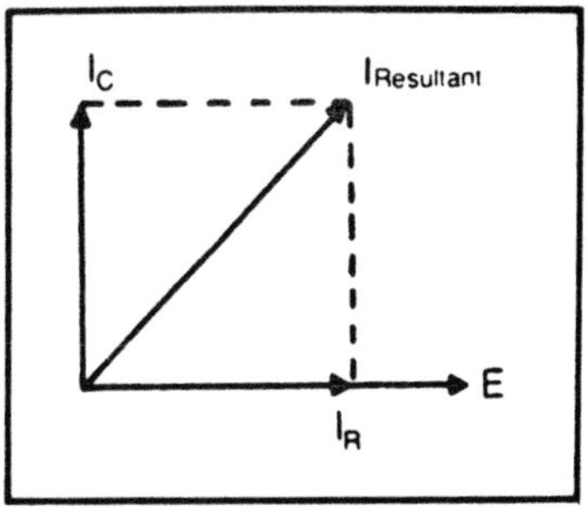

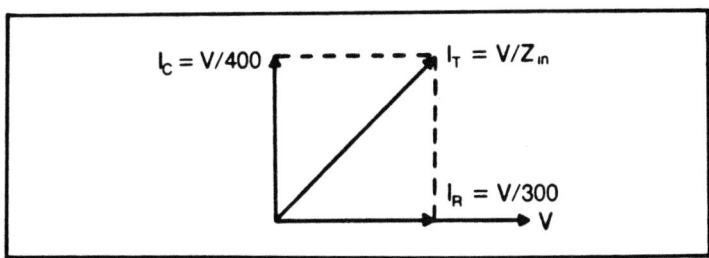

Fig. 4-24. Question 10 vector drawing.

vector diagram can easily be arranged into a right triangle (Fig. 4-26).

Then it follows that the hypotenuse:

$$\left(\frac{V}{Z_{in}}\right)^2 = \left(\frac{V}{X_C}\right)^2 + \left(\frac{V}{R}\right)^2$$

$$\left(\frac{V}{Z_{in}}\right)^2 = \left(\frac{V}{400}\right)^2 + \left(\frac{V}{300}\right)^2$$

Now divide both sides of the equation by V^2

$$\left(\frac{1}{Z_{in}}\right)^2 = \frac{1}{160{,}000} + \frac{1}{90{,}000}$$

Putting the right side of the equation over a common denominator

$$= \frac{90\text{ k} + 160\text{ k}}{(160\text{ k})\,(90\text{ k})}$$

Take the reciprocal and then the square root of both sides:

$$Z_{in} = \sqrt{\frac{(160\text{ k})\,(90\text{ k})}{250\text{ k}}} = \sqrt{57.6\text{ k}} = 240$$

I_C = V/400
I_T = V/Z_{in}
I_R = V/300
V

Fig. 4-25. The voltage lags the current.

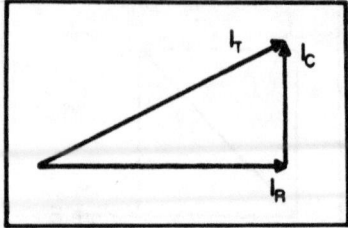

Fig. 4-26. A vector drawing arranged as a right triangle.

Question 11 can be solved by using either method shown above to find the circuit impedance. Then find the current by $i_T = 18 \div Z_{in}$ and then by multiplying i_T by the resistance to obtain the voltage drop across the resistor. But the impedance can also be found by using trigonometric functions. Not all schools of electronics teach these principles since the above method works quite well. We include this section for review by those technicians familiar with these techniques. Again, we construct a triangle (Fig. 4-27).

$$\text{The angle } \theta = \tan^{-1} 20/15 \text{ (read as angle whose tangent is 20/15)}$$

$$= 53° 8' \text{ (look up in table)}$$
$$\text{and } Z_{in} = 20/\sin \theta$$
$$= 20/(0.8)|[\text{look up in table}]$$
$$= 25$$
$$\text{then } i_T = V_{ac}/Z_{in}$$
$$i_T = \frac{50}{25}$$
$$= 2A$$
$$V_R = i_T R$$
$$= 2 (15)$$
$$= 30 \text{ volts (Answer to } Q11)$$

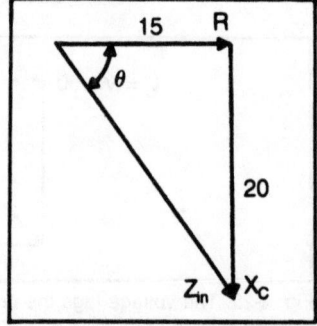

Fig. 4-27. Using the trigonometric functions.

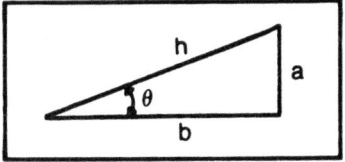

Fig. 4-28. This triangle shows the trigonometric relationships.

Any math book probably contains the trigonometric formulas. Here is a listing of a few common formulas (Fig. 4-28).

$$\sin \theta = \frac{a}{h} \text{ or } \sin^{-1} \frac{a}{h} = \theta$$

$$\cos \theta = \frac{b}{h} \text{ or } \cos^{-1} \frac{b}{h} = \theta$$

$$\tan \theta = \frac{a}{b} \text{ or } \tan^{-1} \frac{a}{b} = \theta$$

Capacitors and resistors in series are often used in circuits with nonsinusoidal waveforms—often with square waves or pulses. *Question 12* deals with this type of situation. Here we need to be aware that capacitors take time to charge up. In fact, the time it takes is proportional to the product of resistance and capacitance.

The time it takes a capacitor to charge or discharge by 63 percent of the total change possible, is the product of R (the resistance of the charge or discharge path) and C (the capacitance of the capacitor).

$$T = RC$$

Before tackling *Q12*, let's examine the circuit in Fig. 4-29. Of course, it's the same circuit but rearranged to emphasize the volt-

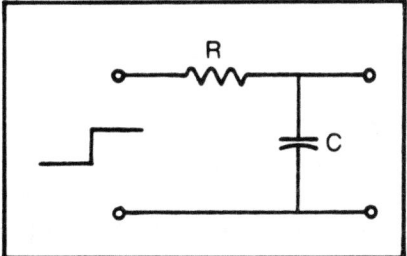

Fig. 4-29. Rearrangement of Fig. 4-11.

age across the capacitor. And as we just said, the capacitor takes time to charge; hence, we would expect the output to start at zero and charge eventually (at least 10 RC time constants) to the input voltage.

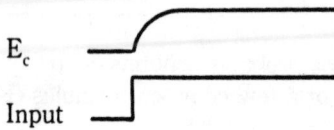

E_c

Input

Now keeping in mind that the voltage around the series circuit must add up to zero at all times, what must the voltage be across the resistor?

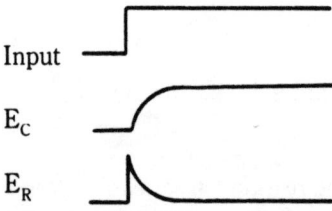

Input

E_C

E_R

Notice that E_C and E_R at any instant equals the input voltage. Also notice that E_R is the waveform shown in answer *a* of *Q12*.

In an inductive circuit like *Question 13*, at the occurrence of a step voltage the inductance will not allow the current to change instantaneously. With no current flow initially, the voltage drop across R is zero and the E_L is, therefore, the applied voltage step. As current builds up the voltage across R increases, the voltage across L decreases. The voltage will change by 63 percent in one time constant.

$$T = L/R$$

$$\text{in this case } T = \frac{1 \text{ mH}}{1 \text{ k}\Omega}$$

$$= 1 \ \mu \text{ second}$$

PARALLEL L, R, AND C TANKS

Inductors and capacitors in parallel exhibit some special characteristics quite useful in electronic circuits. They are used extensively to select frequencies of interest and to reject other frequencies. At low frequencies capacitive reactance X_C is high because $X_C = 1/2\pi fC$. Inductors at low frequency exhibit a low impedance. $X_L = 2\pi fL$. At resonance $X_C = X_L$. In the parallel circuit of *Question 14* with the frequency below resonance, then the X_C is greater than the X_L. With smaller X_L the source will find the inductor an easier path for current to flow. Hence, answer *c* is correct.

Question 15 points out some startling concepts of parallel circuits. Examine the circuit of Fig. 4-30.

We know that $Z_T = Z_1Z_2/Z_1 + Z_2$ from work with parallel resistors. But since currents in the impedances are not in phase, neither are the impedances. Therefore, to solve this equation for a real example we have to take into account the phase angles. Using the j operator is one way to do this.

$$Z_T = \frac{(jX_L)(-jX_C)}{jX_L + (-jX_C)}$$

For *Q15* $X_L = 30$ and $X_C = 40$

$$Z_T = \frac{(j30)(-j40)}{j30 - j40}$$

$$= \frac{-(j)(j)1200}{-j10}$$

but $j = \sqrt{-1}$ and $\therefore (j)(j) = -1$

$$Z_T = \frac{1200}{-j10} \quad \left(\text{note: } \frac{1}{-j} = j\right)$$

$$= j120 \text{ ohms}$$

$$= 120 \text{ ohms in phase with the inductor}$$

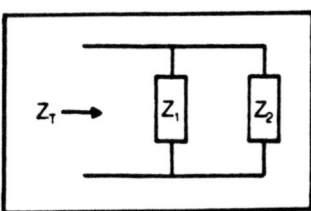

Fig. 4-30. Parallel impedances.

To illustrate a little further with this example, let's find i_L and i_C and then i_T and finally Z_T, which should be the same as just calculated. A voltage is not given so let's assume 120 volts just for easy division.

$$i_L = \frac{120 \text{ V}}{X_L} \qquad\qquad i_C = \frac{120}{X_C}$$

$$= \frac{120}{30} \qquad\qquad\qquad = \frac{120}{40}$$

$$= 4 \text{ A} \qquad\qquad\qquad = 3 \text{ A}$$

But these currents are 180° out of phase as illustrated in this phase diagram.

4 A i_L leads e by 90°

i_T e

3 A i_C lags e by 90°

i_T then is the vector sum of 1 ampere.

$$Z_1 = \frac{120 \text{ V}}{1 \text{ A}}$$

$$= 120 \text{ ohms in phase with } i_L$$

Note that the voltage doesn't alter the result. Try a different voltage and do the same steps, if you are unsure of this.

Also notice that if X_L and X_C are equal, i_T would be zero. In a real circuit this is impossible; X_L can equal X_C but some current will have to be drawn from the source because of resistive losses. It does mean, however, that the effective impedance looking into a parallel LC circuit at resonance can be very, very high. Therefore, a circuit arranged as in *Question 16* would be a high impedance at or near resonance, but X_L becomes very low at lower frequencies and X_C becomes low at higher frequencies bypassing signals not near resonance. A band of frequencies will be passed near resonance. The circuit is a bandpass filter. Answer *d* is correct for *Question 16*.

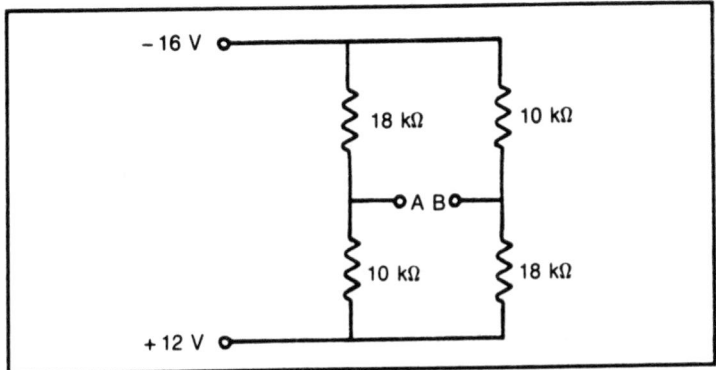

Fig. 4-31. A series parallel circuit.

PARALLEL-SERIES CIRCUIT COMBINATIONS

A series-parallel combination of resistors is shown in *Question 17.* There are, of course, an infinite variety of series and parallel combinations possible. This combination is often encountered in electronics and should be familiar. It is also called a bridge circuit. One approach to solving this circuit is to first obtain the voltage drops across individual resistors, then add voltages around a loop from A to B to find the voltage of A with respect to B. The circuit is shown in Fig. 4-31.

First, let's deal with the +12 V and – 16 V shown on the schematic. When a supply voltage is shown on a schematic without showing a reference, it is assumed that the voltage is with respect to ground. If we drew in the sources as batteries and connected the grounds the circuit would look like Fig. 4-32. At any rate, in this example, the total voltage across each series

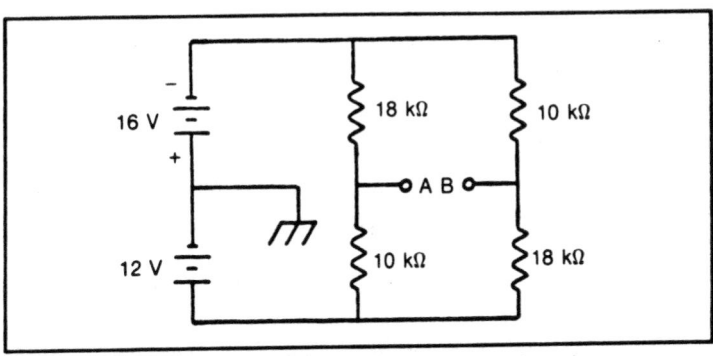

Fig. 4-32. Circuit of Fig. 4-15 with batteries shown as the voltage sources.

65

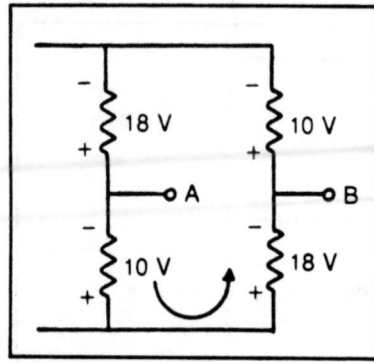

Fig. 4-33. Voltage distribution for the circuit of Fig. 4-15.

combination is 16 V + 12 V or 28 V. Each series leg has 28 kΩ total resistance. Hence, the current in each leg is 1 mA. Let's multiply each resistance by 1 mA and put the voltage drops on each resistor, as in Fig. 4-33. If we sum voltages around the lower loop as indicated by the arrow, the voltage from A to B is:

$$V_{AB} = -10 \text{ V} + 18 \text{ V}$$
$$= +8 \text{ V}$$

Or the voltage at A with respect to ground is $V_{AG} = -10$ V + 12 V = 2 V and B is $V_{BG} = -18$ V + 12 V = -6 V and hence, since A is +2 V above ground and B is 6 V below ground, A is 8 volts above B.

Another possible parallel series combination of resistors is shown in *Question 18*. In this circuit the actual value of R1 can be found by dividing 50 volts by (10 mA + 20 mA) the total current flowing through R1. This value is 1670 Ω (1.67 k). A 20 percent, 1500 ohm resistor can vary from 1500 − .2(1500) to 1500 + .2(1500) or 1200 to 1800 ohms. Since 1.67 k is within this range answer *b* is correct.

ADDITIONAL READING

Larch, E. Norman: *Fundamentals of Electronics,* John Wiley.

Lease, Alfred: *Basic Electronics,* The Bruce Publishing Company, 1965.

Mandl, Matthew: *Fundamentals of Electronics,* Prentice-Hall, 1960.

Edwards, John: *Exploring Electricity and Electronics with Projects,* TAB BOOKS Inc., 1983.

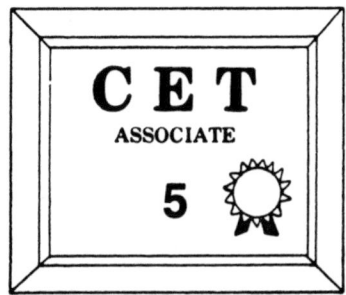

C E T
ASSOCIATE

5

Oscillators, Detectors, Comparators, Demodulators

This chapter covers the subjects of oscillators, detectors, comparators, and demodulators. Let's start with a quick quiz.

QUIZ

Q1. In Fig. 5-1, there are four oscillators, which blocks are they?

    a. A, B, F, G   c. A, D, C, G
    b. A, E, F, G   d. A, C, F, G

Q2. Which block in Fig. 5-1 would be used to decipher correct hue and color-intensity information?

    a. B   c. D
    b. C   d. E

Q3. Which block might be classified as a comparator in Fig. 5-1.

    a. B   c. D
    b. C   d. E

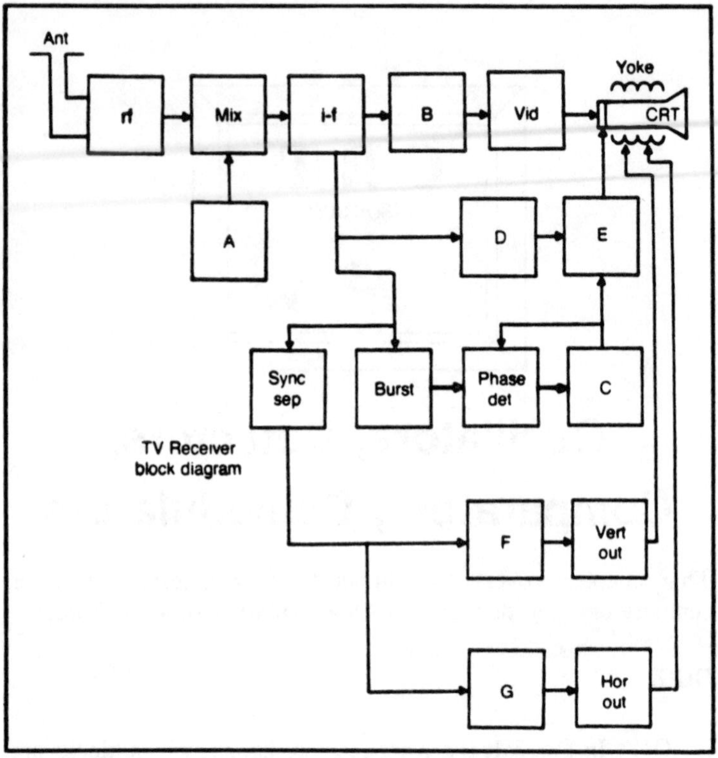

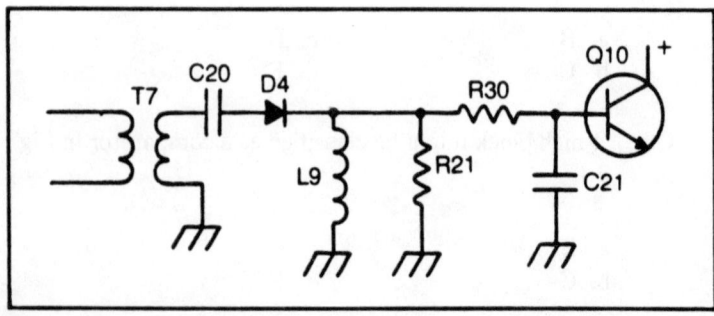

Fig. 5-1. Television receiver block diagram for Q1, Q2, and Q3.

Q4. The circuit in Fig. 5-2 would most likely be used in which block?

a. B   c. C
b. A   d. E

Fig. 5-2. Electronic circuit for Q4.

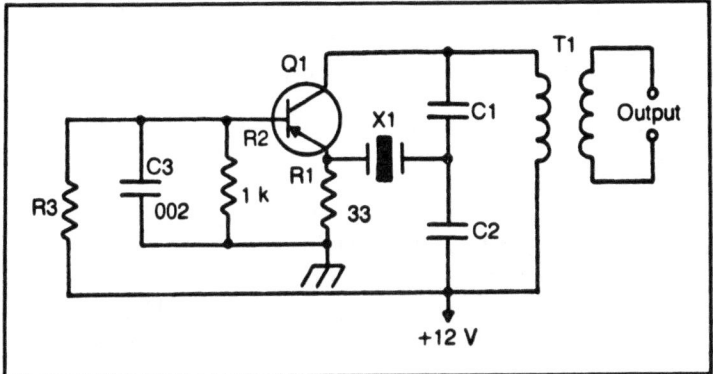

Fig. 5-3. Electronic circuit for Q5.

Q5. The output of the circuit in Fig. 5-3 will be:

    a. dependent upon signal input at Q1 base

    b. continuous oscillating ac waveform

    c. one-shot oscillation frequency depending on the size of R1, C1, C2, and X1

    d. detected as 1/2 of the input waveform

Q6. Feedback that makes the UHF oscillator in Fig. 5-4 work comes from the:

    a. collector to the base via the interelement capacitance of Q1

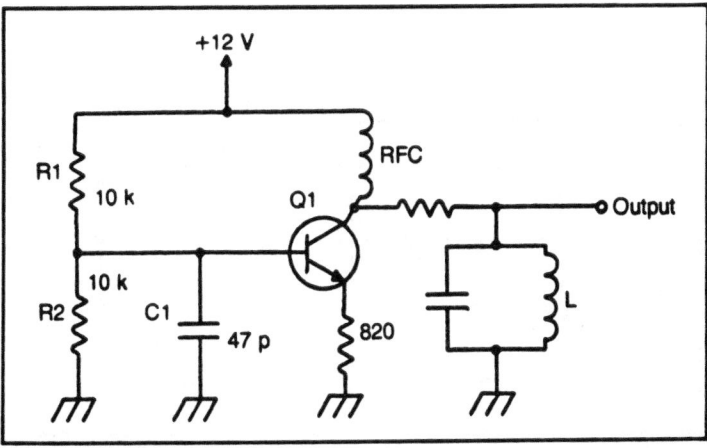

Fig. 5-4. UHF oscillator schematic for Q6.

b. from the rf choke through R1 to the base of Q1

c. from the output to the base, through the air

d. through L and the grounds, to C1

Q7. In Fig. 5-5 what will happen to the output if input A goes positive with respect to B?

a. the op-amp will compare the inputs and cause the output to go negative

b. the output will go positive

c. the inputs will be compared but the voltage at X must be −0.7 volts or more negative before any change will occur

d. Figure 5-5 is not a voltage comparator, but an oscillator

Q8. The detector in Fig. 5-6 is identified as:

a. ratio detector

b. discriminator

c. quadrature detector

d. envelope detector

Q9. The circuit in Fig. 5-7 is:

a. providing 3.58 MHz locking signals to the TV set color oscillator

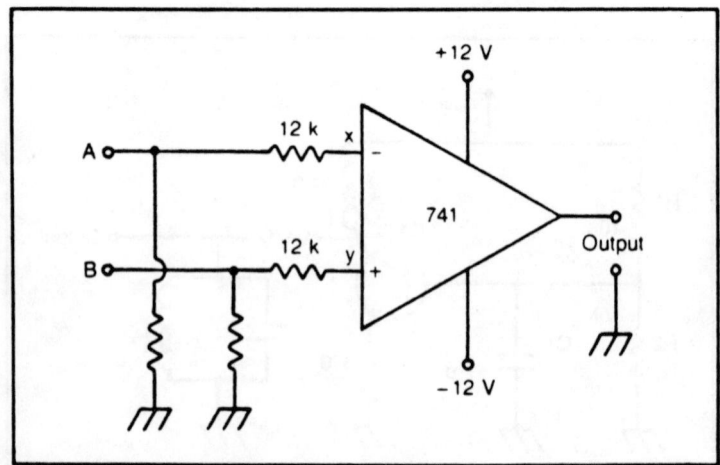

Fig. 5-5. Operational amplifier circuit for Q7.

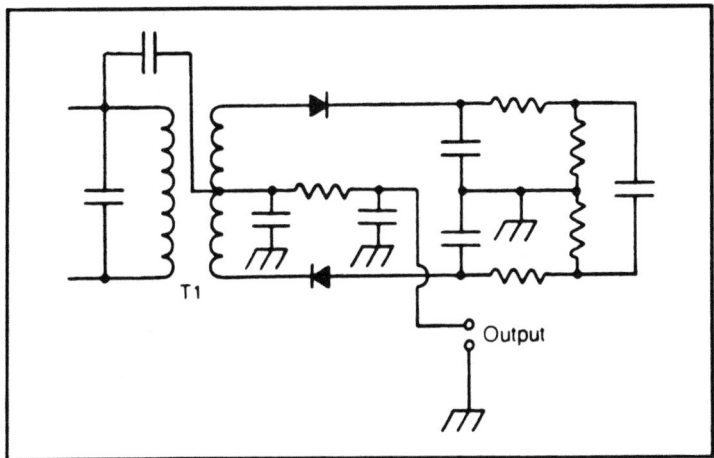

Fig. 5-6. Diode circuit for Q8.

b. a series of bandpass amplifiers
c. a circuit to vectorially recover color difference signals in a color TV
d. a circuit that generates a 3.58 MHz and a 3.58 MHz signal shifted 90° for use in a color receiver demodulator

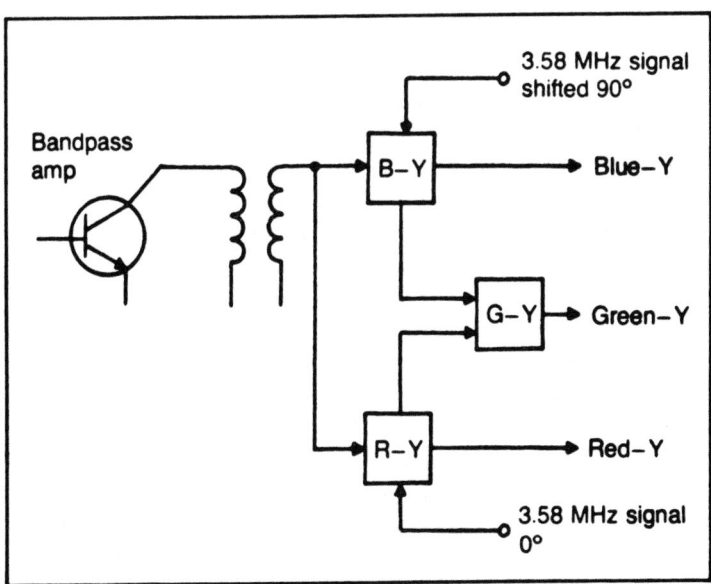

Fig. 5-7. Block diagram for Q9.

Q10. The Fig. 5-8 circuit is:

    a. a circuit designed to be activated when light strikes the LED

    b. a circuit designed to couple a signal from one isolated circuit to another

    c. a photoresistor

    d. a color detector

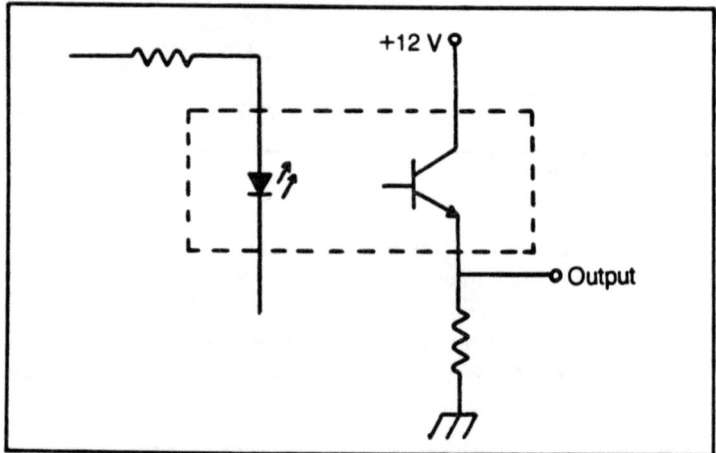

Fig. 5-8. A device schematic for Q10.

While the Associate Exam questions are not related to specific electronics products, the color TV set is used here because it is familiar to nearly all technicians and contains all of the circuits dealt with in this chapter. If you are not familiar with how TV sets work, it would be valuable to you to learn about them now.

OSCILLATORS

Question 1 asks which blocks of Fig. 5-1 have oscillators. The first is "A," known as the 'local' oscillator. This circuit provides a signal to the mixer that is higher than the incoming desired rf signal (the TV station signal) by an amount equal to the i-f (intermediate frequency) being used in the receiver. If the i-f picture carrier signal selected by the manufacturer is 45.75 MHz, then the local oscillator will be running at 101 MHz for channel 2 (picture carrier frequency is 55.25 MHz). Note the i-f frequencies are the difference between the incoming rf signal and the rf produced by the oscillator. The local oscillator frequency is switched to a higher frequency in order that higher TV frequencies such as channel 3, or 4, etc., are selected. Each selected channel's picture carrier is just 45.75 MHz lower than the local oscillator frequency. If the mixer stage then has its output tuned to the i-f frequencies then no matter which station is selected, the output of the mixer is always the i-f frequencies containing the modulation coming from the TV station. The local oscillator/mixer circuitry is known as a heterodyne circuit and the mixing of the oscillator and rf signal to obtain the same i-f frequency for each station is known as heterodyning. The advantage of converting each group of rf signals to a single band of intermediate frequencies is that a single band of frequencies can be more practically amplified than can a broad band of frequencies covering the entire TV broadcast band.

The second oscillator is "C" in Fig. 5-1, the 3.58 MHz color oscillator. We need it in a TV set because the 3.58 MHz color carrier frequency used in TV communications is not transmitted by the TV station, due to limited TV channel bandwidth. Only the 3.58 MHz color information sidebands are transmitted as part of the TV broadcast signal. Since these sidebands have nothing to 'relate to' when they get to the TV receiver, we must reintroduce the 3.58 MHz signal somewhere in the receiver. If we do that we can then recover, or *demodulate*, the color information contained in the sidebands and produce correct hue and color intensity information.

We need two more oscillators. One to produce 60 Hz to deflect the CRT picture vertically at a speed too fast to show any flicker in our eyes. We also need a 15732 Hz oscillator and amplifier to push the CRT beam from left to right on the screen at the single-line rate.

Note that in a TV set only 'samples' of the oscillator frequencies are sent from the broadcast station, but the C, F, and G frequencies we produce in the receiver must be exactly the same as similar timer circuits used in producing the video signal at the transmitter.

COMPARATORS

If you need to guess what answer is correct for *Question 2* then you should be able to narrow the choices down to C, D, and E as possibilities. Since C has already been described as the 3.58 MHz oscillator then it must not be a 'detector' or 'demodulator'. It is used as a reference to help detect the information contained in the color signals relating to color intensity and hue, but it is not a "demodulator." D could be part of the demodulator but it is actually used to separate the color information from the rest of the TV signal and to perform some other operations. E is the demodulator. It is here where the red, green, and blue information is extracted immediately prior to applying it to the picture tube.

Block E compared the phase of the color subcarrier signal sideband information with the 'standard', or 3.58 MHz oscillator signal (coming from C). Both of these signals meet in block E and the hue and color intensity is 'demodulated' or interpreted in E. E then is comparing the incoming color signal with the reference signal. It isn't ordinarily identified as a comparator, but in performing the demodulation of the color signal it does so by comparing color modulation to the reference. The answer to *Question 3* is *d*.

DETECTORS

Figure 5-2 is a commonplace audio or video detector circuit. The design varies greatly but the function is to detect the usable information contained in the i-f signal envelope. Since the envelope varies + or − a zero reference, to detect the amplitude variations of that signal, we first must clip off one half of the signal envelope. We can merely rectify the i-f variations with the diode detector to accomplish this. In Fig. 5-2 we clip off the negative portion and keep the positive half. Then we use a low-pass filter in R30 and C21 so that the rf variations (44 MHz) are smoothed out and Q10 sees merely the audio (if in a radio) or the video signal (if in a TV). The circuit could be called a demodulator also, but it never is. The circuit is used in block B, answer *a* in *Question 4*.

Figure 5-3 is a common crystal-oscillator circuit. Nearly any amplifier circuit can be made to oscillate. To assure that it oscillates at the desired frequency, (perhaps 3.58 MHz) X1 is selected for that frequency. The other circuit components set the proper transistor operating voltages and provide stabilization. The circuit shows no input signal at the base so answer *a* in *Question 5* is incorrect. The circuit has none of the features of a one-shot oscillator, and there is nothing to suggest it is a detector of any type. Other types of oscillators should be studied so that you become familiar with their appearance and applications. Some types in rf work are: *Armstrong*, which uses a "tickler" coil to sustain oscillations; *Colpitts*, recognized by split capacitors in the input circuit; *Hartley*, recognized by a split inductance in the grid/base circuit, and crystal, such as that of Fig. 5-3. In addition there are numerous oscillators used in digital work: TTL one-shot; square-wave generator; multivibrator; monostable; free running; voltage controlled, and others.

As stated above, the Fig. 5-4 circuit can be an oscillator if the circuit values cause high enough gain in the transistor to put some signal back into the base circuit. Unfortunately it is hard to recognize the difference between some amplifiers and some oscillators if there is no direct coupling of the feedback. That is the case in *Question 6*. The feedback is by way of the inter-element capacitance of the transistor. It could be by close proximity of the collector circuit to the base, but that would be unpredictable as to the actual frequency generated.

OPERATIONAL AMPLIFIERS

Op amps can detect minute changes in their inputs. With the type of configuration (shown in Fig. 5-6 of *Question 8*) with both inputs balanced, any minute change in one input will drive the amp into saturation. Saturation output voltage will be slightly less than the supply voltage, + or − 12 V. The circuit can be redesigned to provide feedback from the output to the inputs, which can allow variable output levels corresponding to the level of the input voltages. Note here that if Y goes positive with respect to X, then the output will swing positive. If X goes positive with respect to Y, the output will swing negative since the X input produces an inverted output.

Detector Types

Question 8 asks you to recognize a ratio detector. Two items are important: the diodes are "reversed" and there is a large electrolytic to filter out the rf after detection. A discriminator (Fig. 5-9) looks similar but there is no large filter (5 μF is typical in a ratio detector) and the diodes "face" the same direction. Note that the output of a ratio detector comes from the center of the transformer while the discriminator takes the audio from the diodes. The detector in Fig. 5-2 is an example of an envelope detector. Quadrature detectors combine two components of the FM signal in a gated synchronous circuit. One of the components is shifted 90 degrees out of phase by being passed through an LC combination. When combined the output is the original audio contained in the FM signal. The LC combination is the key to identifying that type of detector in an FM circuit.

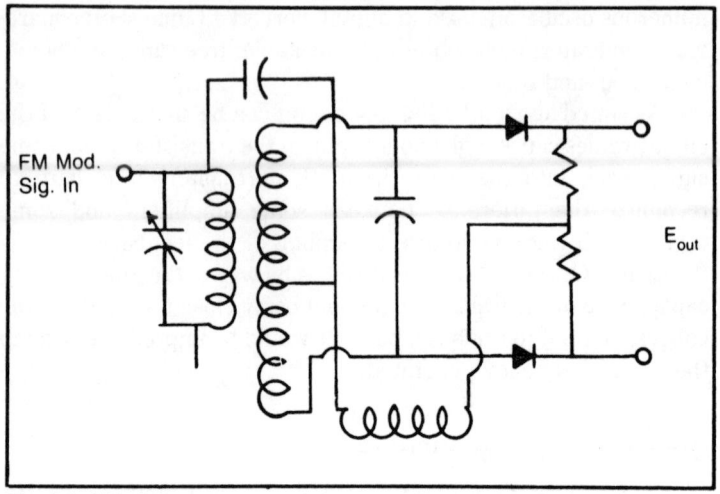

Fig. 5-9. Discriminator.

Color Demodulation

Figure 5-7 increases the information in block "E" of *Question 2*, showing the three blocks that made up the single block. This demodulation is complex. The frequency is high and the components of the signal are both phase and amplitude modulated at the transmitter by the color information. A phase-varying signal represents this information at the output of the bandpass amplifier. Various schemes have been used to demodulate or recover this information. A demodulator 'sampling' the phase-varying signal at a particular phase angle will produce voltages corresponding to the amount and hue of the color originally coded at that phase angle at the transmitter. If the detected signal is to be applied to a grid in a picture tube that corresponds to the red gun and the cathode of that gun containing Y or luminance information, then the demodulator must detect information that corresponds to red minus the luminance Y, or R – Y. In a similar manner B minus Y(B – Y) and G minus Y(G – Y) could be detected but it turns out that G – Y can more easily be made by proper combinations of R – Y and B – Y as indicated in the block diagram. The correct answer to *Question 9* is *c*.

Sometimes our minds get a "set." The circuit of *Question 10* merely asks if you recognize the symbol for an optical coupler. These are used increasingly in computer technology where signal grounds and power supply voltages would be better off not mixed. For instance, isolating a remote sensor from the main process-control computer would remove any shock hazard associated with the computer mainframe, ground faults and so forth. The answer, therefore, has nothing to do with this chapter except to check your "mind set."

ADDITIONAL READING

Adams, Thomas M.: *Detector and Rectifier Circuits*, Howard W. Sams, 1966.

Adams, Thomas M.: *Oscillator Circuits*, Howard W. Sams, 1966.

Gibilisco, Stan: *Basic Transistor Course—2nd Edition*, TAB BOOKS Inc., 1984.

Lytel, Allan: *Handbook of Transistor Circuits*, Howard W. Sams, 1969.

Veatch, Henry C.: *Transistor Circuit Actions*, McGraw-Hill, 1968.

Test Equipment
and Measurements

This chapter contains questions about measurements and test equipment. Use it as a guide. If you are unsure of the material a particular question relates to, and not enough help is contained in this chapter, refer to the reference list at the end of this chapter for further study.

QUIZ

Q1. If a 20,000 ohms-per-volt meter movement is to be used to measure 10 volts at full scale, R_x in this circuit (Fig. 6-1) should be:

a. 200 kΩ
b. 20 kΩ
c. 9 kΩ
d. 180 kΩ

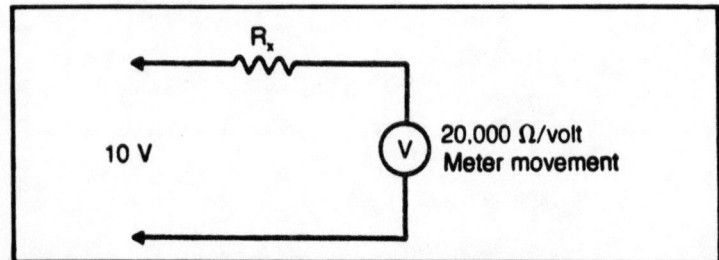

Fig. 6-1. Simple voltmeter circuit for Q1.

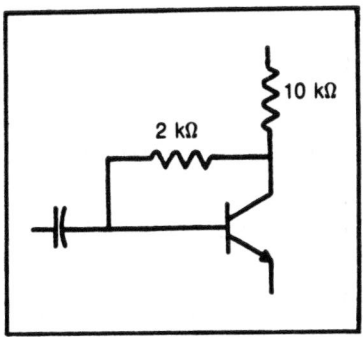

Fig. 6-2. Circuit to be measured in Q2.

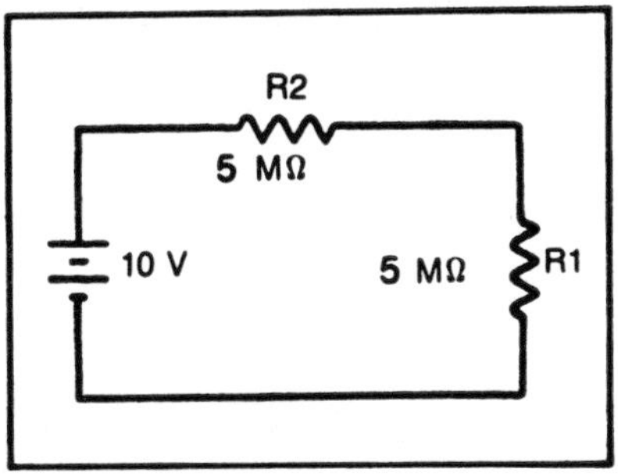

R2
5 MΩ
10 V
5 MΩ R1

Q2. The meter in *Question 1* is used on the 10-volt range to measure the voltage across R1 in the circuit of Fig. 6-2. It will read:

a. 5 volts
b. 10 volts

c. less than 0.5 volts
d. more than 0.5 volts

Q3. In the circuit of Fig. 6-3 a low-voltage ohmmeter was used to measure the 2 k resistance. The reading will be reliable:

a. true
b. false

Q4. The 20,000 ohm/voltmeter movement of *Question 1* is going to be used to build an ammeter with 1 mA full-scale deflection. A shunt resistance will be needed to bypass most of the current. The shunt resistance should be:

a. 1.053 kΩ
b. 0.95 kΩ

c. 20 kΩ
d. 1 Ω

10 kΩ
2 kΩ

Fig. 6-3. Circuit to be measured in Q3.

Q5. The 1 mA meter of *Question 4* is to be inserted at X in the circuit of Fig. 6-4. We should expect the measured current to be:

a. less than 0.5 mA
b. more than 0.5 mA
c. not significantly different than 0.5 mA

Q6. With an oscilloscope in triggered-sweep operation:

a. the trace starts without regard to the trigger
b. vertical deflection is triggered by sweep
c. horizontal deflection is modulated by Z
d. the sweep voltage starts at trigger

Q7. Retrace blanking in an oscilloscope is:

a. not used
b. applied to the Z-axis
c. used on recurrent sweep only
d. used to blank vertical retrace

Q8. Use of an × 10 probe instead of direct connection to a scope:

a. reduces circuit loading
b. increases the effective input impedance
c. decreases the signal to the scope
d. all of the above.

Q9. In the circuit of Fig. 6-5, if you want to see what the

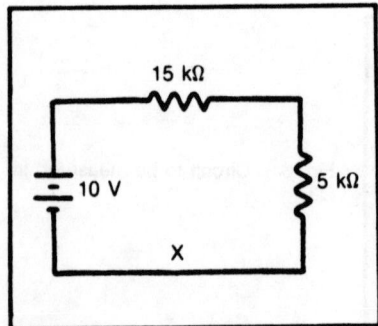

Fig. 6-4. Circuit used for Q5.

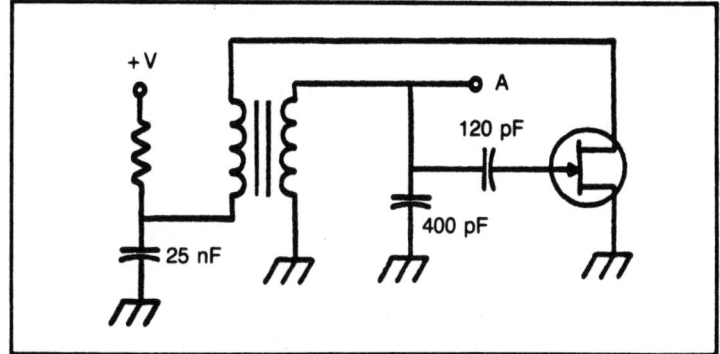

Fig. 6-5. Circuit to be observed with oscilloscope in Q9.

waveform at point A looks like, along with the scope you would use:

a. ×1 probe

c. rf probe

b. ×10 probe

d. high-voltage probe

Q10. If the top of the graticule was set for 0 Vdc, and the sensitivity at 1 V/cm, the waveform shown in Fig. 6-6 when measured with a ×10 probe has a:

a. −2.4 Vdc component

c. −0.24 Vdc component

b. −24 Vdc component

d. 0 Vdc component

Q11. In the waveform shown in Fig. 6-6 the peak-to-peak voltage measurement is:

a. 12 V P-P

c. 0.12 V P-P

b. 1.2 V P-P

d. 24 V P-P

Q12. If the sweep time is calibrated at 10 ms/cm in the waveform of Fig. 6-6 then the frequency of the waveform is:

a. 100 Hz

c. 50 Hz

b. 20 MHz

d. 10 MHz

Q13. A digital voltmeter contains a frequency counter. In order to use the counter to measure voltage the input voltage level:

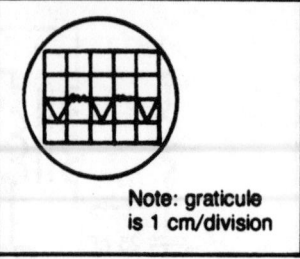

Fig. 6-6. Waveform measured in Q10.

Note: graticule is 1 cm/division

    a. is used to scale time
    b. goes to an analog to digital converter
    c. is applied to a galvanometer
    d. both a and b are correct

Q14. A function generator delivers sine waves, square waves, triangle waves, and others. If a square wave gets attenuated on all frequencies except its fundamental frequency, the result would be:

    a. a sawtooth modified
    b. a "spiked" signal
    c. a sine wave
    d. none of these

Q15. A circuit is to be aligned using a sweep generator and post marker generator. The marker generator is usually a:

    a. continuously sweeping frequency
    b. crystal-generated frequency
    c. constant amplitude signal
    d. none of the above

Q16. The output of a flip-flop used in a binary counter is being checked with a logic probe. The indicator of normal operation would be:

    a. a blinking light   c. a light that is lit
    b. a light that is out   d. none of these

Q17. A logic pulser probe generates:

    a. low duty-cycle pulses   c. various patterns
    b. logic pulses   d. all of the above

Q18. A logic current probe is used to:

    a. there is no such probe
    b. trace current through wire
    c. check turbidity of water
    d. inject signals into nodes

METERS

Proper use of meters is always a concern of electronics technicians. This portion of the chapter deals with some aspects of using meters to test electronic circuits. The sensitivity of a voltmeter can be given in two different ways. Each has to do with the amount of current it takes to cause full-scale deflection of the pointer or needle in a D'Arsonval meter movement. Suppose you have a meter with 20,000 ohms/volt sensitivity and the lowest voltage scale is 1 volt. That is, when the range switch is set at 1 volt, it takes 1 volt applied to the meter input terminals to cause full-scale deflection. The current flowing in the meter will be 1 volt divided by 20,000 ohms or 0.05 mA. Suppose there is a 10-volt scale on this meter. If you apply 10 volts and want full-scale deflection, the meter movement must still have only 0.05 mA flowing. Hence, you need a series resistance to drop most of the 10 volts to still wind up with 1 volt on the meter movement to result in 0.05 mA through the meter. The series resistance (R_x, in Fig. 6-1) must then be 9 volts divided by 0.05 mA, or 180 kΩ.

METER LOADING (VOLTAGE)

Meter loading is a problem every technician should be aware of. Almost any test instrument will have some effect on the circuit to which it is attached. Good usage will minimize this effect. A common cause of error is current loading by the meter. In *Question 2*, a circuit is to be measured with a VOM. The circuit has rather large value resistors and we should suspect this will be a problem. Without the meter the voltage will divide equally across R1 and R2, but the introduction of the 200 k resistance of the meter in parallel with R1, significantly alters the circuit. In fact, R1 of 5 MΩ in parallel with 200 kΩ of the meter is an equivalent resistance of less than 200 k ($\approx$192 k). The new equivalent circuit then looks like Fig. 6-7. The voltage across the 192 k (voltage the meter "sees") is

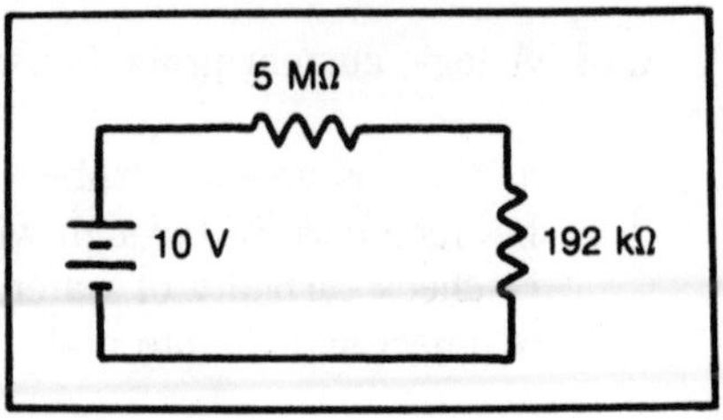

Fig. 6-7. Equivalent circuit.

$$\frac{10 \text{ V } (192 \text{ k})}{5 \text{ meg } + 192 \text{ k}} = 0.396 \text{ V.}$$ Hence, answer c is correct in *Question 2*.

LOW-VOLTAGE OHMMETER

A recent innovation in ohmmeters is the introduction of the low-voltage ohmmeter. This meter is used to measure resistance but uses a low-voltage power source. Remember that ohmmeters (since they operate in unpowered circuits), must provide their own power. Many have two or three batteries for this purpose. An example would be an ohmmeter with a 9-volt battery for high-ohms scales, and a 1.5-volt battery for low-ohms scales; and now ohmmeters with open-circuit output voltages as low as 100 millivolts. The purpose of this low-voltage ohms scale is to measure resistances in parallel with diode or transistor junctions without biasing the junction, thereby giving a parallel current path. The answer to *Question 3* is, therefore, a, true.

Current Measurement

If a meter movement is to be used in measuring current, a common way to change the range of currents to be measured is to put shunts around the meter. Notice that the meter movement of *Q1* (20,000 ohms/volt) could be used directly to measure up to 0.05 mA (or 50 μA). To measure larger current, however, necessitates a shunt. *Question 4* involves calculating the shunt resistance for using the 20,000 ohms/volt meter to measure full scale of 1 mA. A sketch is shown in Fig. 6-8 to help visualize the problem:

$$\text{Since } I_x = 1 \text{ mA } - .05 \text{ mA } = .95 \text{ mA}$$

$$\text{then } R_S = \frac{1V}{.95 \text{ mA}} = 1.0526 \text{ k}\Omega$$

84

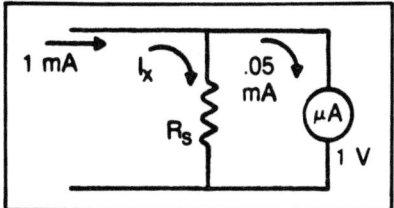

Fig. 6-8. Shunt resistor for making a 1 mA meter scale.

"LOADING" IN CURRENT MEASUREMENT

Using a current meter also causes problems in the circuit being measured. Since the circuit is opened and the meter inserted, the meter's resistance becomes part of the circuit. If we redraw the circuit of *Question 5* to include the meter circuit we get the circuit shown in Fig. 6-9.

The 10 V battery now "sees" a slightly higher resistance. Instead of 20 kΩ it "sees" nearly 21 kΩ, therefore, insertion of the meter reduces the current. If the resistances were accurate, the original current should have been:

$$I = \frac{10 \text{ V}}{20 \text{ k}\Omega}$$

$$= 0.5 \text{ mA}$$

With the increase in the series resistance by insertion of the meter, the current will be approximately

$$I = \frac{10 \text{ V}}{20 \text{ k}\Omega + 1 \text{ k}\Omega}$$

$$= 0.48 \text{ mA}$$

Fig. 6-9. Equivalent circuit to calculate effects of meter "loading" in a current measurement.

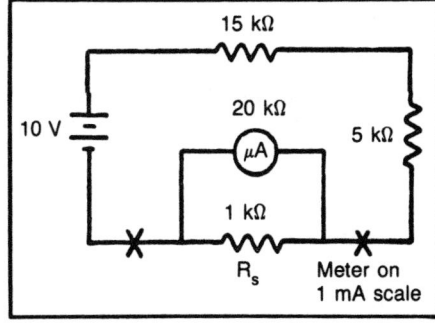

Therefore, the answer to *Q5* is *a*. Less than 0.5 mA, or depending on the situation answer *c* may be correct; 0.02 mA may not be a significant difference in a particular application. A question with two answers equally correct would *not* be included in the Certification Examination. This one was included for discussion only.

OSCILLOSCOPES

Since an oscilloscope is an integral part of most electronic troubleshooting, many questions on the Certification Exam deal with oscilloscopes. Some questions concern oscilloscope operation and some concern using a scope for measurements. *Questions 6 and 7* are examples of operations. In using a triggered sweep scope, you become familiar with various controls that set the generation of a trigger pulse. You may select the trigger source as *External, Internal,* or *Line*. On *External* the trigger generator is connected to the external trigger jack or plug, on *Internal* the trigger is generated from the voltage in a vertical channel; on *Line* from the ac power line. Other controls set the *Level, Slope,* and *Mode* of operation (such as ac fast, dc, ac slow, etc.). In any case, once a trigger has been generated it in turn starts the horizontal sweep generator which normally moves the electron beam from left to right on the CRT screen or display. Hence, the correct answer in *Question 6* is *d*.

A new sweep will not be generated until a new trigger is generated. The *time* the sweep takes to go from left to right is controlled by the sweep time controls. To illustrate these concepts, examine Fig. 6-10. The trigger point, T, has been set at the indicated point by adjusting for positive slope and appropriate level. Thus, the trigger illustrated in B might be generated.

Suppose the sweep time is selected to give a waveform shown in C. Notice the waveform starts at the trigger occurrence. Its time duration, however, is set by the sweep time controls. D and E are different sweep-time settings. The displays generated by these different settings are illustrated in Fig. 6-11.

Z-AXIS

An oscilloscope has an X-, Y-, and a Z-axis. The vertical deflection is the Y-axis. The horizontal deflection is the X-axis and the Z-axis is the beam intensity. Thus, the correct answer to *Question 7* is *b*. The Z-axis is used for blanking horizontal retrace.

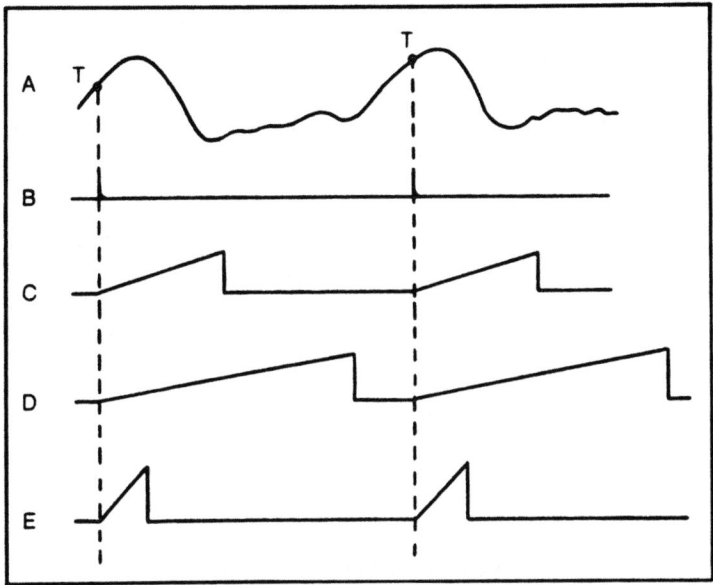

Fig. 6-10. Waveforms in a triggered sweep scope with various sweep speeds.

The Z-axis is sometimes available at the rear of the oscilloscope for external connections.

PROBES AND LOADING

An oscilloscope when used for measurement, loads the circuit to which it is attached. A typical scope input impedance is 1 megohm with input capacitance of 30 pF. A ×10 probe for this scope would have an input resistance of about 10 megohms and an input capacitance of 10 pF. An ×100 probe would have input

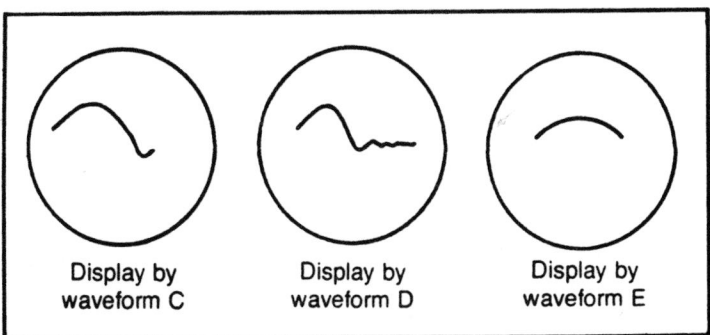

| Display by waveform C | Display by waveform D | Display by waveform E |

Fig. 6-11. Waveforms displayed with the various sweep-speed settings.

resistance of about 100 megohms and an input capacitance of about 3 pF. The attenuation in an ×10 probe is 1/10. In an ×100 probe it is 1/100. Since a ×10 probe attenuates the signal, reduces circuit loading, and increases the input impedance, answer *d* is correct in *Question 8*.

Note that though the input resistance increases 10 times in an ×10 probe and 100 times in an ×100 probe, the capacitance does not decrease by the same factors. The reason for this is that the cable required to attach the probe to the scope adds capacitance to the input capacitance of the scope. Each length of cable adds capacitance. The probe itself adds some capacitance. Figure 6-12 illustrates this point.

The probes we are discussing here have different names to describe the same thing. They are called attenuator probes, low-capacitance probes, and sometimes isolation probes. You should also note that a high-voltage probe is a special purpose attenuator probe normally used to measure high voltages. Since a high-voltage probe also has low input capacitance (2-3 pF) it can be used where capacitive loading is a problem; such as, the tuned circuits in radios, TVs, communication equipment, etc. However, the large attenuation means that the signal being measured must be pretty large in order to get a usable scope pattern.

The answer to *Question 9* should be *b* (a ×10 probe). However, note that the addition of about 10 pF to the tank circuit will detune the circuit. If that detuning is a problem, a ×100 probe may be necessary, or even a ×1000 (high-voltage probe).

SPECIAL-PURPOSE PROBES

Other probes are available. One of these is an rf probe (also

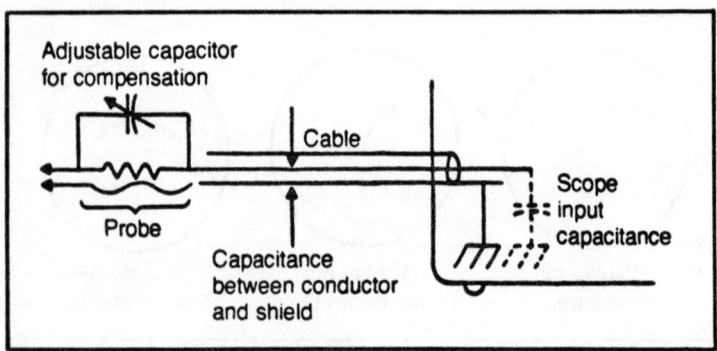

Fig. 6-12. Compensating a scope probe.

called demodulator probe or detector probe). This probe contains a detector circuit. Rf at the input to the probe is rectified and filtered. The output of the probe is dc or if the input rf was modulated with a low-frequency, the probe output will be proportional to the modulation. Current probes are also available to measure alternating currents in a wire.

SCOPE MEASUREMENTS

You will find several questions on the Certification Exam dealing with scope waveform and dc measurement. You will need to know the effects of an attenuator probe, and how to estimate voltages from a scope trace. *Questions 10 and 11* are examples. The answer to *Question 10* is *b*, (– 24 V). Here it is necessary to estimate the average value of the waveform and determine how far that average is deflected from the 0 Vdc reference (top line of the graticule in this example). The waveform is reproduced in Fig. 6-13 to clarify this concept. Since the average value is something less than half way from top-to-bottom of the waveform (a symmetrical waveform would be exactly half way between peaks), a line is drawn in at this estimate. The deflection of this average line from 0 is the dc value. If you had the scope in front of you this estimate could be checked by switching to ac coupling. When switched to ac coupling the average value will coincide with the 0 Vdc line. The waveform would move up (in this case) and be above and below the top line. If the estimate is correct the negative peak would be at – 6 V.

To more accurately check the dc value, set a convenient portion of the waveform on a graticule line with the vertical position control while using ac coupling. In this case, the negative peaks might be easiest. Then switch to dc (direct coupling). The vertical distance the point moves is the dc component of the waveform. Actually, the deflection is measured in centimeters and the proper scale

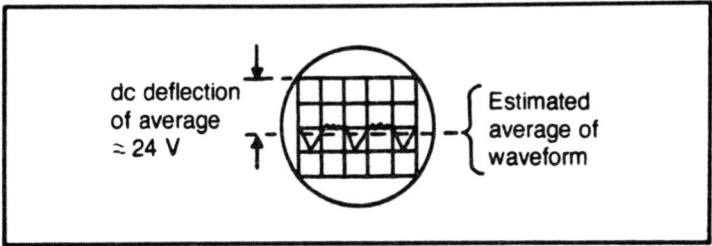

Fig. 6-13. Analysis of scope display.

factors (vertical sensitivity and probe attenuation factor) must be used to determine the voltage. In this case the average value is approximately 2.4 cm down from the top (our dc reference). The sensitivity is 1 V/cm. Therefore, at the input to the scope is a 2.4 Vdc component. However, the attenuator probe reduces the input signal by 1/10. Therefore, the input voltage has a 24 Vdc component in the negative direction.

All the same sensitivities apply to the ac components of the waveform. In this case, the peak to peak deflection is about 1.2 cm. 1.2 cm = 1 V/cm × 10 = 12 V. *Question 11* is therefore, *a*, 12 V.

TIME AND FREQUENCY

An oscilloscope is also used to measure time and/or frequency. Triggered-sweep scopes have very linear sweep in the horizontal direction. That is, the deflection voltage increases at a very constant rate. Time can, therefore, be accurately measured with an oscilloscope. The sweep-time settings are calibrated and can be determined by reading the scales on the knobs. Some scopes even have a digital readout on the screen that displays the time/cm setting. Once time is measured, frequency can easily be determined. For example, in *Question 12* the sweep time is set at 10 ms/cm. The period of the waveform is 2 cm long (measured from some convenient point on the waveform to the next occurrence of that point). Since 10 ms/cm × 2 cm = 20 ms, the period of the waveform is 20 ms.

$$f = \frac{1}{T}$$

$$f = \frac{1}{20 \text{ ms}}$$

$$f = 50 \text{ Hz}, \quad \text{answer } c.$$

COUNTERS

With the advent of inexpensive digital circuits, counters are becoming more and more useful. A wide range of counters are now available. Counters basically operate by counting cycles of an input waveform for a predetermined time period. If, for example, cycles are counted for one second, the number of cycles counted is the same as the frequency. Of course, it isn't too practical to count higher frequencies for one whole second, i.e., 23 MHz would require a count of 23 million. But if 23 MHz was counted for one millisecond the counter would only count to 23,000. If you only counted for 1 microsecond the counter would only count to 23. By appropriate adjustment of the decimal place or of the multiplier, the 23 would be read as 23 MHz. In a counter with five readout digits, the display would probably be arranged to read "over-range" if attempting to count for one second. It would probably read 23,000 kHz if sampled for a millisecond and 23.000 MHz if sampled for one microsecond. A block diagram for a counter is shown in Fig. 6-14.

The waveform of the input voltage is shaped to appropriate trigger pulses for the BCD counter. The counter is able to count sequentially when a trigger is applied. The timer resets the counter and starts it counting from zero. At a time specified by the front panel settings, the timer will stop the counter and enable the "dump gate" which reads the counter outputs (in parallel) into the BCD to 7-segment decoder/drivers. The decoder drivers in turn light up the appropriate display elements. Many of these circuits are now available on a single IC chip.

DMMs

Counters can also be used to construct voltmeters, ohmmeters,

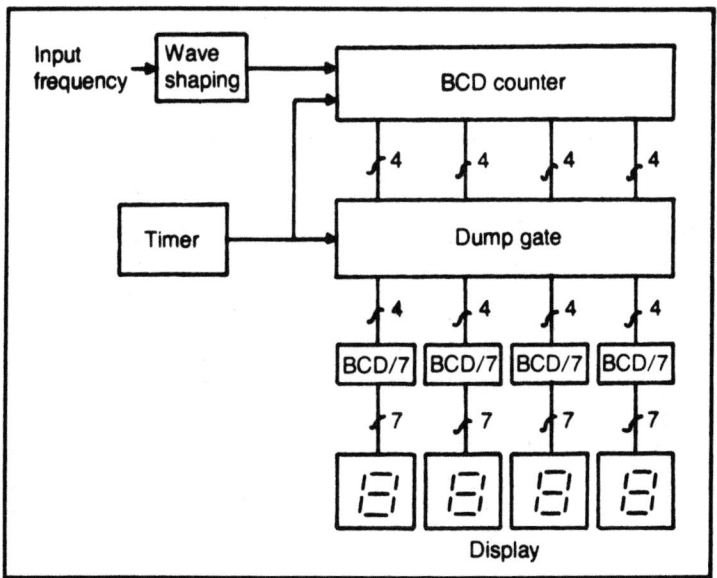

Fig. 6-14. Frequency counter block diagram.

91

milliammeters, capacitance meters, and other special purpose meters. Because of immense production of ICs and improved ICs, these applications are becoming more and more common. The usual functions contained in a digital multimeter (DMM) are: voltmeter, ohmmeter, and milliammeter. The voltmeter is often arranged to measure ac or dc voltages. In all of these applications the desired quantity can be converted to a dc voltage level (by appropriate circuitry) that varies linearly with the unknown quantity. For example, an unknown resistance would be converted to an unknown voltage by applying a voltage to the resistance along with appropriate range resistances in series. The unknown voltage is then applied to a circuit known as an analog-to-digital (A to D) converter. A block diagram of such a circuit is shown in Fig. 6-15.

The circuit functions as follows. The comparator output will allow the clock to trigger the counter until the digital-to-analog (D/A) converter output level matches the input voltage V_x. At that time the counter is stopped and the count transferred to the display. The D/A output increases with each increase of the count in the counter. Shortly after transfer of the count, the counter is reset to zero. This makes the output of the D/A converter go to its lowest level. The comparator switches and the counter starts to count clock pulses. When the D/A output reaches V_x again, the comparator switches and stops the counter. If V_x is larger the count will continue longer. With a smaller V_x the counter will count for less time before the D/A output reaches V_x and shuts off the count thereby transferring the count to the display. Therefore, the

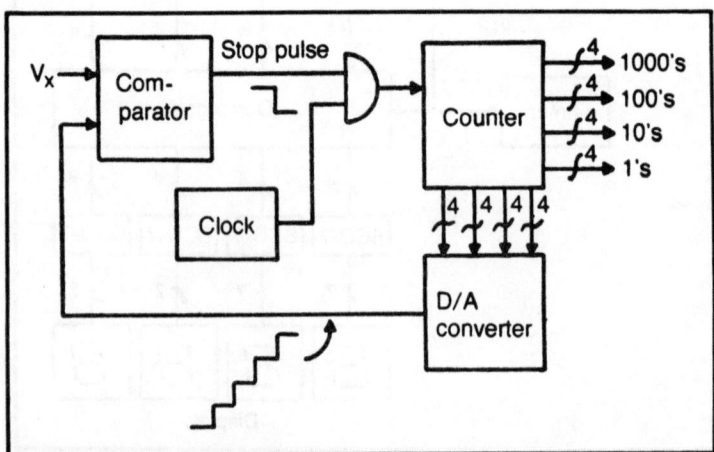

Fig. 6-15. Digital voltmeter block diagram.

transferred count is larger for larger values of V_x and smaller for smaller values.

Suppose we are on a 10-volt range and things will be arranged so that the D/A converter will have an output of zero to 1 volt. Resistors and range switches will be so arranged as to provide V_x to the comparator from 0 to 1 volt. That is, if 5 volts is applied to the meter, V_x will be 0.5 volts. If 7 volts is applied, V_x will be 0.7 and so on. The D/A output will also range from 0 to 1 volt for the full range of the counter. If the counter can count up to 999, a count of 500 would result in the D/A output of 0.5 volts. A count of 700 would produce 0.7 volts. If your input voltage is 8.5 volts, V_x would be 0.85 volts. When the counter reached 850 the D/A output would be 0.85 volts. The comparator will switch, shutting off the counter and transferring the count to the display, which would be arranged to display 8.50 in all likelihood.

This overall circuitry is called an analog-to-digital converter since an analog signal is changed to a digital count. The most straightforward answer to *Question 13* is *b*. A case could be made for answer *a* being correct, since within the A/D converter, V_x "scales" time by stopping the counter at a time determined by the magnitude of V_x. Therefore, answer *d* might be the most correct. Again, let us repeat that these sort of ambiguities will not be part of the Certification Exam and are only contained here for discussion purposes. On a Certification Exam answer *a* might be "more correct" making *d* the correct answer. Or it might be made completely wrong making *b* the correct answer.

CAPACITANCE METERS

Capacitance meters can now be purchased that use electronic counters. These counters count a frequency for a period of time proportional to the time constant, T, of an RC circuit where C is the unknown capacitance. If the capacitor is large, the counter will have longer to count and will, therefore, reach a larger number. The display can, therefore, be calibrated to read the capacitance of the capacitor. R can be used in the charging circuit to change the range of the capacitance checker.

GENERATORS

Technicians use all sorts of generators. Sine-wave generators or oscillators are widely used. All sorts of sine-wave generators are in use from audio frequencies on into the gigahertz region. Sine-wave generators with a small amount of output power are available (such as grid-dip meters) and larger power generators are also available. Sine-wave generators are used for a large variety of things. They are used to inject signals for signal tracing, for alignment, for calibration, and other purposes.

Function Generators

Another class of generators are function generators. These usually come with several types of waveforms available, such as square waves, triangle waves, and sine waves.

Square wave testing of amplifiers and circuits can be an important technique, especially if frequency distortions might be present, like phase-shift and amplitude impairments. For example, if a square wave is applied to a low-pass circuit that allows only the fundamental frequency to pass, the output will be a sine wave at the fundamental frequency. The answer to *Question 14* is *c*.

Alignment Generators

Many generators are used for alignment of tuned-circuit amplifiers. A generator that generates a single frequency is often used when one frequency is to be amplified by a tuned circuit. For example, the i-f circuits in an AM radio can be aligned by applying the i-f frequency to the input and adjusting the circuit for maximum passage of the i-f frequency. Traps are also often adjusted with application of a single-frequency sine wave signal.

When a tuned amplifier is used to pass a spectrum of frequencies a sweep generator is often used to send signals to the unit under test. The frequencies of interest are swept back and forth usually at a 60 Hz rate. A block diagram is shown in Fig. 6-16.

The input amplitude is constant over the range of frequencies. At some of the input frequencies the amplifier under test will be more efficient than others; or, in other words, at some frequencies

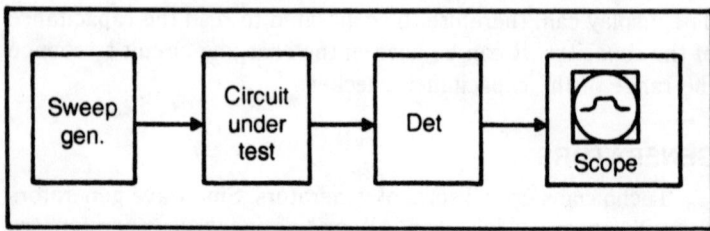

Fig. 6-16. Sweep alignment generator.

more voltage will pass through the circuit under test than will pass through at other frequencies.

If a detector is used at the output of the circuit under test, to separate the variations of amplitude and then send them to an oscilloscope, the circuits "response" curve may be viewed. Because the sweep generator is changing frequency, it is difficult to construct dials or even counters in the sweep generator to calibrate the frequency being applied to the circuit under test. An alternate scheme uses a separate marker generator (often contained in the same instrument with the sweep generator). The marker generator is usually capable of generating several specific frequencies each controlled by a crystal. Answer *b* is correct for *Question 15*. Adding the marker generator to the block diagram is shown in Fig. 6-17.

LOGIC TEST EQUIPMENT

In recent years many new pieces of test equipment have been manufactured to check logic circuits used in all kinds of applications. Logic probes are in this category.

Logic Probes

A very simple logic probe could be built, as in Fig. 6-18, with a resistor and an LED.

If the red probe is attached to a positive voltage the LED will

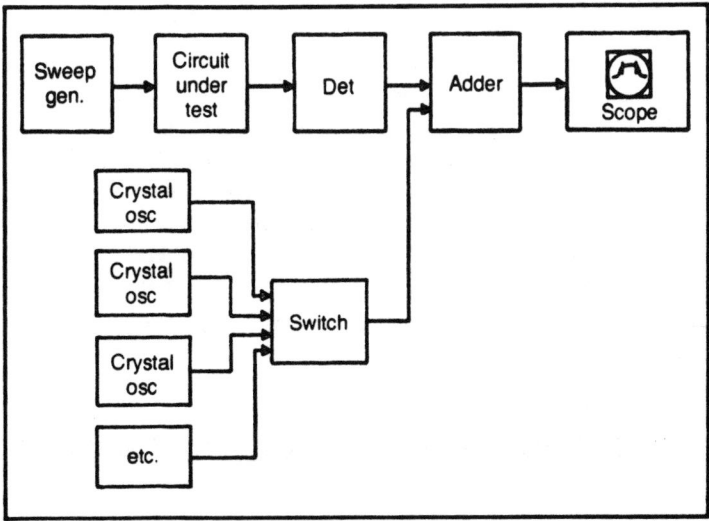

Fig. 6-17. Post sweep-marker generator.

95

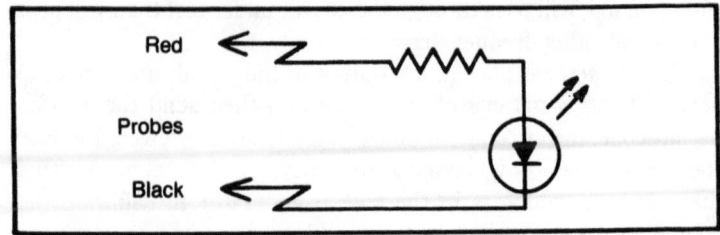

Fig. 6-18. Simple logic probe.

be lit. If the logic level is 0 volts the LED will be out. In a simple probe such as this care must be used to make sure that voltages are not excessive for the probe circuit and also that polarity is observed.

Many probes are commercially available. One example is the Hewlett Packard probe shown in Fig. 6-19.

This probe will show a dim light when attached to an open node, get bright when attached to a logic "1," and go out when attached to a logic "0." The logic probe when attached to a node containing pulses (low-, and high-logic levels, sequentially) will blink. The answer to *Question 16* is, therefore *a*.

A switch position also allows for "memory," that is, a position where a seldom occurring pulse will latch an internal circuit and light the indicator. This is a very useful feature for detecting transients on the power lines and glitches on other lines that should be high or low all the time.

Many companies also make a logic pulser, a kind of portable generator. An example of this kind of probe is shown in Fig. 6-20.

This particular probe generates a pulse with a very low duty-cycle. That is—the pulse is very short with respect to the time it is off. This probe can be programmed to generate a variety of pulses, the highest rate of which is 100 pulses per second. At the 100 Hz rate the pulse is on for 10 μs and off 10 ms. A pulse source such as this can be used to cause logic gates to operate, flip-flops to toggle, and other circuits to switch. The answer to *Question 17* is *d*. Coupled with the logic level probe the logic pulser is a powerful troubleshooting tool.

HP 545A Logic Probe

Fig. 6-19. Sample of a logic probe. (© Copyright Hewlett-Packard Company.)

HP 546A Logic Pulser

Fig. 6-20. Sample logic pulser. (© Copyright Hewlett-Packard Company.)

Another probe in the logic probe family is the current probe. This probe costs a little more but is a valuable aid in some troubleshooting situations. A sample of this kind of probe is shown in Fig. 6-21.

An adjustment on this probe changes the threshold at which the light in the probe blinks. The intensity of the light is proportional to the current flow in a wire adjacent to the probe tip. More current in the wire causes the light to become brighter. Less current, less brightness.

On a computer board, one line goes to many different ICs. For example, a data line might go to 32 different RAM memory chips as well as to several logic chips. Suppose one of the chips has a short to ground. How do you find which chip is shorted? Voltage checks will show the line as 0 volts, but any one of the ICs (if shorted) could cause the problem, so could a solder bridge on the line itself. The current probe along with the logic pulser is very valuable in finding this kind of problem. Inject a signal anywhere on the line and trace the current path, with the current probe, to the shorted spot. Answer *b* in *Question 18* is the correct choice.

Logic Analyzers

A good many logic analyzers are being produced. Since most meaningful information in digital based products is in the voltage levels on many lines simultaneously, it is advantageous to be able to "look" at several lines all at the same instant. Further, the clarity is extended if all lines can be looked at in steps of time, or sequentially. This is accomplished in logic analyzers by combining the CRT display with digital computer concepts and memory. As patterns occur in the device under test, these patterns are stored in the analyzer for specified times, and then displayed on the CRT in one of several formats; octal, hexadecimal, decimal, binary,

HP 547A Current Tracer

Fig. 6-21. Sample current probe. (© Copyright Hewlett-Packard Company.)

timing, or map mode. Analyzers have a possibility of 16 or 32 input lines, depending on the model. The sample display in Fig. 6-22 shows a partial program listing displayed in hexadecimal, with the sixteen address lines showing information under the A column and the 8 data lines showing information under the B column.

The same information is shown in binary format in Fig. 6-23. The timing mode is shown in Fig. 6-24.

By inputting the lower order address lines on 8 of the inputs to the analyzer and causing them to move the CRT electron beam to the right as the magnitude of the address increases; and by inputting the higher order address lines on 8 other inputs to the analyzer and causing these eight to move the beam down as the magnitude of these addresses increases, a memory map is displayed. A picture of such a map is shown in Fig. 6-24 courtesy of Hewlett Packard.

Line No.	A Hex	B Hex
200	06A2	36
001	06A3	00
002	0BF0	00
003	06A4	2C
004	06A5	C3
005	06A6	9B
006	06A7	06
007	069B	34
008	0BF1	03
009	0BF1	04
010	069C	7E
011	0BF1	04
012	069D	FE
013	069E	0A
014	069F	C2

Fig. 6-22. Analyzer's hexidecimal display. (© Copyright Hewlett-Packard Company.)

Line	A	B
No.	Bin	Bin
00	0000011010100010	00110110
001	0000011010100011	00000000
002	0000101111110000	00000000
003	0000011010100100	00101100
004	0000011010100101	11000011
005	0000011010100110	10011011
006	0000011010100111	00000110
007	0000011010011011	00110100
008	0000101111110001	00000011
009	0000101111110001	00000100
010	0000011010011100	01111110
011	0000101111110001	00000100
012	0000011010011101	11111110
013	0000011010011110	00001010
014	0000011010011111	11000010

Fig. 6-23. Binary program display. (© Copyright Hewlett-Packard Company.)

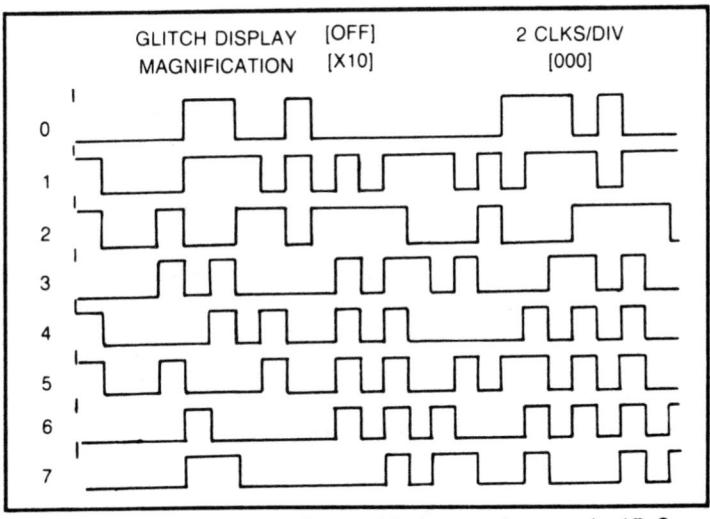

Fig. 6-24. Eight data-bus lines displayed in timer analyzer mode. (© Copyright Hewlett-Packard Company.)

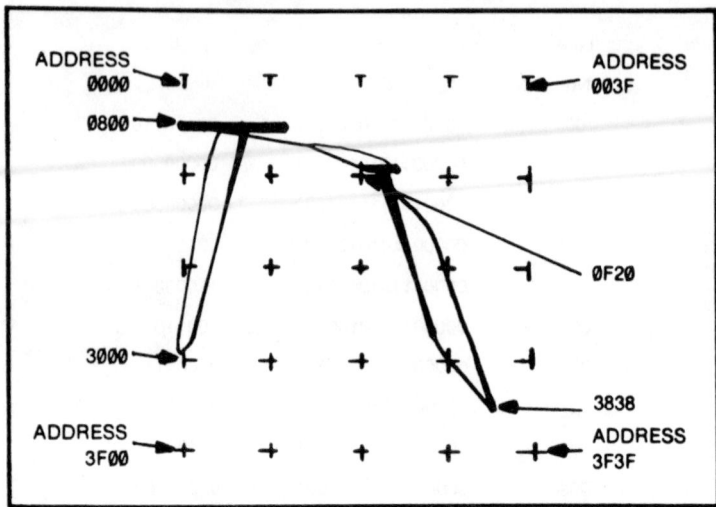

Fig. 6-25. Map-mode display. (© Copyright Hewlett-Packard Company.)

The map displays the activity of the address bus. If addresses, or a group of addresses, are displayed but they were not programmed this way give a clue as to how the sequence occurred, leading to a solution to the problem. The analyzer is useful in debugging software problems.

Spectrum Analyzers

Spectrum analyzers are found in some audio shops and in communications work for analyzing output of a transmitter. The purpose of a spectrum analyzer is to display the energy developed by complex waveforms as a function of frequency—the frequency spectrum. In Fig. 6-26 is a graphic presentation of the spectrum caused by modulating a carrier (f_o) with a single frequency (f_1).

In testing an audio amplifier a single frequency is sent to an amplifier. Distortion in the amplifier will generate harmonics of this single frequency. A spectrum of this is shown in Fig. 6-27.

A spectrum analyzer works by utilizing a section that examines the input waveform and comparing it to a sweeping (or frequency modulated) carrier in a modulator. See Fig. 6-28. As the sweep generator deflects the electron beam in the scope horizontally, it also changes the frequency of the VCO (voltage-controlled oscillator).

As the varying frequency of the VCO is presented to the modulator and compared to the input, sidebands are generated.

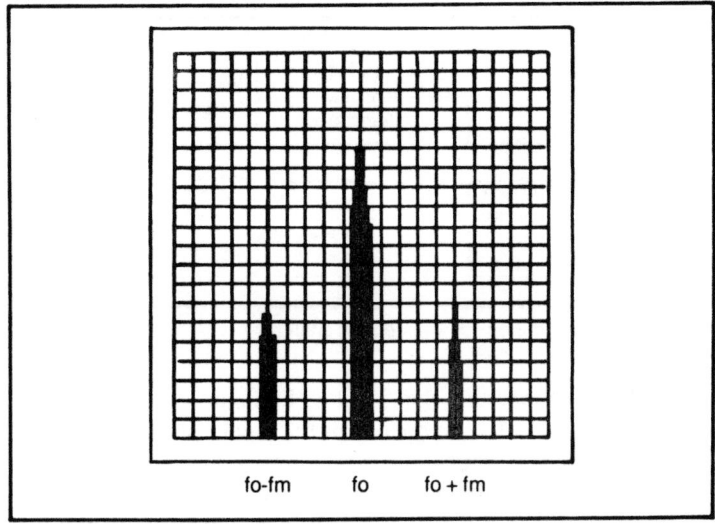

Fig. 6-26. Frequency spectrum of a modulated carrier.

Suppose the input waveform is a single frequency sine wave at 1 MHz with no distortion. At a particular instant of time the output of the VCO might be 0.5 MHz. The modulator will therefore produce energy at 1 MHz, 0.5 MHz, and at 1.5 MHz. These are all outside the range of the narrow-band amplifier resulting in no

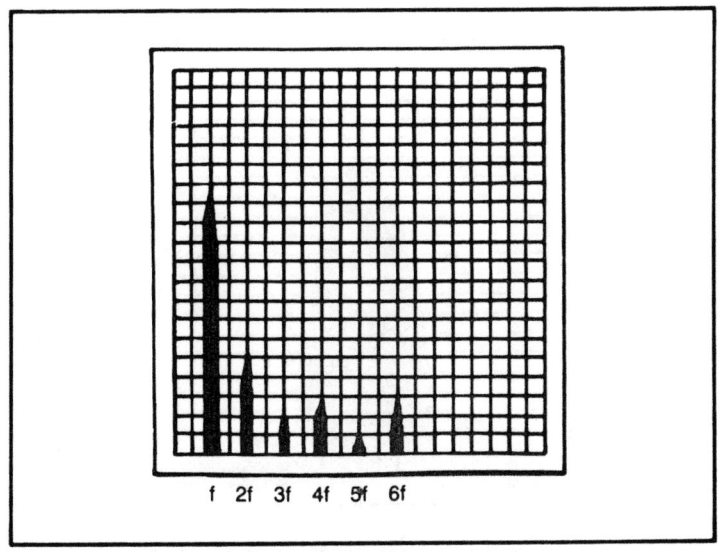

Fig. 6-27. Spectrum caused by distortion in an amplifier.

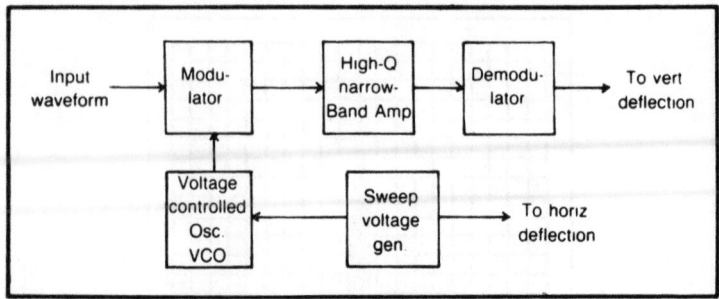

Fig. 6-28. Block diagram of a spectrum analyzer.

vertical deflection. As the VCO gets higher in frequency it approaches the 1 MHz frequency of the input. The sidebands will start to contain energy within the low-frequency narrow-band (remember the modulator output has sum and difference frequencies) of the narrow-band amplifier. That energy will then cause deflection. The display will show a single spike at the fundamental frequency of the input signal.

A transmitter output, of course, contains many frequency components. An amplitude modulated carrier from an AM radio station would have sum and difference frequencies at many frequencies, because the audio modulation contains many frequencies. The band-width is, of course, limited at the transmitter

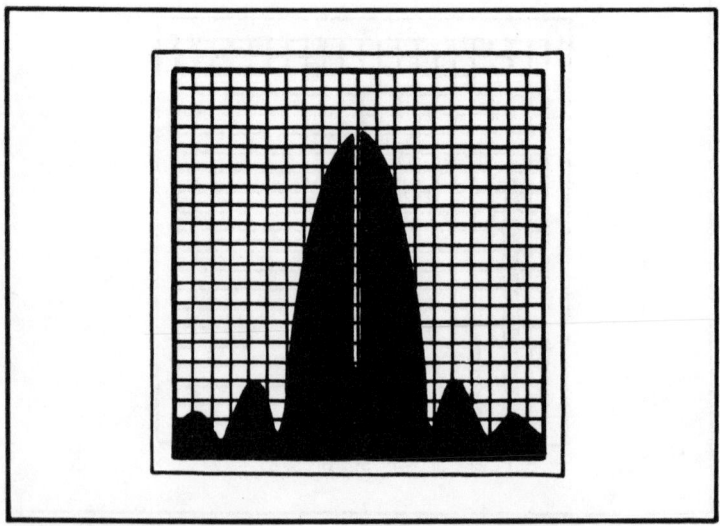

Fig. 6-29. Frequency spectrum of an amplitude modulated carrier.

102

and regulated by federal standards. A frequency spectrum of an AM modulated carrier is depicted in Fig. 6-29.

ADDITIONAL READING

Buchsbaum, Walter H.: *Tested Electronics Troubleshooting Methods,* Prentice-Hall, 1974.

Cameron, Derek: *Advanced Oscilloscope Handbook for Technicians and Engineers,* Reston Publishing Co., 1977.

Herrick, Clyde W.: *Electronic Troubleshooting: A Manual for Engineers and Technicians,* Reston Publishing Co., 1974.

Lenk, John D.: *Handbook of Electronic Meters; Theory and Application,* Prentice-Hall, 1969.

Lenk, John D.: *Handbook of Practical Electronic Tests and Measurements,* Prentice-Hall, 1969.

Luetzow, Robert H.: *Interfacing Test Circuits With Single-Board Computers,* TAB BOOKS Inc., 1983.

Prentiss, Stan.: *Complete Book of Oscilloscopes,* TAB BOOKS Inc., 1983.

Robinson, Walter.: *Handbook of Electronic Instrumentation, Testing, and Troubleshooting,* Reston Publishing Co., 1974.

C E T

ASSOCIATE

7

Electronic
Components Nomenclature

This chapter covers the terminology used to describe electronic component parameters.

QUIZ

Q1. The resistor in Fig. 7-1 is:

a. a 47 K resistor, 5% tolerance
b. a 4700 ohm resistor
c. a 470 ohm resistor
d. a resistor which has an actual measurement within 1% of the marked value

Q2. The wattage of the resistor is:

a. 1/4th watt
b. 10 watts
c. 5 watts
d. cannot be ascertained from the markings

Q3. Color coding of a 5%, 6.8 ohm resistor will be:

a. green, purple, black, gold
b. blue, grey, silver, gold
c. blue, blue, silver, gold
d. blue, grey, gold, gold

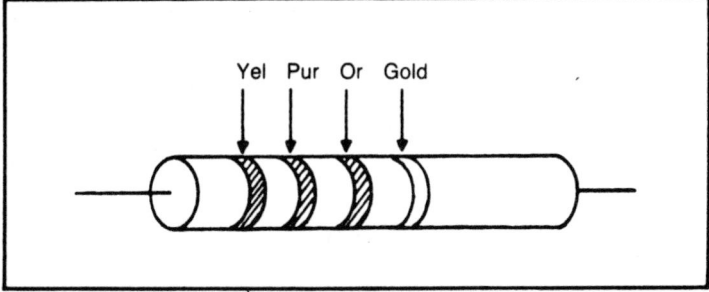

Fig. 7-1. Resistor (see Q1 and Q2).

Q4. The resistor in Fig. 7-2 is:

   a. marked wrong—should be marked R4
   b. a safety component and should be replaced with the exact value part
   c. one that may vary in size
   d. part of a multi-resistor pak

Q5. A disk capacitor with the marking 47 k will most likely be:

   a. a 47 picofarad capacitor
   b. a 0.047 microfarad capacitor
   c. a 47 k resistor that looks like a capacitor
   d. a 47 microfarad capacitor

Q6. In Fig. 7-3 which symbol shows the standard transistor lead configuration?

   a. 1   c. 3, 4, and 5
   b. 2   d. there is no standard

Fig. 7-2. Circuit for Q4.

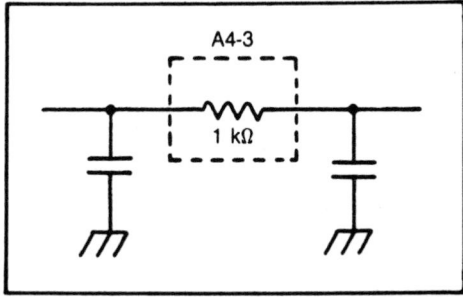

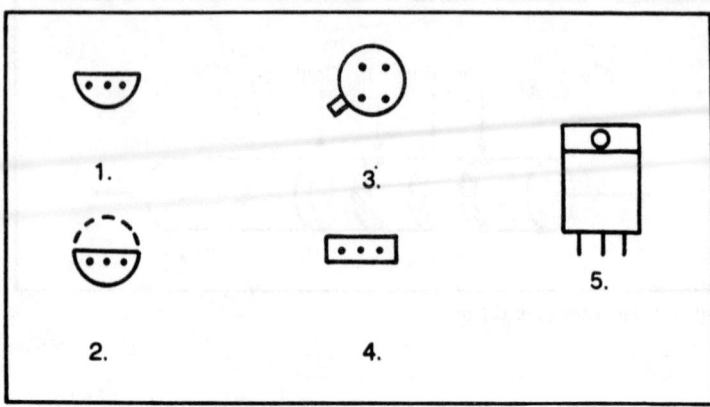

Fig. 7-3. Transistor packages.

Q7. Figure 7-4 represents:

    a. a bipolar transistor c. an FET
    b. an SCR   d. a Darlington transistor

Q8. If V_B is 20 V, R1 is 500 ohms and R2 is 500 ohms, what will be the voltage across D1 (Fig. 7-5)?

    a. 10 V
    b. 11.2 V
    c. 20 V
    d. impossible to determine from the information given

Q9. In Fig. 7-6 which leg is the drain?

    a. a   c.
    b

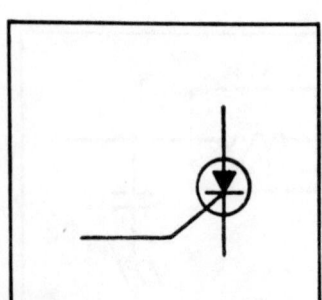

Fig. 7-4. Solid-state component for Q7.

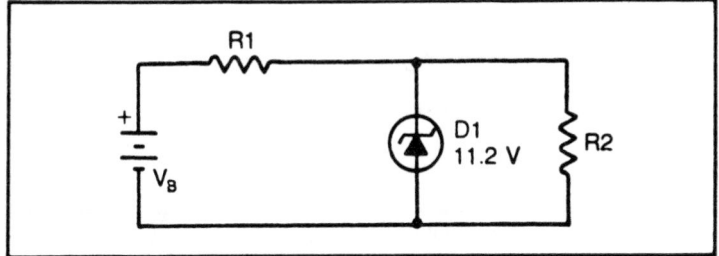

Fig. 7-5. Zener regulator for Q8.

Q10. The component in Fig. 7-7 is a wire with a black pencil-lead-appearing cylinder not directly connected, but loosely slipped over the wire. Which symbol represents it?

a. a   c. c
b. b   d. d

Q11. Identify the symbols in Fig. 7-8.

a. AND gate, NOT gate, Exclusive-OR gate
b. AND gate, NOR gate, Exclusive-NOR gate
c. NAND gate, diode rectifier, Exclusive-OR gate
d. AND gate, NAND gate, NOR gate

Q12. Power supply voltages to operate the U4 chip in Fig. 7-9:

a. are connected to pin 1
b. are connected to pin 2
c. are connected to pin 3
d. are frequently not shown on schematics

Q13. The component in Fig. 7-10 is:

a. a beam-power pentode
b. a tetrode section of a multisection tube

Fig. 7-6. JFET for Q9.

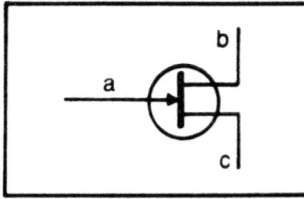

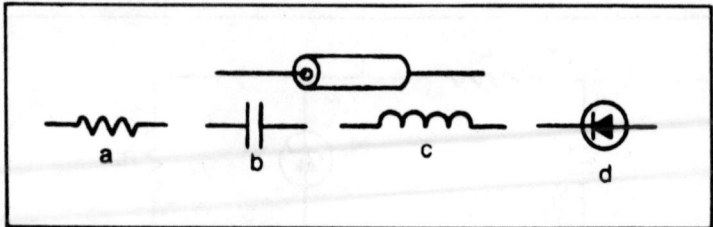

Fig. 7-7. Electronic component for Q10.

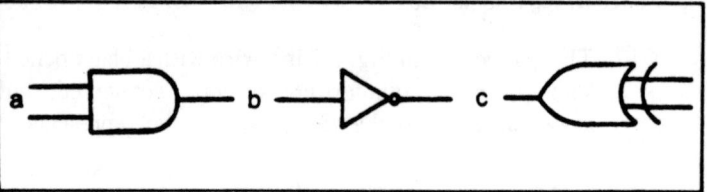

Fig. 7-8. Logic symbol to be identified in Q11.

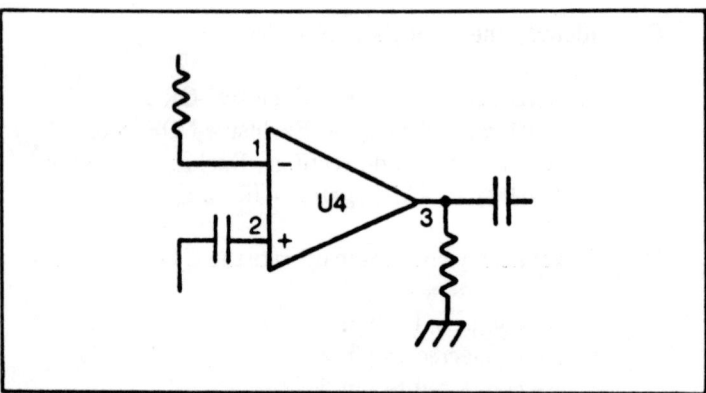

Fig. 7-9. Op-amp circuit for Q12.

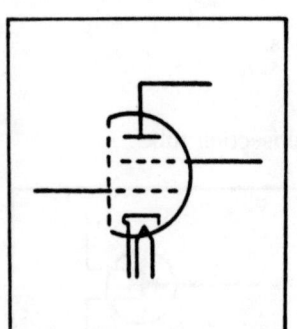

Fig. 7-10. Electronic component for Q13.

c. a gas-filled dual tetrode rectifier

d. a triple diode/tetrode tube

Q14. Match the following:

(1) RFC   (m) center conductor

(2) coax   (n) relay coil

(3) HOT   (o) flip-flop

(4) latch   (p) radio-frequency coil

(5) RL   (q) horizontal output transformer

(6) CRT   (r) kinescope

(7) TO-5   (s) round chip-package type

ELECTRONICS INDUSTRY STANDARDS

Any study of standard notation and symbology in the electronics industry is a futile experience. At or about the time transistor circuitry took over from tube technology any serious efforts by manufacturers or their standards associations to maintain standards appear to have disappeared. Tube types, Morse code, and resistor color-code bands are just about the only items you can be sure of. Because of this giant problem, technicians spend large amounts of time, needlessly verifying the size and function of electronic components. Unmarked components are not a serious problem in manufacturing. For instance, a design modification may call for a change of a diode for frequency, power, or voltage reasons. The production technicians might then need to know that the 'blue' colored diode should always be removed and replaced with the new 'yellow' diodes. To the servicer in the field undisclosed identification of components and arbitrary notation and symbols on service data is a nightmare that costs over a million dollars worth of time each *month*! The format of schematics and item number assignment for various components varies from manufacturer to manufacturer. It may even be different from one product to another that is produced by the same manufacturer. Because of this problem, technicians can only do their best and attempt to recognize components by the symbols that are "most prevalent" during the present period of time.

RESISTORS

Resistor color codes have traditionally been best remembered by technicians by using a phrase to remember the color sequence from 0 to 9. A helpful mnemonic is: "Better Be Right Or Your Great Big Venture Goes Wrong." Better stands for Black, which is the color used for zero; Brown represents 1; Red, 2; Orange, 3; Yellow, 4; Green, 5; Blue, 6; Violet, 7; Grey, 8; and White, 9. In *Question 1* the resistor shown in Fig. 7-1 has the 1st significant digit Yellow or 4. The second is Purple, or 7; and the multiplier—or better said— the number of zeros following the 2 significant digits is Orange, or 3. It is 47000 ohms, or 47 k. Note that the colors go from Black to White in a natural progression. That helps you if you are a little rusty and seldom have need to identify resistor sizes. Also be aware that the color code works only above 9 ohms. Other rules are needed for smaller size resistors (under 10 ohms).

In *Question 2, d* is correct. Carbon resistors still are made in physical sizes that are standard: 1/2 watt, 1 watt, and 2 watt sizes. In micro electronics work a 1/4-watt resistor is generally identifiable by physical size. Wire-wound 2-, 5-, and, 10-watt resistors have been identifiable in most cases by physical size. The over-2-watt resistors often have the wattage printed on them. Wattage of nonflammable resistors are not marked. They are generally smaller in physical size than carbon or wire-wound resistors for the same wattage values.

Under-10-ohm resistors present some difficulty for technicians. They are frequently used in power amplifier and power supply circuitry where heat causes discoloration of the color bands. For instance, a Blue, Grey, Silver, Silver might appear to have four bands of the same color after some use. A resistor value of 1 to 10 ohms uses a Gold third band. Gold means 'divide by 10'. (When it is the third band rather than the fourth band, it is a divider, not the tolerance indicator.) So, if the first band is Red and the second is Red and the third is Gold, you count the Red closest to an end of the resistor as a 2. The second significant figure indicator is Red, therefore also a 2. That is 22 (twenty-two). Divide by 10 and the value is 2.2 ohms. The fourth band means the tolerance, or how far the resistor may actually measure from the indicated value. No fourth band means it may vary up, or down, as much as 20%; Silver means 10% and Gold 5%. In the early days of radio 20% resistors were common. In TV 10% was most often used and in digital circuits anything with tolerances more than 5% is rare, with 1% resistors encountered frequently. A Blue, Grey, Gold, Gold resistor as in *Question 3*, is a 6.8-ohm resistor and may actually measure anywhere from 6.46 to 7.14 ohms.

The stitched box surrounding the 1 k resistor in *Question 4* indicates it is part of a multi-resistor pak. The pak may be identified as A4 and the Fig. 7-2 section will be the third resistor from the dotted end. The resistor paks invariably contain resistances of the same value and are molded into shapes identical to IC chips— including 14-pin dip (dual-in-line packages). IC dip packages are usually black, resistor paks are usually blue or white.

CAPACITORS

Question 5 asks about a '47 k' marked capacitor. The answer *b* is correct. The small physical size of this type of capacitor forced manufacturers to find a way to identify the part with less digits. So the micro-microfarad base quantity was agreed upon and the k multiplier then referred to a thousand $\mu\mu$F. Then 47 k is 47000 micro-microfarad, or 0.047 microfarad. The half-dozen or so early attempts at standard capacitor identification such as: Body-End-Dot; Color Bands; Arrow Boxes; Edge Dots, and so forth are not used anymore. Most often encountered capacitors have the sizes printed on them as well as the breakdown voltage. However, lately, more capacitors are seen in electronics products with secret identification. This requires using the circuit location and service data to determine the correct value.

SEMICONDUCTOR DEVICES

The *Question 6* is a little misleading since it asks for a standard that does not exist. Since the earliest days of transistor circuitry there has been no standard lead configuration adopted by the manufacturers. Those parts that do contain the E, B, C locations marked on them, are a blessing for working technicians. If these aren't on the part, which is the most common condition, then manufacturers reference numbers must be consulted, or the replacement component package may have an outline drawing showing the lead locations. Inserting a transistor in a circuit the wrong way will destroy the transistor, and perhaps others along with it. Soldering it in more than once will tend to ruin the PC board traces. The best procedure is to make sure each lead is in the proper place, even though this takes valuable time and is tedious.

Question 7 asks you to identify the SCR symbol. You should also be prepared to identify gate, anode, and cathode and know the SCR function. The SCR symbol is one that has not varied from its original appearance. It can however be confused with the triac, or the diac (Fig. 7-11).

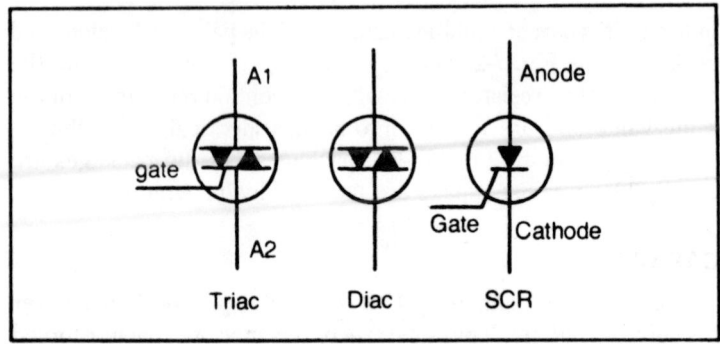

Fig. 7-11. Triac, diac, and SCR symbols.

In *Question 8*, answer *a* is correct. The voltage source (20 V) will divide equally between the resistors leaving + 10 V from the D1 cathode to the anode. D1 will serve no purpose unless some circuit function should cause the voltage to rise to over 11.2 volts at the D1 cathode. Then D1 will conduct, keeping the voltage at 11.2. Note the zener symbol. It is the symbol most commonly used. A diode symbol with a small 'z' inside the circle is also used. You will also see zeners without the circle enclosure and you will find them identified as CR; D; Z; X, and other part numbers.

Field-effect transistors (FETs) of all types are included in the Certification Exams. Know their advantages, their symbols, and how they are used. The answer to *Question 9* is that the JFET or junction-field-effect transistor is ordinarily drawn with the drain at *b*. Fortunately most schematics do show Source (s); Gate (g) and Drain (d) locations. JFETs are covered in Chapter 9.

Many semiconductor circuits may need a small amount of inductance inserted, after the printed circuit board is designed, to eliminate parasitics. The drawing in *Question 10* (Fig. 7-7) is a ferrite sleeve that serves as an rf choke in rf tuners, horizontal output stages in TV sets and many other circuits. It is used to suppress unwanted rf oscillations, harmonics, etc. There is no identification and in a circuit it may have the appearance of a diode with the cathode band obliterated, or it may seem to be a burned resistor.

LOGIC SYMBOLS

More details of logic appear later in this book. You should familiarize yourself with these components. In *Question 11*, *a* is correct. All CETs should be familiar with the military symbols for gates. These are now the most commonly used symbols in digital work. IEEE Std 91-1984 may replace these symbols. See Fig. 7-16 for examples.

OPERATIONAL AMPLIFIERS

In the operational amplifier shown in Fig. 7-9 of *Question 12* answer *d* is correct. Where the product uses multiple chips that derive power from a common power supply, the supply pins on the chips may not be shown, merely the signal pins are shown. Sometimes the power supply pins are shown in the schematic legend as a note.

OTHER ELECTRONIC COMPONENTS

Multisection tubes like the one in *Question 13* may be located far from each other, schematically. To show that a section is a part of a dual or triple envelope the stitched line is used on one side of the circle. Note that four elements in a tube (not counting the filaments) make it a tetrode.

The items listed in *Question 14* as *(1)* through *(7)* are commonly used acronyms or words and you should relate them to the *m* through *s* names with little trouble. There are dozens of other commonly used acronyms in electronics. The more familiar you are with the common symbols and usage, the easier your technical work will be. Much of the terminology and present-day usage can only be gained by experience.

INTERNATIONAL STANDARD NOTATION

Many years ago it became evident that the method of identifying electronics components and noting component values had some problems. The problems were primarily encountered by service technicians but also, to a lesser degree, by engineers and others who work with electronic circuitry.

Figure 7-12 shows the most common method of schematically

Fig. 7-12. Capacitor value markings, old style.

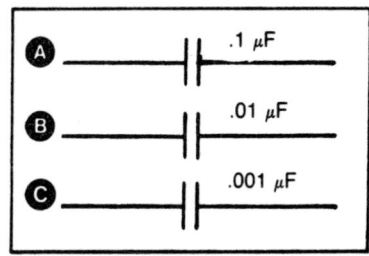

identifying the size of the capacitors. A severe problem is created when the decimal point in A or C is an original typographical omission, or if it becomes lost in later reproductions or photocopies of the print. The decimal point takes up as much space as any other character and on small capacitor packages may be rubbed off or easily undetected. It is also possible that 0.1 μF is written 100 nF, or more commonly: 100,000 pF, or 100 k. Take your pick!

A more positive method of identification is the IS, or International Standards as adopted by ISA. Here in Fig. 7-13 are the same three capacitors of Fig. 7-12 with IS identification.

In Fig. 7-13, item A still has the space problem, but there is no decimal point. In item B the F is dropped for farad since capacitors always have farads as a unit. In B one character is eliminated to conserve space without sacrificing understanding. In C four characters are removed and the possibility of a decimal error is eliminated. The confusion factor that 1000 k, .001 μF, or 1000 pF can generate in technicians of all ages and experience levels is eliminated. Note that if a capacitor multiplier is micro-micro, pico is used. So a 47 $\mu\mu$, or 0.000047 microfarad is in International Standards $\mu\mu$47p.

The resistor problems are similar. Try to repair a unit by replacing a 3.3 k with a 33 k because the decimal point 'got lost' and you will be in trouble. Also note that 1 k can be written 1000 Ω and 3.3 k can be written 3300 (Fig. 7-14). Now look at Fig. 7-15.

What problems have been solved for technicians? First is the elimination of the ohms character (Ω), which is impossible to reproduce on common typewriters and has always been a problem. A second problem solved is the illusive decimal point. The R could be dropped in a resistance that has a value of 100 R since resistance is always resistance; however, it will be needed for those resistors between 1 and 10 ohms (1.5 ohms will be 1R5, as an example).

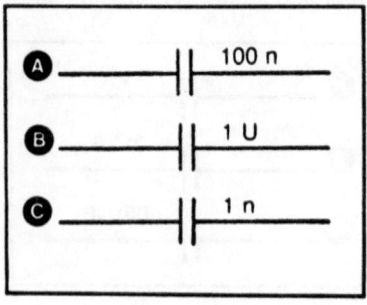

Fig. 7-13. Capacitor value markings, International Standard.

114

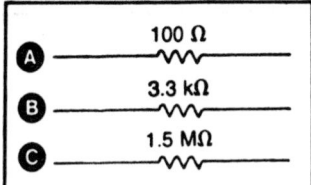

Fig. 7-14. Resistor value markings, old style.

Fig. 7-15. Resistor values in International Standard.

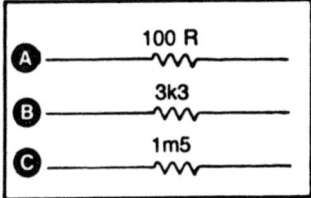

International Standards will be used more and more in the future. Try it on some sample resistors and capacitors so that you are familiar with it. It is used in some questions in this text.

A new standard for computer and logic symbols has been developed by the International Electrotechnical Commission (IEC).

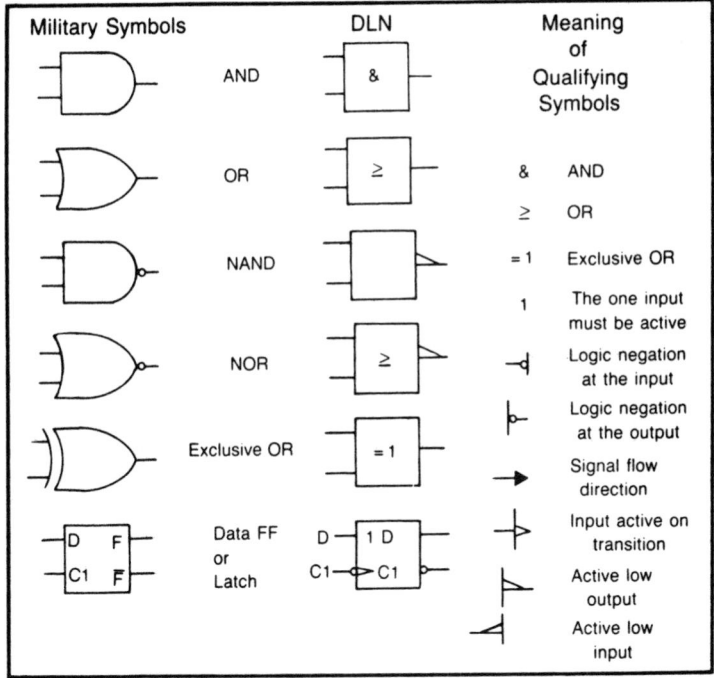

Fig. 7-16. Some logic notations in DLN.

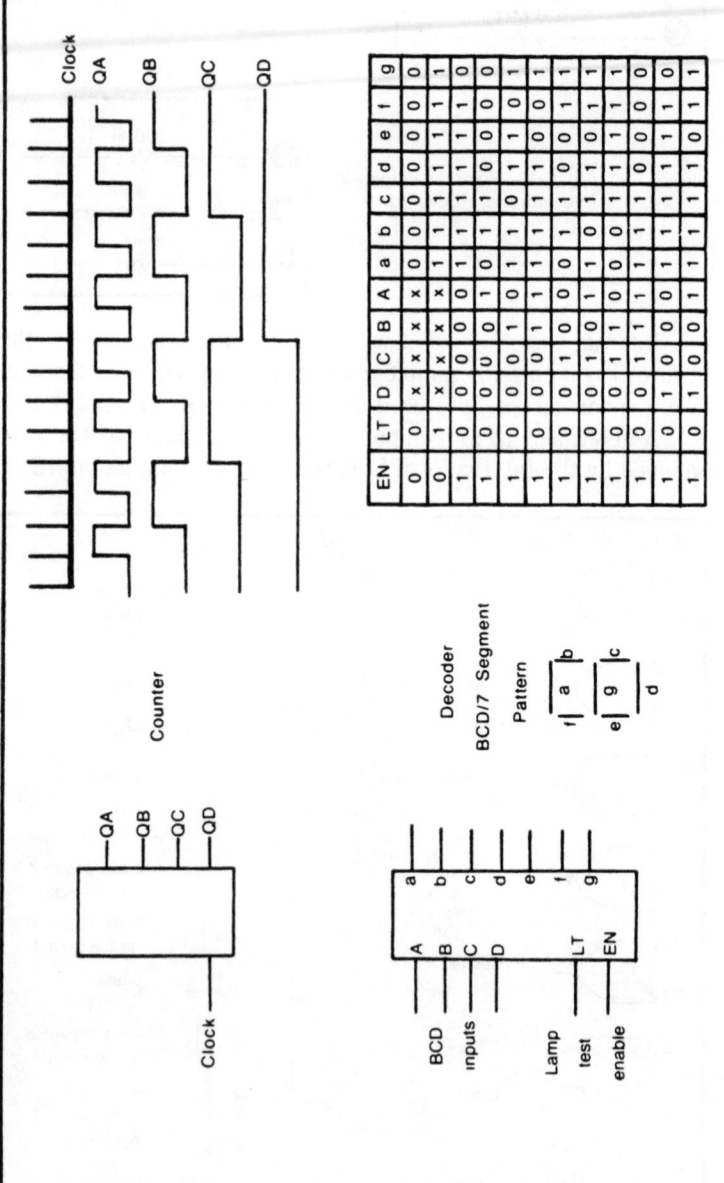

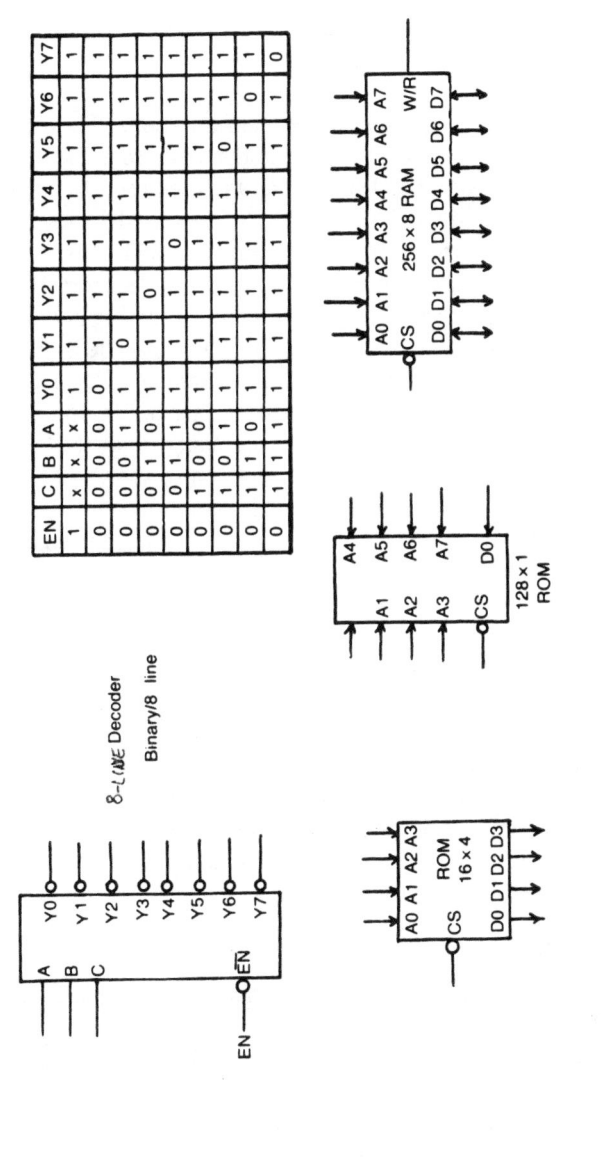

Fig. 7-17. Some computer symbols.

117

In the United States the Institute of Electrical and Electronics Engineers has published the standard in its IEEE Std 91-1984. A few logic devices are shown in Fig. 7-16 and compared to the military notation. Notice the rectangular box is the basic symbol in this system. Meaning is portrayed in the qualifying symbols either in or out of the rectangle.

Figure 7-17 depicts a few complex logic functions found in computers.

Counters can take on various configurations. The one shown here is a binary counter, counting in this case from 0000_2 to 1111_2. Some counters count to 1001_2 or 9_{10} and then reset to 0000_2. Such a counter is called a BCD counter, a binary coded decimal counter.

Many different kinds of encoders and decoders are also available. One example is the BCD/7-segment decoder; shown here with one enable line and a lamp-test input. By looking at the patterns of "1's" shown in the truth table, for particular BCD inputs, you should be able to find the number. For example, if the BCD inputs are 0100_2 or 4_{10} the outputs that are "1" are b, c, f, and g. If these outputs are connected to an LED 7-segment display the "4" should illuminate. A binary to 8-line decoder is also shown in the figure.

A couple of different read-only-memory symbols are also shown. The one with the four address lines (A_0 through A_3) can address 16 different locations, since $2^4 = 16$. Since there are four data lines the ROM is said to be a 16×4 ROM. A 128×1 ROM is also shown. A RAM (random-access-memory) symbol is also shown. Note that the data lines are shown with arrows in and out and also note the presence of a Write/Read enable line. When this line is high the Write function is enabled and information is stored from the data lines to the address selected by the address lines. When low a Read function would be enabled.

Manufacturers of integrated circuits make available data books that contain specifications for their computer chips. These are often referred to by technicians working in computer based products.

ADDITIONAL READING

Cirovic, Michael: *Integrated Circuits, A User's Handbook,* Reston Publishing Co., 1977.

Douglas-Young, John,: *Technicians Guide to Microelectronics,* Park Publishing Co., 1978.

Faber, Rodney B. and Russell L. Heiserman: *Introduction to Electron Devices,* McGraw-Hill, 1968.

Hughes, Fredrick W.: *Workbench Guide to Practical Solid State*

Electronics, Parker Publishing Co., 1979.

Jones, Thomas H.: *Electronic Components Handbook,* Reston Publishing Co., 1978.

Turner, Rufus P.: *Solid State Components,* Howard W. Sams, 1974.

Warring, R. H.: *Electronic Components Handbook for Circuit Designers,* TAB BOOKS Inc., 1983.

Semiconductors

This chapter contains questions on diodes, transistors, and other semiconductor devices. This review will cover operation, safety precautions, and testing of these devices.

QUIZ

Q1. A forward-biased diode made of germanium will have a voltage drop such that the anode will be:

a. positive with respect to the cathode
b. negative with respect to the cathode

Q2. The symbol for a zener diode is:

a. 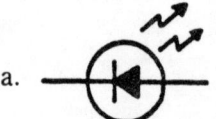 c.

b.  d.

Q3. In the circuit of Fig. 8-1 the voltage at A with respect to B should be:

a. positive   c. alternating
b. negative

Q4. If the zener diode opens in the circuit of *Question 3,* the output voltage will:

a. increase   c. remain the same
b. decrease

Q5. The bipolar transistor in Fig. 8-2 is:

a. an NPN, biased correctly
b. an NPN, biased incorrectly
c. a PNP, biased correctly
d. a PNP, biased incorrectly

Q6. A transistor is biased at saturation with a sine wave signal input to the circuit. The output clips 180° of the input. This is:

a. class A operation   c. class C operation
b. class B operation   d. none of these

Q7. Figure 8-3 is a/an:

a. common-base amplifier
b. common-emitter amplifier
c. common-collector amplifier
d. none of these

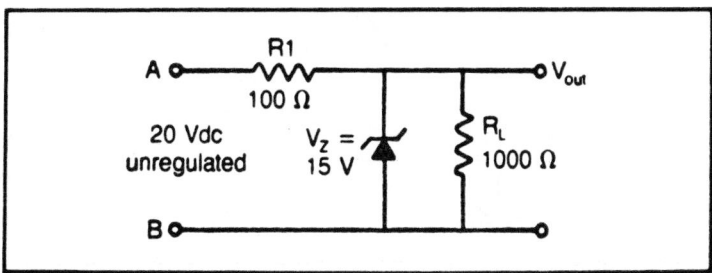

Fig. 8-1. Zener regulator for Q3.

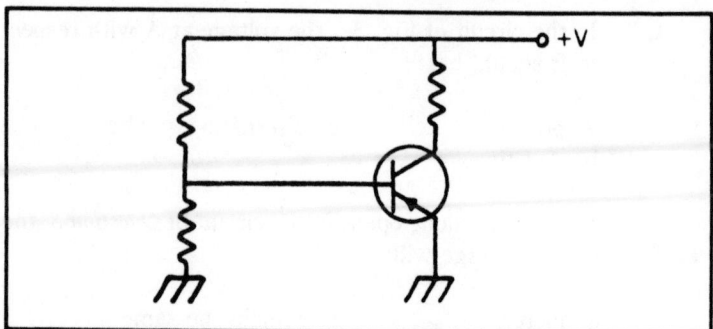

Fig. 8-2. Transistor amplifier for Q5.

Q8. Suppose in the circuit of Fig. 8-4 that the generator creates a voltage signal that produces a signal current i_e of 2 mA. The collector signal current i_c will be:

a. approximately 2 mA
b. beta times i_e
c. since beta = 1 in common base circuits a and b are both correct
d. none of these

Q9. If in the circuit of Fig. 8-4 it takes 0.01 volt of signal to create i_e of 1 mA the voltage gain is:

a. undeterminable   c. 100
b. unity   d. less than one

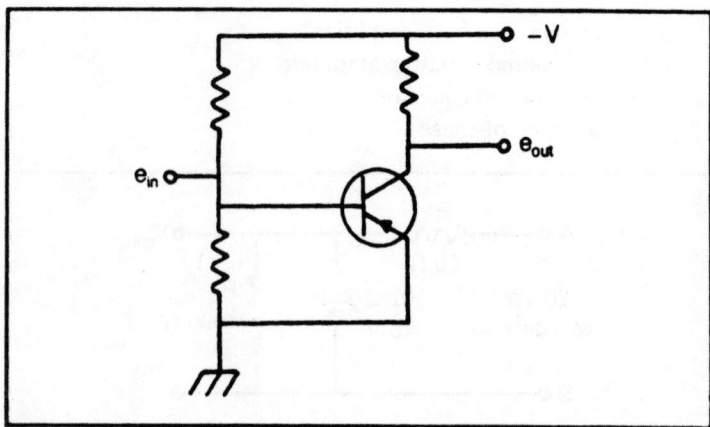

Fig. 8-3. Transistor amplifier for Q7.

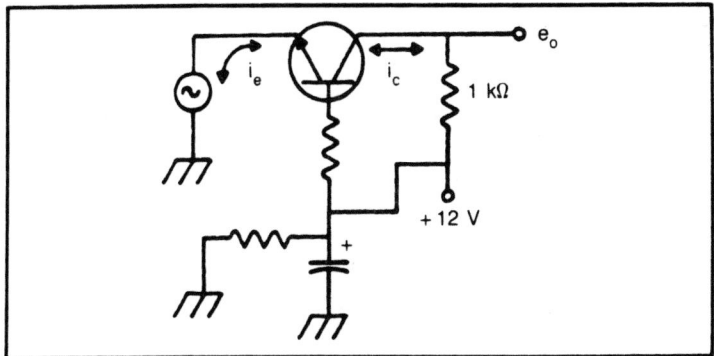

Fig. 8-4. Currents in common base amplifier, Q8.

Q10. An ohmmeter on the × 100 scale is being used to measure
a transistor. The red lead is positive with respect to the
black lead. A low reading is measured when the red lead
is on the base and the black lead is on the collector of
a PNP transistor. This measurement is:

    a. normal
    b. not normal

Q11. A unijunction transistor has:

    a. an emitter   c. three leads
    b. a negative resistance   d. all of the above
       region

Q12. The symbol in Fig. 8-5 is:

    a. an N-channel unijunction c. an N-type SCN
    b. an N-type SCR   d. an N-type MOSFET

Fig. 8-5. Solid-state device for Q12.

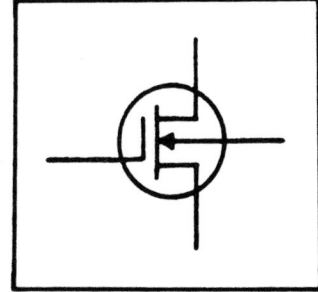

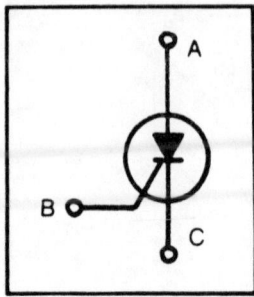

Fig. 8-6. Silicon Controlled Rectifier symbol, Q13.

Q13. In the symbol of the SCR in Fig. 8-6 terminal C is:

a. the cathode   c. the gate
b. the anode   d. none of these

Q14. Figure 8-7 is the symbol of:

a. a triac
b. a silicon-controlled switch
c. a diac
d. none of these

DIODES

The following circuit (Fig. 8-8) is biased such that current will flow easily through the circuit. If the positive terminal of the battery is connected through circuitry to the anode of a diode and the negative terminal is connected through circuitry to the cathode, the diode is forward biased. Electrons will flow in the direction of the arrow and hence voltage drops are as shown. The answer to *Question 1* is, therefore, *a*. If the diode is turned around (as shown in Fig. 8-9), the voltage drops are still in the same direction. How-

Fig. 8-7. Solid-state device for Q12.

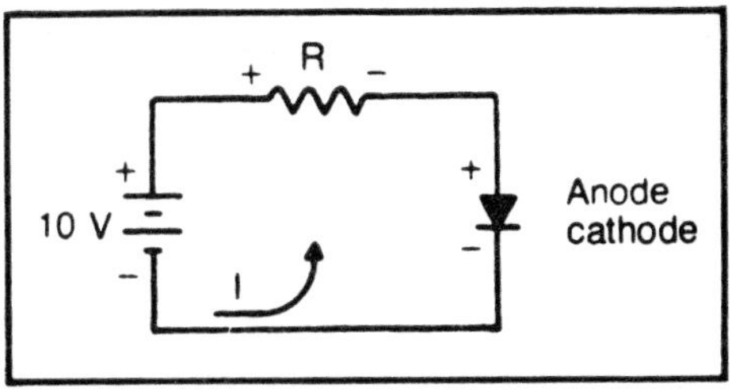

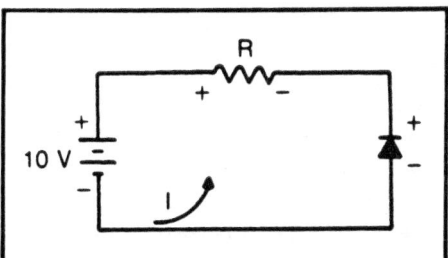

Fig. 8-8. Forward-biased diode.

ever, the diode is now reverse biased. Therefore, current is quite small. The voltage drop on the resistor is almost zero, hense the back-bias on the diode is nearly equal to the battery voltage, 10 volts. When the diode is forward biased the magnitude of its voltage drop is approximately 0.6 V (silicon diode).

In replacing diodes, four things are important to know. First, I_{Fmax}, the forward current maximum rating is important to know. Suppose R in Fig. 8-8 is 10 ohms ± 10%. I_{max} will occur when R is minimum and the diode is forward biased.

$$I_{max} = \frac{10 \text{ V} - 0.6 \text{ V}}{10 - 10(.10)} \quad \begin{array}{l} \text{(voltage drop across the diode)} \\ \text{(minimum resistance)} \end{array}$$

$$= 1.044 \text{ amperes}$$

Select a diode in this case with I_{Fmax} greater than 1.044 amps. Second, PIV—the peak inverse voltage rating is important to know if the diode is to be reverse biased. Suppose the circuit of Fig. 8-10 is to be built. What should PIV be?

The highest voltage in the reverse direction occurs when the capacitor is charged to peak value and the input voltage goes to its peak value with terminal A negative with respect to B. We might redraw the circuit at that instant to give Fig. 8-11.

Hence, the reverse voltage applied to the diode is 110 (1.414) + 110 (1.414) = 311 volts. In many places the 110-volt ac line volt-

Fig. 8-9. Reverse-biased diode.

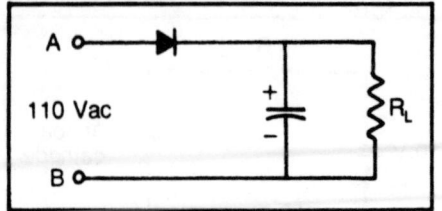

Fig. 8-10. Half-wave rectifier circuit.

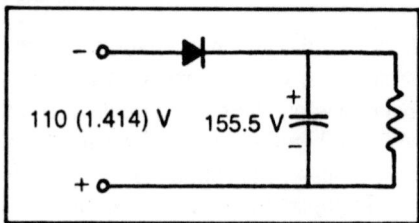

Fig. 8-11. Instantaneous voltages in a rectifier circuit.

age is closer to 120 Vac. If the above source voltage was from such a power system then the actual applied inverse voltage could be as high as 340 volts. In that case, the selected diode must have a PIV (peak inverse voltage) greater than 340 V. The third thing important to know is what the diode material is. Is it germanium, silicon, or some other material? The fourth important factor is the physical characteristics. Will it fit? If it's a stud-mounted diode, does the stud need to be insulated? Is the stud the anode or the cathode? All other physical factors need to be considered. An exact replacement, of course, takes care of all these considerations (provided of course, that the exact replacement really is just that, and isn't mismarked or a "bad" part).

Another diode (useful for its special characteristics) is the zener diode. In the zener diode symbol the cathode portion is shown as a bent line resembling the letter Z (Fig. 8-12).

Fig. 8-12. Zener diode symbols.

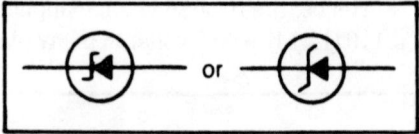

I recommend, ETA/s, the symbol on the right in Fig. 8-12. The answer to *Question 2* is *d*. Zener diodes are important in voltage regulations. These diodes have a range of operation when reverse biased, that exhibits almost constant voltage for a wide range of currents. In order to reverse bias a zener a positive voltage must

126

be sent to the cathode and a negative sent to the anode. In *Question 3* this means A must be positive with respect to B, hence answer *a* is correct.

In the circuit of Fig. 8-13 with a zener diode normal operation is such that the voltage drop across R1 is $V_B - V_Z$. The current through R_1 (I_T) is $I_Z + I_L$ where I_Z is the zener current (electron current shown on drawings) and I_L is the load current. As long as the operation is in the normal range I_T is constant and changing the load current I_L changes I_Z inversely. Let's put in some numbers and explore this further. Let $V_B = 10$ volts, $V_Z = 5$ volts and R1 = 1000 ohms. I_T must then be constant at 10 V – 5 V/1000 =, which is equal to 5 milliamps. Suppose $R_L = 2000$ ohms. Then $I_L = 5/2000 = 2.5$ mA. If $I_T = 5$ milliamps and $I_L = 2.5$ milliamps then I_Z must equal 2.5 mA. Suppose that R_L opens up. Then I_L is surely 0 mA. But I_T must still be 5 mA. Let's change R_L now to 1000 ohms. Then I_L wants to be 5 mA and I_Z wants to be 0 milliamps. Or, the zener diode is no longer in the zener region. It is starved for current. A further increase in the load takes the circuit out of normal operation. For example, suppose R_L changes to 500 ohms. Now the circuit current I_T must increase since $R_1 + R_L = 1500$ ohms and 10 volts/1500 ohms = 6.67 mA. The load voltage is now 6.67 mA × 500 = 3.33 volts. The zener is now off or not "broken down."

In *Question 4* a circuit is present and a trouble introduced. The zener is opened. In that case the circuit now looks like Fig. 8-14.

$$V_{out} = 20 \text{ V} \quad \frac{1000}{1000 + 100} = 18.2 \text{ volts}$$

Therefore, V_{out} increased from 15 volts to 18.2 volts.

The subject of diodes usually covers tunnel diodes. The symbol is shown in Fig. 8-15. This diode, when slightly forward biased, exhibits negative resistance. That is when the voltage is increased the current decreases. It is possible to build an oscillator using this characteristic with the circuit shown in Fig. 8-16.

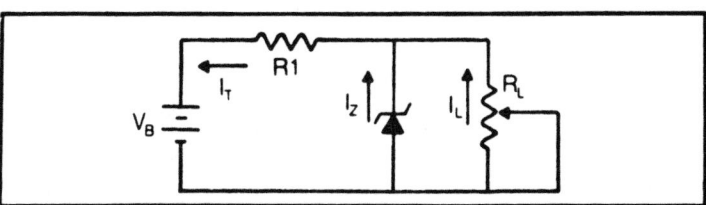

Fig. 8-13. Current in Zener regulated circuits.

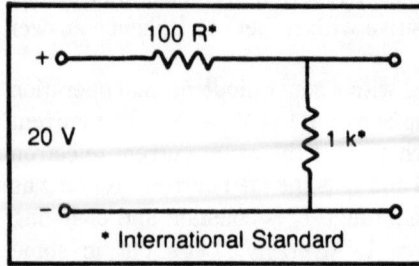

Fig. 8-14. Equivalent circuit.

However, because of difficulties in keeping the diode in the negative resistance range, and other problems, the tunnel diode has not been used much in practical circuits. On the other hand, another diode, the "varicap" diode or varactor is very useful. This diode is normally reverse biased. Since a reverse biased junction is essentially electrons separated by a dielectric, it has capacitance. Since the capacitance varies (separation of the carriers) as the reverse voltage varies, the diode is useful in construction of voltage-variable oscillators. Special diodes are also available for fast switching, noise generation, and other special needs.

THREE-LEAD SEMICONDUCTORS

A very useful three-lead semiconductor device is the bipolar

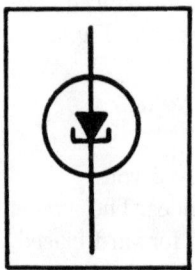

Fig. 8-15. Tunnel-diode symbol.

Fig. 8-16. Tunnel-diode oscillator circuit.

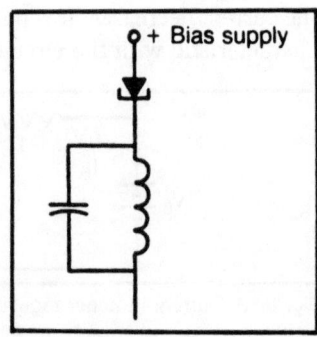

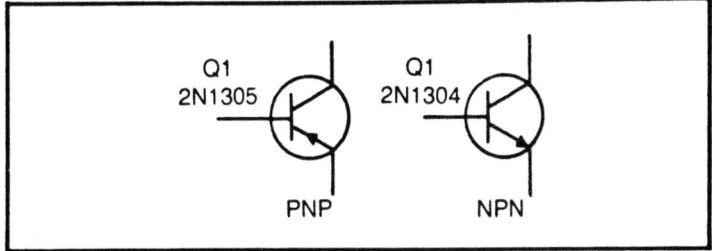

Fig. 8-17. Bipolar transistor symbols.

transistor. There are many varieties and types of bipolar transistors. The symbols for an NPN and for a PNP are shown in Fig. 8-17.

TRANSISTOR AMPLIFIERS

Bipolar transistors are used as amplifiers. To make them operate they must be properly biased. To amplify, the collector-base junction must be reverse biased and the base-emitter forward biased. A forward biased junction is very much like a forward biased diode. In the circuit of Fig. 8-18 the base is tied through the resistor to the negative terminal of the battery, while the emitter is tied to the positive terminal of the battery. The arrow is in the direction of conventional current flow; that is, opposite to electron flow. If the battery is connected to cause electrons to flow in a direction opposite to the arrow; the junction is forward biased. A forward biased silicon junction has about 0.6 volts drop. A germanium junction has about 0.3 volts drop if biased in the forward direction.

The collector-base junction of Fig. 8-19 is reverse biased.

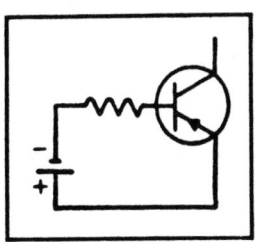

Fig. 8-18. Biasing the base-emitter junction.

Fig. 8-19. Biasing the collector-base junction.

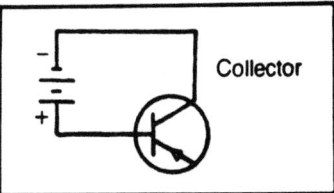

129

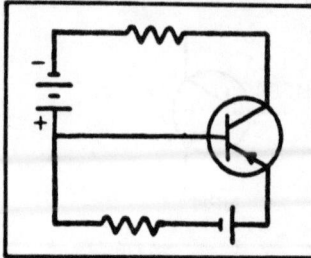

Fig. 8-20. Proper amplifier bias polarities.

(Think of the collector lead also having an arrow pointing in—like the emitter.) Since the negative battery terminal is connected to the collector through the resistor and the positive battery terminal is connected to the base, the electron flow would be in the direction of the arrow; if there was one, and if current flowed. But this is reverse bias so no current flows. Putting the two concepts together in Fig. 8-20 gives a properly biased amplifier.

With the base-emitter conducting, electrons will be "injected" into the base. These electrons will cause current to flow in the collector lead also. This current will be h_{FE} times the base current. The h_{FE} is the dc current gain. In equation form:

$$I_C = h_{FE} I_B$$

Let's look at the circuit of *Question 5* redrawn as in Fig. 8-21 with voltage drops shown.

Note that the voltage drops across the power supply voltage divider are as shown. Further note that these drops are such that they would *reverse* bias the base-emitter junction and *forward* bias the collector-base junction. This is incorrect for proper operation of the amplifier. Hence, this is an improperly biased PNP transistor.

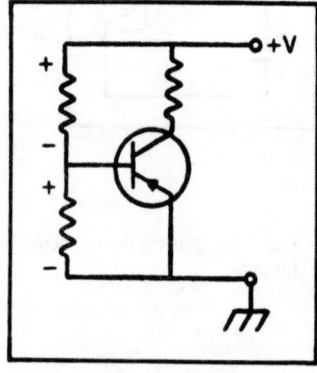

Fig. 8-21. Improper amplifier bias polarities.

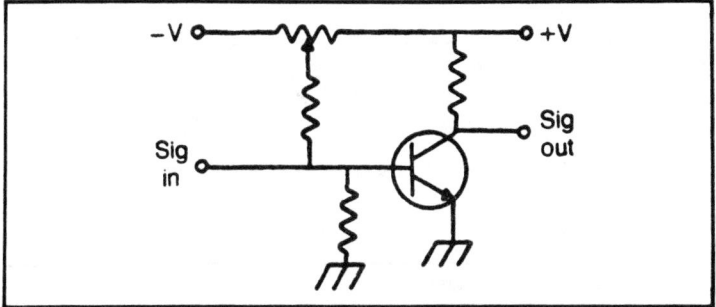

Fig. 8-22. Demonstration circuit for adjusting classes of amplifier operation.

With the circuit of Fig. 8-22 the base-emitter bias can be adjusted from highly positive to highly negative. If the bias is highly negative the base-emitter junction is reverse biased. Decreasing the negative voltage to the point where signal starts to affect the output on the positive signal peaks would be approaching Class C operation. That is, output signal change for less than 180° of input signal. At some point in decreasing the negative voltage, the output signal would vary for 180° of the input signal. That bias is called Class B bias. Increasing the bias positively would eventually reach an area of bias where signal output would change for the entire 360° of input signal. This area is Class A operation. Further increasing bias voltage in the positive direction would establish another point where for half the input cycle the output would not vary because the transistor would be saturated for that half cycle. This is another Class B operational bias. Increasing bias more positively would reduce output signal variation to less than 180° of the input signal. This would again be Class C operation. Eventually, if the bias is positive enough the signal could not bring the transistor out of saturation. The answer to *Question 6* is *b*. Digital circuits are normally biased either into saturation or at cutoff, that is, on or off.

CE, CC, or CB Amplifiers

Amplifiers are sometimes classified by the terminology common-emitter, common-collector or common-base amplifiers, depending upon the common connection between the input signal and the output signal. For example, if the base is common to the input signal and to the output signal, the amplifier is a common-base amplifier. Since it is almost an unwritten rule that signal flow is depicted on schematics from left to right, a common-base amplifier is often depicted as in Fig. 8-23.

131

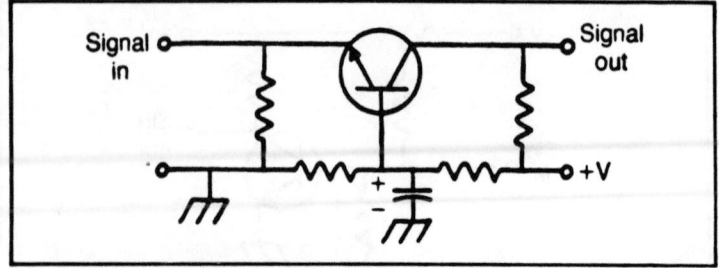

Fig. 8-23. Common-base amplifier.

But no matter how the circuit is drawn, if the input and output signals show the base as their common terminal, it is a common-base amplifier. These amplifiers find use when a high input impedance is needed.

Common-collector amplifiers are often called emitter followers; because the output signal taken from the emitter follows almost one for one what the base signal is. Figure 8-24 shows an emitter-follower schematic or common-collector amplifier schematic. Of course, the signal is developed from base to ground and from emitter to ground. But *signal-wise* the collector is virtual ground. Collector voltage does not vary with either input or output signal. Therefore, the collector is "common" to the input and to the output signals.

The common-emitter amplifier is the most commonly used transistor amplifier because it has current gain and voltage gain. A common-emitter amplifier is shown in Fig. 8-3. In this case, ground happens to be also common for the emitter as well as the input signal and the output signal.

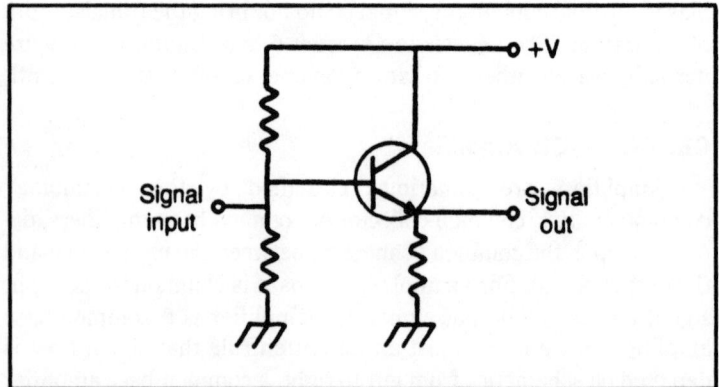

Fig. 8-24. Common-collector amplifier.

CIRCUIT CALCULATIONS

Since common-emitter amplifiers are widely used, this discussion will take them up first. If you came across the circuit of Fig. 8-25 in the certification test and you were asked what the collector dc voltage was, could you determine the value? If you could, you should not have trouble with bias problems on the exam. If, in addition to the information given in the circuit, you were also told this was a Class A amplifier, you should be able to get close to the answer without any calculation since in order to amplify a signal linearly for 360° of the input signal the transistor should be biased somewhere in the middle, between saturation and cutoff. If the transistor was cut off the collector voltage would be 10 volts in this case. If it were saturated the collector voltage would be nearly 0 volts. For an amplifier you should expect the collector to be about halfway between these extremes at 5 volts. But with the information contained in the drawing the collector voltage can be calculated. Start by calculating the base to ground voltage. Since the base draws very little current, this voltage will be determined by the voltage divider R1, R2.

$$V_{BG} = \text{voltage base to ground} = \frac{1.2 \text{ k}}{1.2 \text{ k} + 8.2 \text{ k}} \times (10 \text{ V})$$

$$= \frac{12}{9.4} \text{ volts}$$

$$= 1.28 \text{ volts}$$

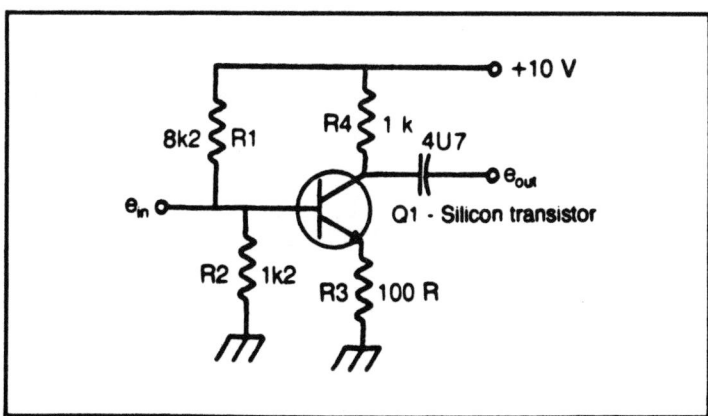

Fig. 8-25. Circuit used for calculations.

If the transistor is silicon, the base-emitter voltage drop will be about 0.7 volts. Hence the voltage from emitter to ground should be:

$$V_{EG} = 1.28 - 0.7$$
$$= 0.58 \text{ volts}$$

The emitter current must equal:

$$I_E = \frac{0.58 \text{ V}}{100 \text{ ohms}}$$

$$= 5.8 \text{ mA}$$

Since the emitter current and collector current are almost identical then:

$$I_C = I_E = 5.8 \text{ mA}$$

This is a good approximation. The collector voltage to ground then is:

$$V_{CG} = 10 \text{ V} - I_C \, R4$$
$$= 10 \text{ V} - (5.80 \text{ mA}) \, 1 \text{ k}$$
$$= 4.2 \text{ volts}$$

Suppose a signal is applied at the base with respect to ground, could you calculate the output signal? Say that e_{in} is 20 mV P-P; that is, the base voltage varies from 1.28 up to 1.3 volts and down to 1.26 volts. With no bypass capacitor on the emitter its voltage will also vary by 20 mV P-P (or near enough, anyway). Therefore, I_E will vary by:

$$\Delta I_E = i_e = \frac{20 \text{ mV}}{100 \text{ ohms}} = 0.2 \text{ mA}$$

$$\text{and } \Delta I_C = i_c = i_e$$

$$\text{hence: } e_o = i_c \times 1 \text{ k}$$
$$= (0.2 \text{ mA}) \, (1 \text{ k})$$
$$= 0.2 \text{ volts P-P}$$

The voltage gain:

$$A_v = \frac{e_o}{e_{in}}$$

$$= \frac{0.2}{20 \text{ mV}}$$

$$= 10$$

In this common-emitter circuit the voltage gain is easier to figure just by noting that since the signal current in the emitter resistor is the same as the collector signal current the voltage gain must be the same as the ratio of collector resistance to emitter resistance:

$$A_v = 1 \text{ k}/100 = 10$$

With the emitter bypassed, however, none of the above holds true. Since the emitter voltage stays constant there is no "built-in" degeneration. Or, saying it another way, all of the signal results in a base current swing. The collector current change then is the ac current gain, h_{fe}, times the base current change. These are both dependent on the transistor parameters. Voltage gains of 100 are common and much higher is possible. In this configuration both current gain and voltage gain are exhibited.

The common-base circuit in Fig. 8-26 is the same as that in *Question 8*. The currents drawn are dc currents; therefore, they are capital letters. Also they are drawn the way electrons would flow in the circuits. Many references will draw all the currents either into or out of the transistor and let the signs take care of direction.

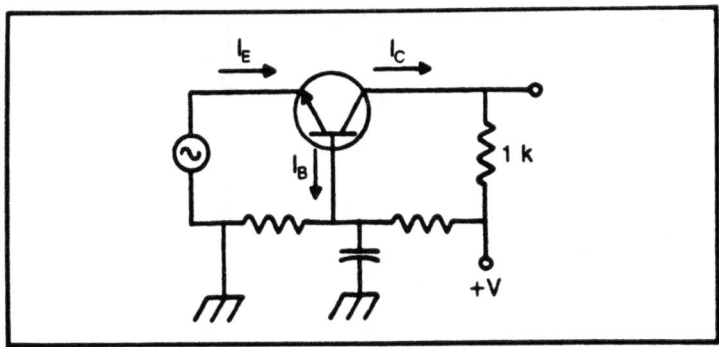

Fig. 8-26. Common-base circuit of Q8.

That is, if a current is drawn into the collector and it is later found that the current has a negative sign it means the current flows out. Anyway, the way they are drawn here is the way electrons would flow in the properly biased transistor. Since electrons can't disappear, the current in must equal the current out.

$$I_E = I_B + I_C$$

Or rearrange the equation:

$$I_C = I_E - I_B$$

Note that since I_B is very small I_C is always slightly less than I_E. If the signal input voltage causes a slight increase in I_E, I_B, and I_C will increase. If I_E decreases slightly I_B and I_C will also decrease. In other words signal currents will behave much the same as dc currents. To indicate signal voltages and currents it is normal to use lowercase letters as in Fig. 8-27.

$$i_e = i_c + i_b$$

or rearranging

$$i_c = i_e - i_b$$

with i_b very very small

$$i_c \approx i_e$$

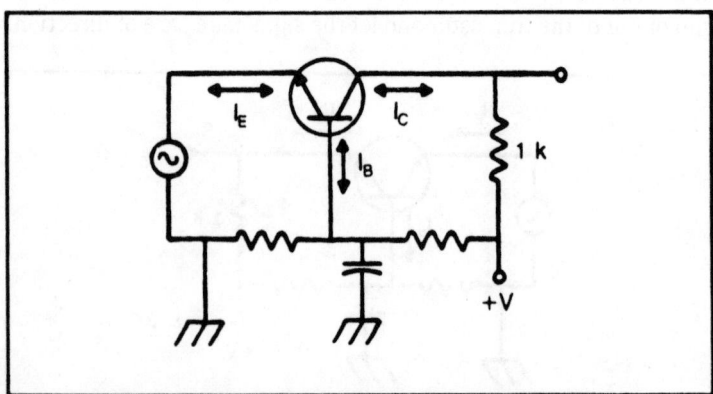

Fig. 8-27. Signal currents in common-base circuit.

136

Hence, if the signal voltage causes a signal current i_e of 2 mA the collector current is almost 2 mA. Answer *a* is correct for *Q8*. If a signal of 0.01 volts creates a current of 1 mA, most of the 1 mA flows to the collector and hence through the 1 k collector resistor resulting in a signal voltage change of 1 volt. The voltage gain then is:

$$A_v = \frac{1 \text{ volt}}{0.01 \text{ volt}}$$

$$= 100 \quad \text{(answer to \textit{Question 9} is } c\text{)}$$

A common-collector circuit is shown in Fig. 8-28. Again, the base to ground voltage can be calculated ignoring the base current.

$$V_{BG} = \frac{1 \text{ k}}{2 \text{ k}} (-10)$$

$$= -5 \text{ volts}$$

If the transistor is made of silicon the base-emitter drop is 0.7 volts, hence:

$$V_{EG} = -5 \text{ V} + 0.7$$
$$= -4.3 \text{ volts}$$

and from this

$$I_E = \frac{V_{EG}}{R} = \frac{-4.3}{200} = 21.5 \text{ mA}$$

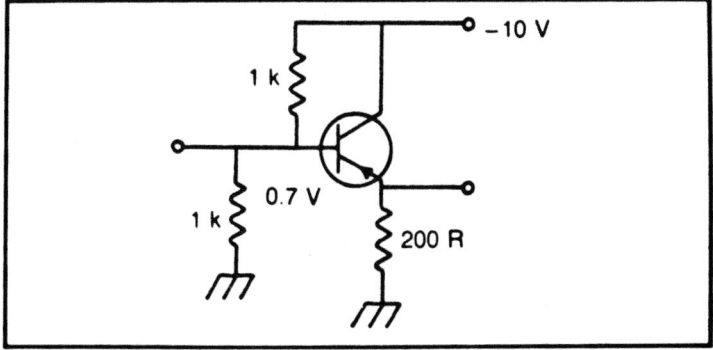

Fig. 8-28. Common-collector circuit.

Note that the input signal causes the base voltage to vary around the 5-volt level. For example, let's suppose the input voltage causes the base voltage to change from − 5 V to − 6 V. If that's the case, the output voltage goes from − 4.3 to − 5.3; still 0.7 volts away from the base voltage. If the input causes the base voltage to go to − 4 volts the output changes to − 3.3 (still 0.7 volts more positive than the base). Hence, while the input signal is two volts peak-to-peak the output is two volts peak-to-peak. This example ignores some things like the nonlinearity of the transistor. However, the output signal voltage will be only slightly less than the input signal voltage.

$$A_v \text{ is almost } 1$$

The base current change required to change the emitter current is:

$$\Delta I_B = \Delta I_E / h_{fe}$$

The change in emitter current:

$$\Delta I_E = \frac{5.3}{200} - \frac{3.3}{200} = \frac{2}{200} = 10 \text{ mA}$$

If the transistors small signal current gain is 50 (not an exceedingly high current gain), then:

$$\Delta I_B = \Delta I_E / h_{fe}$$

$$= \frac{10 \text{ mA}}{50}$$

$$= 0.2 \text{ mA}$$

It can be seen from these examples that the following conditions exist in the various amplifier configurations.

Circuit Configuration	A_v Voltage Gain	A_I Current Gain
Common Emitter	>1	>1

| Common Base | >1 | ≈1 |
| Common Collector (Emitter-Follower) | ≈1 | >1 |

MEASURING DIODES AND TRANSISTORS

An ohmmeter is often used to check diodes and transistors. A semiconductor junction when forward biased is a low resistance, and when reverse biased it is a high resistance. Not all meters have the positive terminal of the internal battery (or voltage source) attached to the red lead. If the red lead is positive, when it is connected to the anode of a semiconductor diode, and if the black negative lead of the ohmmeter is attached to the cathode lead; the diode is forward biased provided that the voltage is large enough (Fig. 8-29). If the junction is good the resistance will be low, maybe 10 ohms. If the leads are reversed the resistance will be high, maybe 10 kilohms.

In measuring transistors the same sort of thing occurs. If the junctions are looked at, as if they were diodes, the equivalents of Fig. 8-30 will prevail. If the positive red lead is on the base of the PNP for example, and the black lead on the collector, the junction is reverse biased and the reading should be high. *Question 10* stated the reading was low, hence, *b* "not normal" is the correct answer.

OTHER SEMICONDUCTOR DEVICES

There are many types of semiconductor devices. This section will cover some of these devices. The symbol for a *unijunction transistor* is shown in Fig. 8-31. The N material between base 1 and base 2 acts like a conductor with some resistance. If current is flowing in the base 1 emitter circuit; however, the resistance is very low between base 1 and base 2. The base 1 emitter has a re-

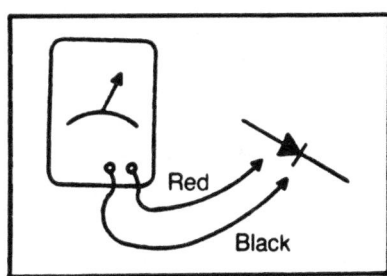

Fig. 8-29. Ohmmeter diode test.

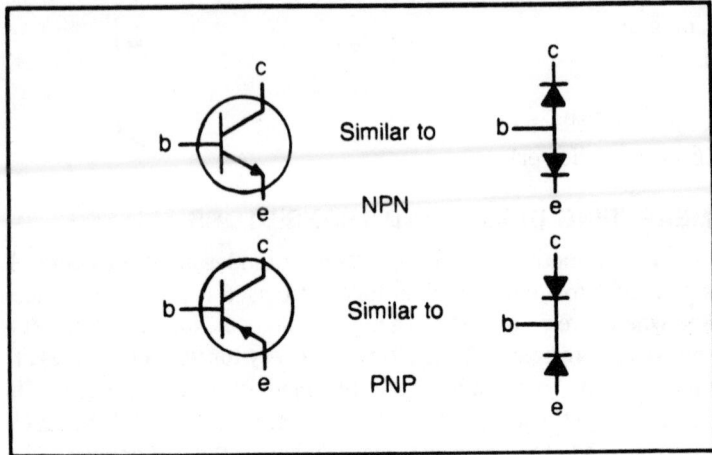

Fig. 8-30. Diode representation of transistors.

gion (when forward biased) of negative resistance. Like the tunnel diode, in this region increases of forward bias result in decreased current. This characteristic is useful in building a simple oscillator. Since the unijunction transistor has an emitter, and it has this area of negative resistance, and it has three leads, the answer to *Question 11* is *d*.

Another very useful semiconductor device is the *junction field-effect transistor* (JFET). There are two kinds of JFETS; the n-channel and the p-channel. Each has a gate, a drain, and a source (Fig. 8-32). While JFETs are useful they have not been applied as extensively as their cousins, the *isolated gate field-effect transistors* (IGFET). This transistor is also known as a MOSFET (*metal-oxide semiconductor FET*). The JFET (like the unijunction) consists of a P-doped or N-doped silicon bar that acts like a resistance between the source and drain. The gate is diffused into the bar making a PN junction between the gate and the bar. If the junction is forward biased and it increases current in the bar between the source and drain, the transistor is operating in the enhancement mode. If re-

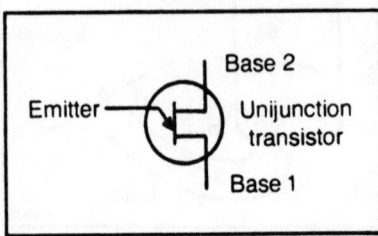

Fig. 8-31. Unijunction transistor symbol.

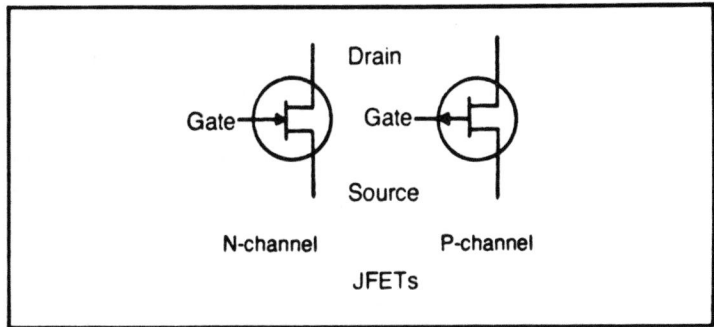

Fig. 8-32. Junction field-effect transistor (JFET).

verse bias decreases current, the transistor current is being depleted. The transistor is said to be operating in the depletion mode. From the symbols in Fig. 8-33 it can be seen that the correct answer to *Question 12* is *d*.

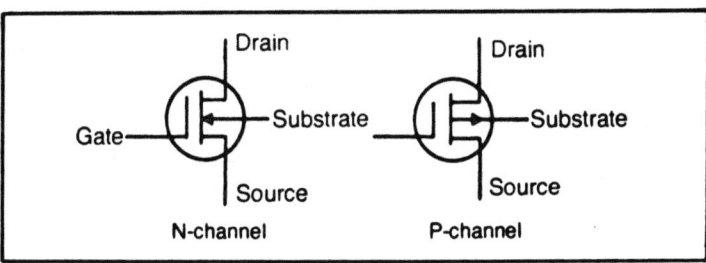

Fig. 8-33. Metal-oxide semiconductor field-effect transistors (MOSFET) or isolated-gate field-effect transistors (IGFET).

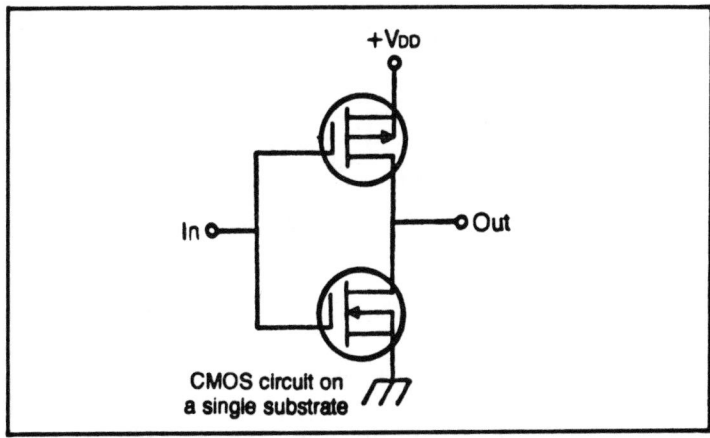

Fig. 8-34. Complementary metal-oxide semiconductor device.

The MOSFET is useful because it utilizes small amounts of power and it has a very high input impedance. By combining N-channel and P-channel FET devices on a single substate, a pair of complimentary *FETs* are created. A whole family of devices using these techniques have been devised and gained widespread use in computer technology. These are called *CMOS* devices (pronounced see-moss), see Fig. 8-34.

THYRISTORS

A large group of semiconductor devices having three or more junctions have been developed. These are called *thyristors*. Some thyristor symbols are shown in Fig. 8-35. The SCR behaves like a gas-filled triode, except current in the gate starts conduction instead of voltage on a grid. With positive voltage at the anode (with respect to the cathode) the SCR will not conduct normally. Application of positive voltage on the gate (with respect to the cathode) will cause gate current to flow. The gate current will "turn-on" the SCR. Anode current will flow. If the anode to cathode voltage is above a certain breakover voltage the SCR can conduct without gate current. This would not be allowed in most applications, since the advantage of the SCR is in controlling the turn-on with a small gate current. From the SCR symbol it can be seen that the correct answer to *Question 13* is *a* (the cathode). Note that positive

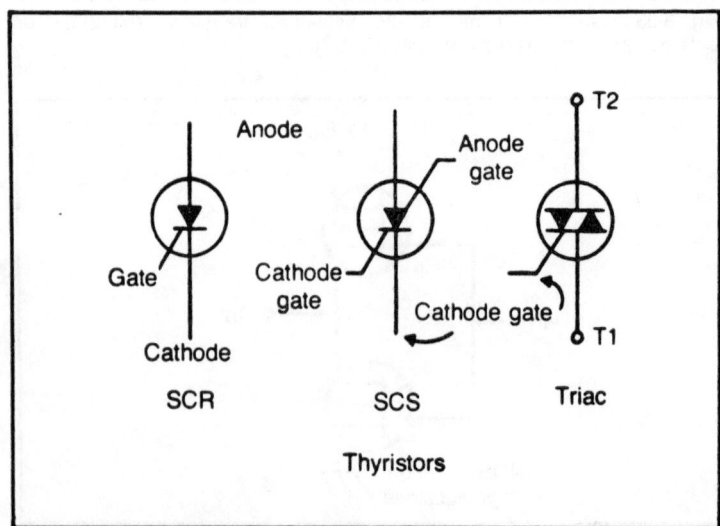

Fig. 8-35. Thyristors (PNPN devices).

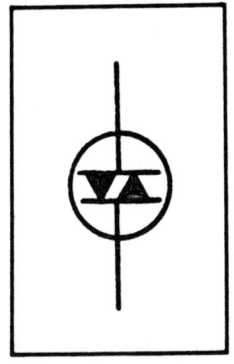

Fig. 8-36. Diac.

voltage applied to the cathode of the SCR (with respect to the anode) will not result in current flow. The SCR acts like a back-biased diode regardless of gate current.

The *silicon-controlled switch* (SCS) is designed so that it can be turned on with either polarity of gate voltage. Like the SCR, reverse voltage from anode to cathode will not result in current regardless of gate pulses. The *triac*, however, can be turned on in either direction with either polarity of gate pulse.

A diac symbol is shown in Fig. 8-36. The diac has only two junctions like a transistor. Therefore, it is not a thyristor. The diac stays a high impedance with either polarity of terminal voltages until a critical voltage is reached. Beyond this voltage the diac goes into an avalanche mode and becomes a low impedance. The answer to *Question 14* is *c*.

INTEGRATED CIRCUITS

Many of the transistor and diode devices can be incorporated on a silicon chip. When many devices are combined to form complex circuitry on a single chip, the result is called an integrated circuit or IC for short. There are many package varieties of ICs including 8, 10, and 12 lead TO-5 "can" types. Dual in-line packages or DIPs are quite common in 8 lead, 14 lead, 16 lead, and many more leads (for larger packages).

Many varieties of linear integrated circuits are now available. Complete audio i-f sections, for AM, FM, and TV are available in IC packages. Chroma demodulators, chroma subcarrier, stereo multiplex decoders, audio amplifiers, and many other IC chips are available. Operational amplifiers are also available in many IC varieties.

ADDITIONAL READING

Douglas-Young, John: *Technicians Guide to Microelectronics,* Parker Publishing Co., 1978.

Hoft, Richard G., ed.: *SCR Applications Handbook,* International Rectifier Corp., Semiconductor Division, 1974.

Horn, Delton T.: *Basic Electronics Theory—with projects and experiments,* TAB BOOKS Inc., 1981.

Jones, Thomas H.: *Electronics Components Handbook,* Reston Publishing, 1978.

Larson, Boyd: *Transistor Fundamentals and Troubleshooting,* Prentice-Hall, 1974.

Veley, Victor F.: *Semiconductors to Electronics Communications Made Easy,* TAB BOOKS Inc., 1982.

Warring, R.H.: *Understanding Electronics—2nd Edition,* TAB BOOKS Inc., 1984.

Digital Concepts

This chapter covers concepts of digital electronics pertinent to the technician of today. This rapidly expanding field should be understood by almost all electronics technicians. Computer techniques are invading almost every electronics area.

QUIZ

The first five questions pertain to the circuit in Fig. 9-1.

Q1. In this circuit if input A and B are both open (no connection), the output voltage will be:

 a. +5 volts   c. −5 volts
 b. nearly zero volts   d. none of these

Q2. The base to ground voltage with the same conditions as in *Question 1* would be:

 a. about 0.6 volts   c. about 0.2 volts
 b. +5 volts   d. −5 volts

Q3. If input B is grounded and input A left open the output would be:

 a. +5 volts   c. −5 volts
 b. nearly zero volts   d. none of these

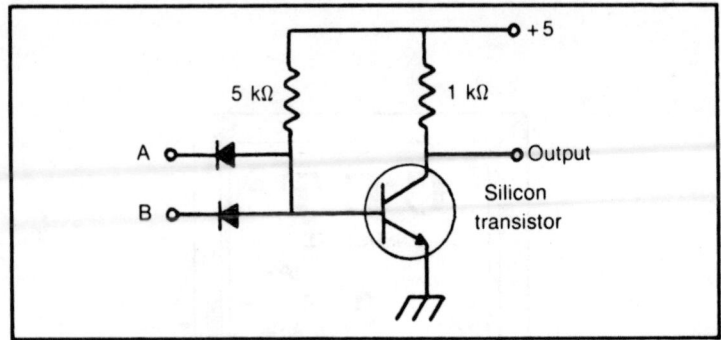

Fig. 9-1. Logic gate for Q1 through Q5.

Q4. If positive logic is assumed the circuit is:

a. a NAND gate   c. an AND gate
b. a NOR gate   d. none of these

Q5. If negative logic is assumed the circuit is:

a. a NAND gate   c. an AND gate
b. a NOR gate   d. none of these

Questions 6 through 10 refer to the circuit in Fig. 9-2.

Q6. The signal at G could best be described by the logic equation:

a. G = BC   c. G = A + B
b. G = CD   d. none of these

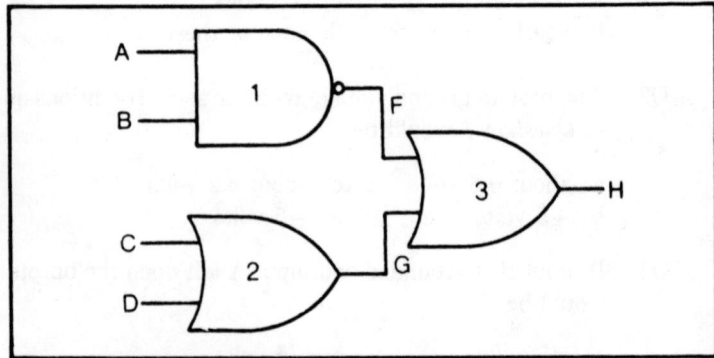

Fig. 9-2. Logic diagram for Q6 through Q10.

146

Q7. If A = "1" and B = "1" the signal at F will be:

    a. logic 1
    b. logic 0

Q8. If positive logic is assumed with "1" = +5 volts and "0" = 0 volts and if A, B, and C equal 0 volts and D equals +5 volts, H must equal:

    a. +5 volts   c. 2.5 volts
    b. 0 volts   d. none of these

Q9. If A and B are logic 1 and if C and D are both logic 0, H is:

    a. logic 1
    b. logic 0

Q10. The equation that describes H is:

    a. $\overline{A + B}$ (CD)   c. $\overline{AB}$ + C + D
    b. AC + BD   d. none of these describe H

Q11. An SR flip-flop is:

    a. monostable   c. bistable
    b. astable   d. none of these

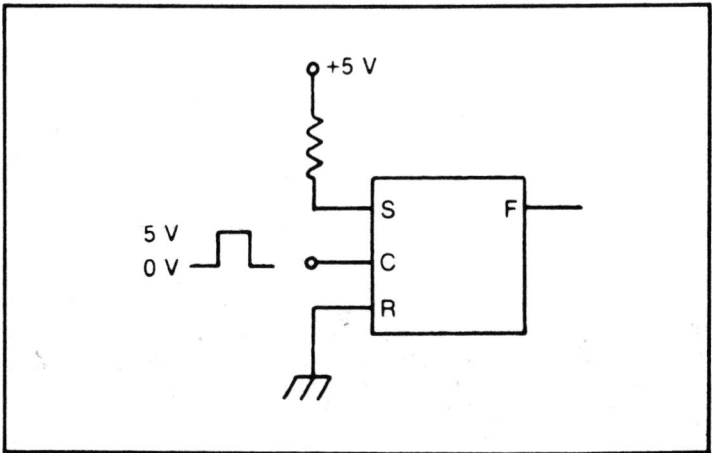

Fig. 9-3. S-R flip-flop and input for Q12.

Q12. After the SR flip-flop in Fig. 9-3 is clocked the output at F will be:

    a. +5 volts
    b. nearly zero volts
    c. undeterminable

Q13. The toggle flip-flop changes state with each trigger:

    a. true
    b. false

Q14. Data flip-flops are used for:

    a. counters   c. tri-state buffers
    b. A-to-D converters d. memory

SWITCHING CIRCUITS

At the heart of all computer-digital circuits is the switch. Understanding the transistor switch is, therefore, fundamental to a thorough understanding of digital computers. (Another field of study is involved in understanding computers from a programmer's viewpoint, which is different than an electronics technician's viewpoint.)

In switching circuits little power is consumed in the active device, which is the transistor. The circuit discussion below illustrates why this is the case. Note that when SW1 in Fig. 9-4 is in the A position there is no bias to supply base current for the transistor. The transistor is, therefore, OFF; that is, no collector current flows. With no collector current flowing the collector voltage is +5 volts. The power dissipated in the transistor is I_C (5 V), which is: 0(5)

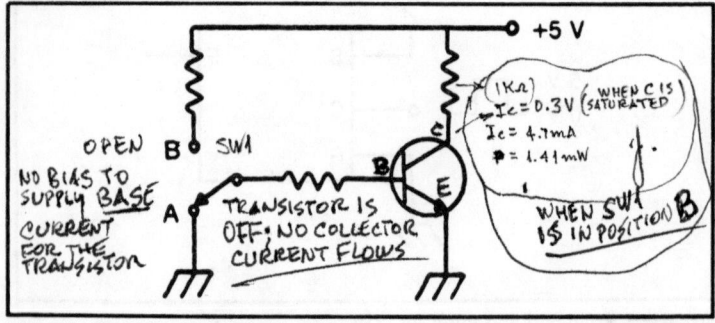

Fig. 9-4. Fundamental switching circuit.

= 0 watts. (Actually a small amount of leakage current does flow in the transistor. It is in the microampere range.)

When SW1 is in position B the base-emitter junction is forward biased. Resistances are chosen to cause enough current in the base circuit to produce saturation. If the transistor is saturated, the collector voltage is very low, about 0.3 V for silicon. Let's assume a load resistance in the collector of 1000 ohms. The collector current then is:

$$I = \frac{E_T}{R} = \frac{5\,V - 0.3\,V}{1000} = 4.7\,mA$$

Then

$$P = I \cdot V$$
$$P = (4.7\,mA)\,(0.3\,V)$$
$$= 1.41\,mW$$

Hence, in either the ON or OFF state the transistor consumes very little power.

LOGIC GATES

This basic transistor switch can be coupled with other circuit components to make various computer gates. Diodes, for example, can be used to form gates and make a useful (if obsolete) logic device when coupled with transistor switches. Let's examine such a circuit in Fig. 9-5.

Assume that inputs A and B are derived from collectors of transistors similar to those in this circuit. In other words, if the collector "driving" A is OFF, A will be +5 volts. If the collector

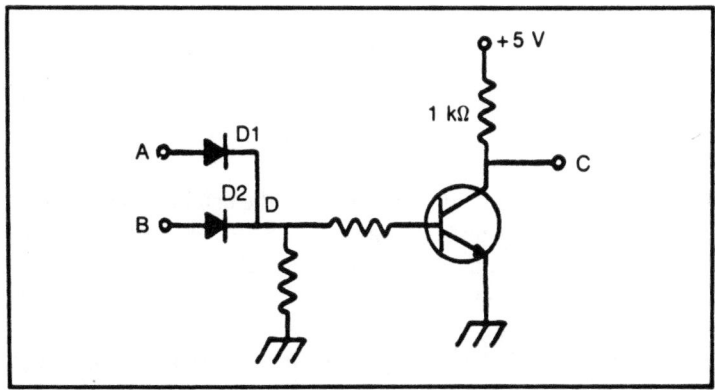

Fig. 9-5. A computer gate circuit.

"driving" A is ON the voltage will be 0.3 volts. The same voltage level may occur at B independent of A. To describe the circuit output at C (the dependent variable in this case) we need to examine all possible combinations of A and B. If A and B are both low (0.3 volts) the diodes cannot conduct. There will be no base current, hence the transistor is OFF and C is +5 volts. Suppose A is high (+5 volts) while B remains low. D1 becomes forward biased, D2 remains OFF. The +5 volts forward biases the base-emitter junction and the transistor goes ON. The voltage at C drops to 0.3 volts. In fact, either A or B high will result in C low. A and B both high will only further drive the transistor on and C will remain low. The following table summarizes these statements.

A	B	C
Low	Low	High
High	Low	Low
Low	High	Low
High	High	Low

In digital circuits we speak of logic levels of "1" and "0". Sometimes true and false are used instead, with true the same as logic 1 and false the same as logic 0. If the numerals "one" or "zero" are to be used for logic levels they are set apart by quote marks when used in sentences and not preceded by the word "logic" or the words "logic level."

For positive logic the higher voltage level is considered a "1" or True. A "0" is the lower voltage level. If the circuit above is used in a positive logic system, the following table shows "1" = High and "0" = Low.

A	B	C
0	0	1
1	0	0
0	1	0
1	1	0

This is now called a truth table because the original work in logic was done using True and False assignments to sentences connected by connectives such as AND, OR, and NOT.

Notice that if this circuit is used in a negative logic system where "1" = low voltage and "0" is the high voltage, the negative logic truth table will be quite different in appearance (even though it's the same circuit).

A	B	C
1	1	0
0	1	1
1	0	1
0	0	1

If the circuit of Fig. 9-5 is separated into logic functions, the diodes make up a logic gate, while the transistor is an inverter or NOT circuit. For the transistor if the input at D is high the output at C is low. C is said to equal "not D" in this case. A bar over a letter is used to indicate NOT. Thus:

$$C = \overline{D}$$

Another way of saying the same thing is in a truth table.

C	D
0	1
1	0

Redrawing the gate in the Fig. 9-5 circuit and leaving off the inverter gives the circuit in Fig. 9-6. Note that in this circuit, the input at D goes high when either A or B goes high.

A	B	D
Low	Low	Low
Low	High	High
High	Low	High
High	High	High

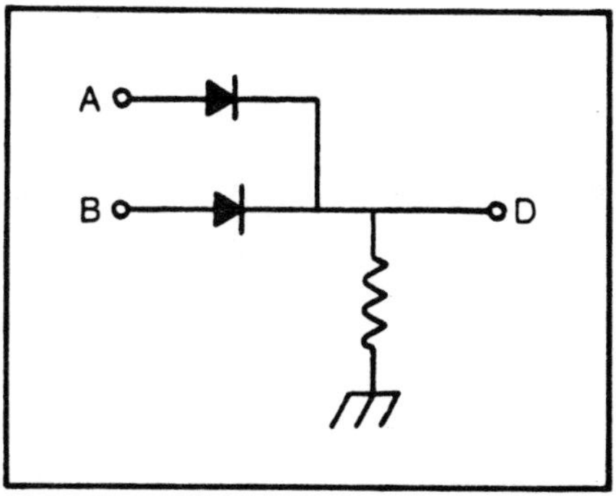

Fig. 9-6. Gate from Fig. 9-5.

If a positive logic system is involved, the truth table with "1" = high and "0" = low is:

A	B	D
0	0	0
0	1	1
1	0	1
1	1	1

This means that if either A or B are "1" the output D is "1" this is an OR gate.

Note also that if negative logic is the system that contains the circuit of Fig. 9-6, then "1" equals zero or low voltage and "0" equals +5 volts (or high). In this case, the truth table looks quite different. Substituting low = "1" high = "0" in the voltage table gives a truth table that looks like this:

A	B	D
1	1	1
1	0	0
0	1	0
0	0	0

We get a "1" out only when both A and B are "1". All other variations of A and B give a "0" output. Now the circuit is functioning as an *AND* gate.

There are a few logic circuits that use negative logic. Most designers use positive logic circuits. Let's now examine the positive logic AND gate in Fig. 9-7. Here, if either or both inputs are ground, the output D is low. Only if both inputs are high ("1" for positive logic) we do get a "1" out.

A	B	D
0	0	0
0	1	0
1	0	0
1	1	1

You may wish to draw the table for negative logic for this circuit. You should be able to see that it will be an OR logic function for negative logic.

If this circuit is followed by an inverter it will be the same as the circuit of *Question 1 to Question 5* (Fig. 9-1). When A and B are left open the transistor will saturate if the dc current gain of the transistor is 5 or greater. Assuming saturation the output will

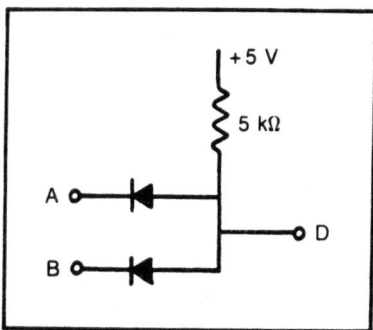

Fig. 9-7. Positive logic AND gate.

be nearly 0 volts (actually about 0.3 volts). This is the answer to *Question 1*.

Since the base-emitter is forward biased, the voltage drop across it is 0.6 or 0.7 volts (silicon junction). The answer to *Question 2* is, therefore, *a*.

This circuit is a positive-logic AND gate followed by a NOT circuit. If a truth table is drawn for AND and a column is used to show the inverse of the AND we get:

			Output
A	**B**	**A•B**	$\overline{\text{A•B}}$
0	0	0	1
0	1	0	1
1	0	0	1
1	1	1	0

Note that if either A or B is at zero volts (logic 0) the output is "1" or high (*Answer a, Question 3*.)

The name of this circuit is taken from the combination of the NOT function and the AND function, NOT AND shortened to NAND. (*Answer a, Question 4*.) An OR followed by an inverter is a NOR. The truth tale for the NOR is:

A	**B**	$\overline{\text{A + B}}$
0	0	1
0	1	0
1	0	0
1	1	0

If the above circuit is used in a negative logic system, the positive logic AND will be an OR for negative logic. The OR followed by an inverter will give the NOR function described above in the NOR truth table. The answer to *Question 5* is, therefore, *b*.

LOGIC SYMBOLS

The symbols in Fig. 9-8 are used in drawings for the AND gate. The OR gate symbols are shown in Fig. 9-9. These symbols are in pairs. That is, if the second AND gate symbol is used on logic diagrams, the second OR gate symbol would also be used. The Electronics Technicians Association, International prefers the first symbols. A small circle at the input or output line indicates an inverter. Examples of this are shown in Fig. 9-10.

COMBINATIONAL LOGIC

These gates can be seen on logic drawings in many combinations. The combination for *Q6 through Q10* is shown in Fig.

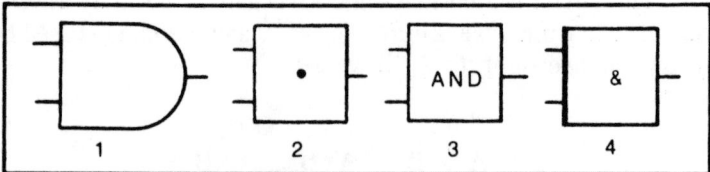

Fig. 9-8. AND gate logic symbols.

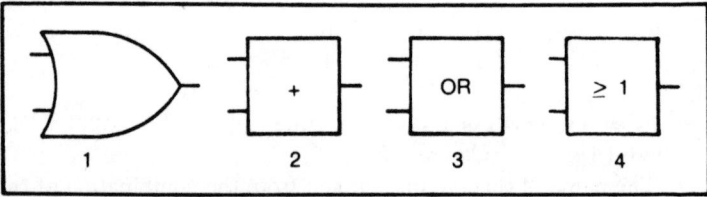

Fig. 9-9. OR gate logic symbols.

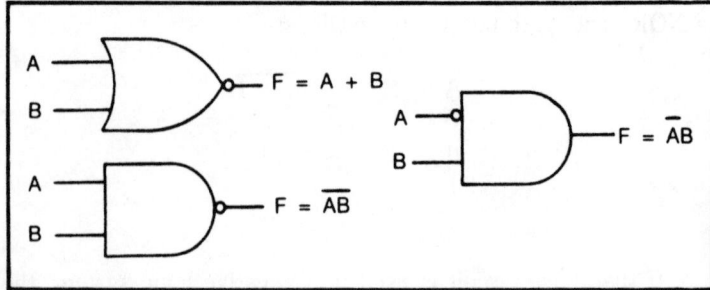

Fig. 9-10. Inverter symbol used with logic symbols.

154

9-2. Since gate 2 is an OR gate, the output, G, should be C OR D. Hence, C + D is the correct representation for G. The answer then to *Question 6* is *d* (none of these).

In *Question 7* it is given that A is a logic 1 and that B is a logic 1. The NAND gate should, therefore, have a logic 0 output.

Positive logic is used in *Question 8*. A, B, and C are, therefore, "0" while D = "1". Since G = C + D then G = "1" + "0" which is equal to "1".

$$F = \overline{AB} = \overline{0 \bullet 0} = \overline{0} = 1$$
$$H = F + G = 1 + 1 = 1$$

The answer then to *Question 8* is logic "1" which = +5 volts.

By similar logic the answer to *Question 9* is *b*, logic 0.

To figure out *Question 10* let's first take each gate individually.

$$F = \overline{AB}$$
$$G = C + D$$

and since H = F + G
by substitution then

$$H = \overline{AB} + (C + D)$$
$$= \overline{AB} + C + D$$

Working with equations such as these is Boolean algebra. There are many books available for further study in this field. See the bibliography at the end of this chapter.

FLIP-FLOPS

Switching circuits that are arranged to have feedback by cross-coupling collectors to bases are called multivibrators (Fig. 9-11). This type of feedback is regenerative in the active portion of the transistors operating ranges. The networks in 1 and 2 of the circuit of Fig. 9-11 can cause the multivibrator to be astable, bistable, or monostable. If the coupling networks are primarily resistive the circuit will be bistable. If the networks are primarily capacitive the circuit will be astable (an oscillator). If one network is capacitive and the other resistive the circuit will be monostable (one stable state). All three are used in digital circuitry. All flip-flops are bistable multivibrators. Therefore, the answer to *Question 11* is *c*. Another name for the monostable multivibrator is the one shot. See Fig. 9-12. A special bistable circuit is the Schmitt trigger. This circuit changes state when the single input is above or below a

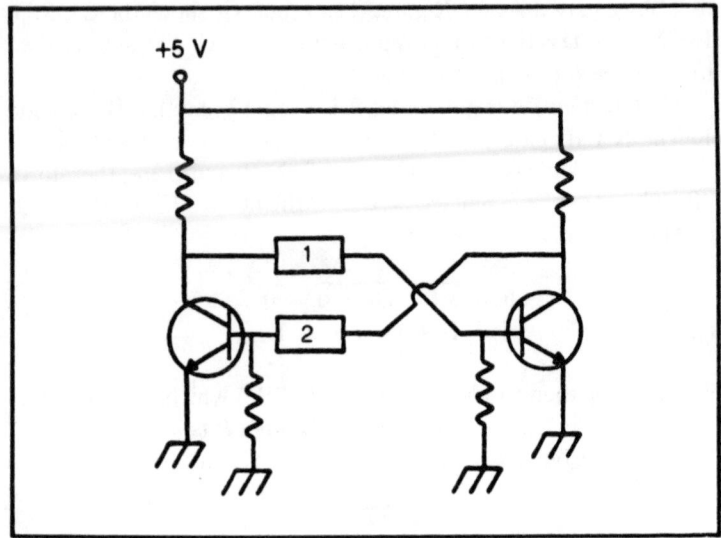

Fig. 9-11. Transistor flip-flop.

particular level. It is often used to "square up" slow changing signals.

There are several types of flip-flops. Perhaps the simplest of these is the set-reset flip-flop without a clock input. It is shown symbolically in Fig. 9-13. Note that it contains four signal lines (power connections are seldom shown). The inputs are normally shown on the left. They are S for the set input and R for the reset input. The outputs are often named for the particular function of the flip-flop. F designates *F*unction. For example, if the flip-flop were the fourth flip-flop in a data register, the outputs might be labeled D4 and $\overline{D4}$. The outputs are derived from the collectors of the transistors. If one transistor is ON the other is OFF, hence, the outputs are always complementary. That is, when F = "1",

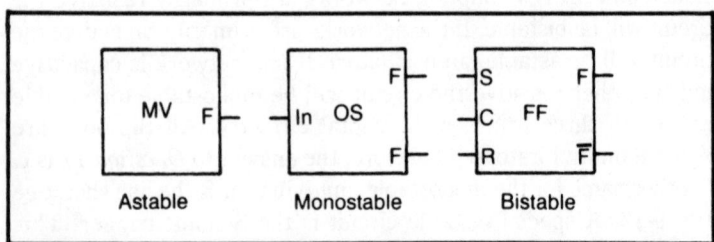

Fig. 9-12. Multivibrator symbols.

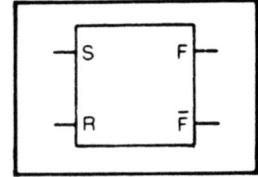

Fig. 9-13. Set-reset flip-flop.

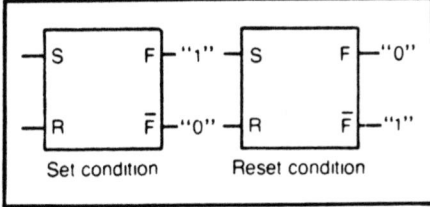

Set condition   Reset condition

Fig. 9-14. Conditions of a flip-flop.

$\overline{F}$ = "0". When F = "0", $\overline{F}$ = "1". A flip-flop is said to be *set* when the F output is a logic 1. The flip-flop is said to be *reset* when the F output is a logic 0. See Fig. 9-14.

A set-reset flip-flop will be *set* after the application of certain input conditions, namely S = "1", and R = "0". It will be *reset* after application of the conditions that S = "0" and R = "1." If S and R are both logic 0 the flip-flop will stay in whatever condition it was in. The condition of a logic 1 on both inputs is forbidden. These conditions are summarized in technical manuals with a truth table. The table needs to account for all possible combination of input and the *present* state of the flip-flop in order to describe how the flip-flop will react to the inputs. Let's use F to represent the *present* state of the flip-flop and F' to represent what the flip-flop will go to after the application of the input conditions. This together with applying the behavior of the set-reset flip-flop will give the following truth table.

Table 9-1. Truth Table for S-R Flip-Flop.

Notes	R	S	F	F'
No change	0	0	0	0
No change	0	0	1	1
Output sets	0	1	0	1
Output stays set	0	1	1	1
Output stays reset	1	0	0	0
Output resets	1	0	1	0
Not allowed	1	1	0	ϕ •
Not allowed	1	1	1	ϕ •

• ϕ is a symbol that means this condition is forbidden. It is formed by the combination of the 0 and 1 overlayed. If 1's are applied the outputs are unpredictable.

157

Perhaps an easier way to show the flip-flop action is to use a slightly different truth table. In this truth table the F output is shown in the "future" by labeling the column F_{t+1}. This means that the column will contain the state of the F output at time t + 1. "t" is implied as the time the inputs are applied.

R	S	F_{t+1}
0	0	F_t
0	1	1
1	0	0
1	1	ϕ

If the flip-flop has a clock input the change of the output is inhibited until the clock occurs. Usually the edge of the clock pulse causes the output transition and either edge may be used. Some flip-flops trigger on the positive-going edge of the clock input and some trigger on the negative-going edge. The tables are the same. In the first table, F goes to F' when the trigger occurs. In the second table "t" can be thought of as the trigger time. For example, when R is 0 and S is 0 on the first line above, the output will stay at whatever it was at time "t"; i.e., F_t. If it was "1" at time t it will stay 1 at t + 1.

In the circuit of *Question 12* the S input is tied to +5 volts and the R input to 0 volts. If +5 volts = logic 1 then 0 volts is a logic 0. A "1" on the S input and a "0" on the R input will set the flip-flop, so F output will go to +5 volts, logic 1. (Note that if negative logic is used the output still goes to +5 volts, but it would be called a logic 0.)

Another common type of flip-flop is the J-K flip-flop. It is symbolized in Fig. 9-15. J can be thought of as the set input and K as the reset input. The letter Q is not unique; it is often replaced with a symbol significant of the flip-flops function. The J-K flip-flop responds exactly the same as an RS flip-flop except that J and

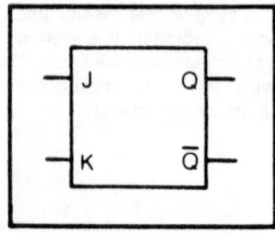

Fig. 9-15. J-K flip-flop.

K inputs can be logic 1 at the same time. When they are, the flip-flop will complement. If Q was a logic 1 (set) it will go to logic 0 (reset). Each table form is shown here.

K	J	Q	Q'		K	J	Q_{t+1}
0	0	0	0		0	0	Q_t
0	0	1	1		0	1	1
0	1	0	1		1	0	0
0	1	1	1		1	1	$\overline{Q}_t$
1	0	0	0				
1	0	1	0				
1	1	0	1				
1	1	1	0				

Both tables are repeating the same rules that applied to the SR flip-flop except when J and K are both logic 1. That is: the flip-flop remains in whatever state it was in if J and K are "0", it sets if J = "1" and K = "0", it resets if J = "0" and K = "1" and it *toggles* if J and K are both "1." If the flip-flop has a clock input the output will be affected only at the appropriate trigger time (either leading or trailing edge may be used for trigger).

Many J-K flip-flops are internally arranged such that the omission of connections to the J-K inputs will be the same as tying J and K to logic "1". Hence, without the J-K inputs the flip-flop will toggle when a trigger is applied. (At successive trigger pulses the output will alternate between "1" and "0".)

A toggle flip-flop behaves like a JK flip-flop with only a clock input. The toggle flip-flop symbol is shown in Fig. 9-16 with its truth table. The answer to *Question 13* is *a* (true).

Another flip-flop is called the data flip-flop. It usually has a clock and it has only one logic level input as in Fig. 9-17. It behaves in the following manner. A logic 1 on the input will become "stored" in the flip-flop when it is clocked. That is the output will go to a

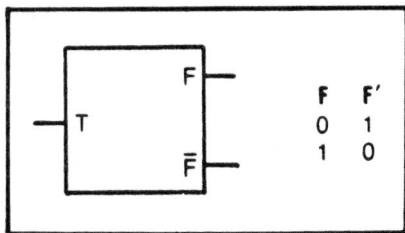

Fig. 9-16. Toggle flip-flop and truth table.

159

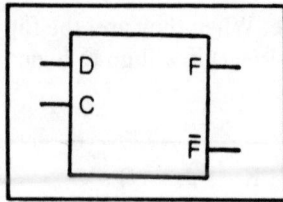

Fig. 9-17. Data flip-flop.

logic 1 after the trigger. A logic 0 will likewise be "stored." The truth tables for a data flip-flop are shown here.

D	F	F'	D	F_{t+1}
0	0	0	0	0
0	1	0	1	1
1	0	1		
1	1	1		

Data flip-flops, as the name implies, are used to store data. They are used in registers, or memory. *Question 14* is, therefore, answer *d*. The data flip-flop is often incorporated in large scale integrated chips (LSI chips). When so made, the result is a random-access memory or RAM.

ADDITIONAL READING

Horn, Delton T.: *Using Integrated Circuit Logic Devices*, TAB BOOKS Inc., 1984.

Larson, Boyd: *Transistor Fundamentals and Servicing*, Prentice-Hall, 1974.

Maloney, Timothy J.: *Industrial Solid-State Electronics*, Prentice-Hall, 1979.

Namgostar, M.: *Digital Equipment Troubleshooting*, Reston Publishing, Inc., 1977.

Paynter, Robert T.: *Microcomputer Operation, Troubleshooting and Repair*, Prentice-Hall, 1986.

Slater, Michael and Barry Benson: *Practical Microprocessors, Hardware, Software, and Troubleshooting*, Hewlett-Packard Co., 1979.

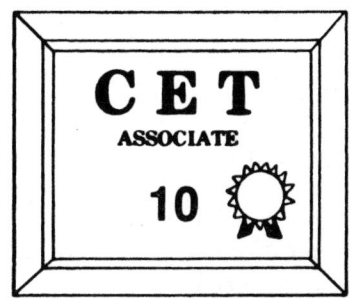

C E T
ASSOCIATE
10

Computer Basics

Let's start with a quick quiz.

Q1. A microprocessor based system is:

a. bus oriented   c. controlled by software
b. versatile   d. all of these

Q2. A byte is usually understood to be:

a. 4 binary bits   c. 32 binary bits
b. 8 binary bits   d. all of these

Q3. Three-state drivers are often used to drive bus lines.

a. true
b. false

Q4. In microcomputers RAM is used for:

a. permanent storage   c. temporary storage
b. address decoding   d. none of these

Q5. Assembly language is:

a. machine language
b. BASIC
c. mnemonic groupings
d. none of these

Q6. A logic probe is used to probe points in the logic circuit of Fig. 10-1. The probe indicated a "1" at B, pulses at A, but logic 0 at F. This means that:

a. NAND gate 1 could be bad
b. NAND gate 1 or OR gate 3 could be bad
c. OR gate 2 is good
d. none of these

Q7. In probing points C and D (of Fig. 10-1) with a logic probe, both points indicated that pulses were present. G then should:

a. blink or be logic 0
b. be logic 1 or blink
c. be logic 0
d. be logic 1

Q8. In probing the circuit of Figure 10-1 with a logic probe it was found that the probe blinked at F, G, and H. This shows that:

a. OR gate 3 is okay
b. OR gate 2 is okay
c. NAND gate 1 is okay
d. at least one input gets through to H

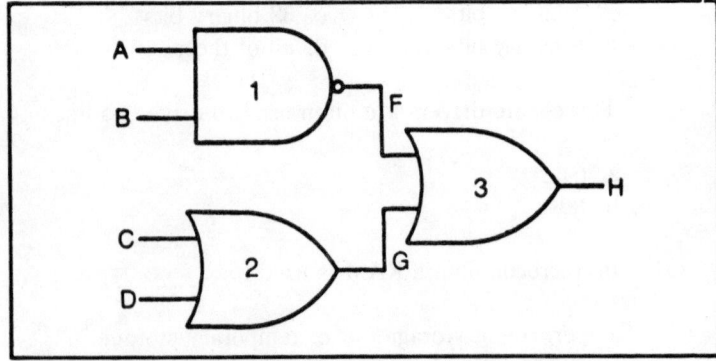

Fig. 10-1. Logic circuit for Q6 through Q8.

162

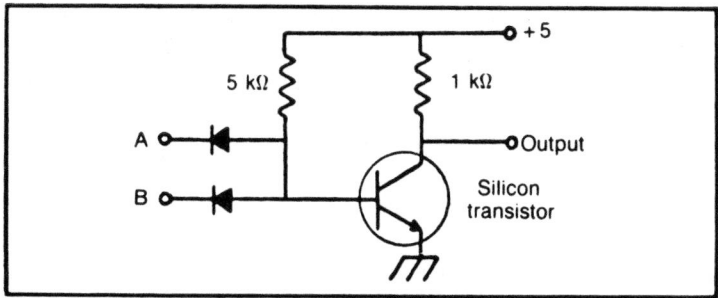

Fig. 10-2. Logic circuit for Q9.

Q9. In circuit of Fig. 10-2 input B was tied to ground and then a pulser was applied to A. A logic probe at the output showed a logic 1. Assuming positive logic:

a. this is normal
b. the transistor is probably bad
c. the diode at A is probably bad
d. none of these

Q10. A logic analyzer indicates:

a. the logic state of many points
b. rise and fall times
c. hex codes
d. a and c

WHAT IS A MICROPROCESSOR?

The microprocessor is an integrated circuit. It is a chip that contains all the computational and control circuitry for a small computer. It outputs and inputs information on pins that can be "bussed." Sequences of operations are controlled by "software." The answer to *Question 1* is *d.*

FUNDAMENTAL PRINCIPLES

Microprocessors operate in a series of steps, moving along from step to step. At each step information on the bus pins stabilizes in some unique pattern of "1's" and "0's." Some pins are called data pins. These pins feed the data bus. These pins are sometimes inputs to the microprocessor and sometimes they are outputs to external circuitry. If there are eight of these data pins, the microprocessor is an 8-bit microprocessor. If there are four pins, it is a 4-bit microprocessor. There are 16-bit microprocessors also. The arrangement of data lines in groups of 4, 8, and 16 is related to the binary base of all computers. Because of the many times that it is necessary to refer to these groups, a system of "names" have evolved for these groupings. These names are tabulated here:

- A bit is one binary digit.
- A nibble is four bits.
- A byte is two nibbles or 8 bits.
- A word is 16 bits.
- A large word is 32 bits.
- A quadword is 64 bits.

The answer to *Question 2* is *b*.

TRI-STATE BUFFER

A bus is a line or connection that can be shared by various independent signal sources or signal destinations. Suppose two devices want to put a signal on a bus. It can be seen from the drawing in Fig. 10-1 that if A is high, Q1 would be ON holding the bus low. If B was low, Q2 would be OFF and (if Q1 wasn't there) the bus would go high. If A and B are going to both drive the bus, some accommodation must be made to prevent this conflict. A three-state driver is used. That is, the output of the driver will be

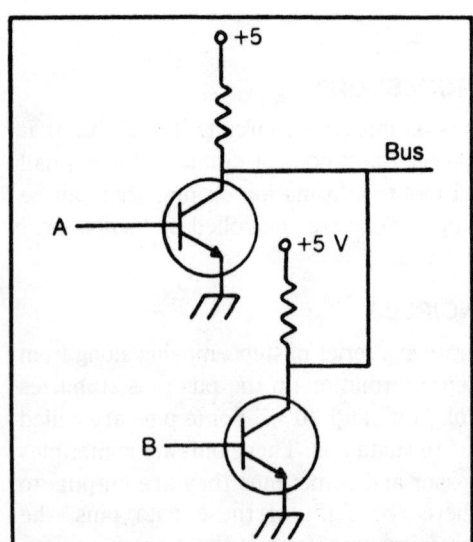

Fig. 10-3. Illustration of bus conflict.

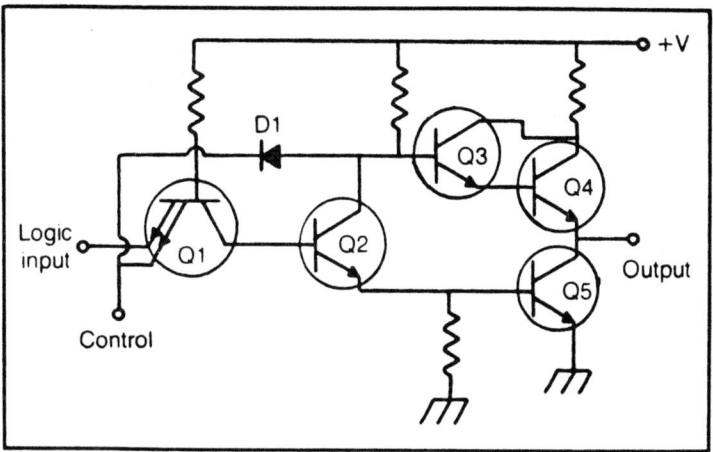

Fig. 10-4. Tri-state driver.

arranged so that it can be "1", or "0", or floating. One such circuit is shown in Fig. 10-4.

When the control input is low, D1 is forward biased holding Q3 base low. Q3 is OFF; therefore, Q4 is OFF. With control low the collector of Q1 is also low so Q2 must be OFF. Q5 is, therefore, also OFF. The output is "floating." With control high the output will follow the dictates of the logic input. If logic input is high, Q1 collector is high, turning Q2 ON. Q2 ON turns ON Q5 and turns OFF Q3, Q4. The output, therefore, goes low. If logic input goes low with control still high, the collector of Q1 goes low shutting Q2 OFF. With Q2 OFF the base of Q3 goes high turning Q3, Q4 ON. Q5 is OFF with Q2, hence, the output is forced high by Q3, Q4. It can be seen that in order to keep the bus from the paradox of trying to be high and low at the same time, no two three-state drivers can be enabled at the same time. Three-state drivers or logic elements with three-state outputs are, therefore, used to drive bus lines. The answer to *Question 3* is *a*.

BUS LINES

Signal lines associated with a microprocessor are normally grouped into three categories: data bus lines, address bus lines, and control bus lines. These are shown diagrammatically in Fig. 10-5.

The 16 address lines (usually labeled A0 through A15) are controlled by a program counter in the microprocessor. If no instructions are brought into the microprocessor to change it, the program counter will count from zero to $(2^{16} - 1)$ or 65,535 and

165

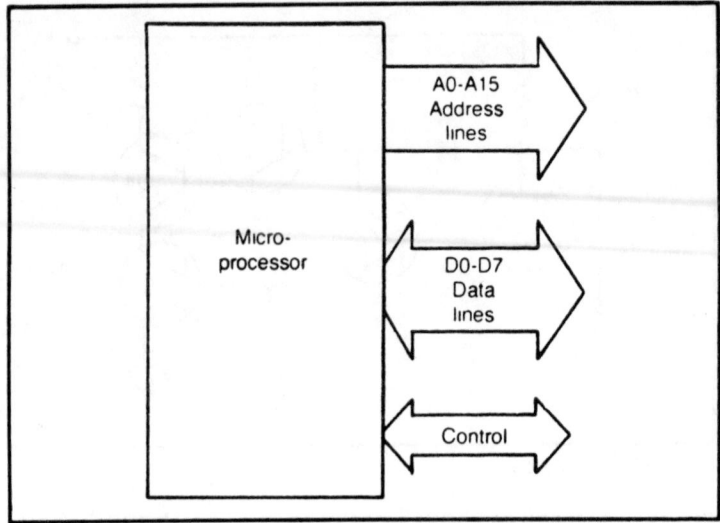

Fig. 10-5. Block diagram of a microprocessor.

start over again. (The number of combinations possible in a 16-bit register is 2^{16}. Therefore, a counter can count from 0 to $2^{16} - 1$.) The P.C.s (program counters) outputs feed the address bus lines, A0 to A15. Normally, however, information is brought into the microprocessor to alter this sequence. The P.C. can be made to skip counts or change to a previous count or, in fact, go to any count desired. Addressing is, therefore, program controlled. This information is brought into the microprocessor by means of the data-bus lines, D_0 through D_7 (or D_0 through D_3 for a 4-bit microprocessor, or D_0 through D_{15} for a 16-bit microprocessor, etc.).

THE MICROCOMPUTER

The microprocessor by itself can do very little. It needs some external devices to make it into a usable microcomputer system, or microprocessor control system. The microcomputer needs a place to store the instructions to tell the microprocessor what to do. The microcomputer also needs a way to interact with people or other machines.

ROM

Read-Only Memory is used to store permanent program material. When a microprocessor is powered up, the P.C. (program

166

counter) is normally reset to zero. The P.C. starts counting from there. The address lines, therefore, are all zero to start. A program is stored in ROM (Read-Only Memory), starting at address zero, that gets the microcomputer into whatever mode it needs to be in to do its work. This program is often called the resident monitor. If the computer has a keyboard, for example, one of the jobs the resident monitor needs to do is to "read" the keyboard to see if a key has been pressed. Other portions of the resident monitor, instruct the microprocessor on how to handle the information from the keyboard, and still others arrange for the display.

RAM

The *Random-Access Memory*, RAM, is the read/write memory. That is, information can be stored there temporarily and later retrieved. Any information stored in RAM is lost when power is removed from the system. The answer to *Question 4* is *c*. Home microcomputers are often referred to by the amount of RAM available. For example, an 8 K machine, has 8192 bytes of Random-Access Memory available for temporary storage. When a particular address is written to, or read from, in RAM, 8 bits of data are involved, or one byte.

LANGUAGE

The pattern of ones and zeros stored in the computer ROM or RAM is the only "knowledge" the computer has other than the pattern of wiring (the way things are hooked together). This sequence of bytes of data is a machine language program. When certain patterns of data are presented to the microprocessor on the data bus, the microprocessor "interprets" these patterns, decoding or operating on this machine language. Patterns of ones and zeros are very meaningful to the microprocessor then, but are pretty meaningless to people. To help people, higher level language or symbols are needed. Manufacturers of microprocessors list, in some fashion, the patterns of ones and zeros (the machine language) that are of particular importance to the microprocessor as instructions. The manufacturer also lists a mnemonic or name for each instruction and details of how the instruction will be interpreted by the microprocessor. The ordering of the instructions, along with data (necessary to some instructions) is called the machine language program. If the mnemonics are listed in the program order, the program is said to be listed in *assembly language*. Assembly language is not so easy to use either, so many machines have available a method of presenting and interpreting a higher level language, such as BASIC, FORTRAN, COBOL, or some other. Because BASIC is easy to use, it is often used in home computers. The answer to *Question 5* is *c*.

TROUBLESHOOTING MICROCOMPUTERS

There are many books written on the subject of troubleshooting microcomputers, and many books written on computers. The purpose of this section is to review only those troubleshooting subjects that every beginning technician should be on speaking terms with.

An oscilloscope is, of course, necessary in troubleshooting along with other meters. But one of the special tools pertaining to computers is the digital logic probe. This common tool is easy to use and is used for switching circuits of all types. The logic probe is designed for a particular family of logic. TTL (Transistor-Transistor Logic) is widespread and, hence, logic probes are available for this family. CMOS (Complementary Metal-Oxide Semiconductor) families are also widespread and these probes are also available. Some probes can be switched from one to the other or used on both. The probe is connected to the power supply of the logic being probed. A light in the probe indicates the state of the voltage attached to the probe tip. A high voltage (+ 5 volts for TTL, + 15 for CMOS) lights the light (usually an LED). A low voltage puts the light out. A blinking light indicates pulses on the point.

Question 7 concerns itself with testing a logic circuit and a logic probe. If AND gate 1 was operating properly the probe should blink at F with the conditions stated. But, if the input to OR gate 3 is shorted to ground the probe at F would not blink. Hence, even though answer *a* is correct, answer *b* is better because it is more inclusive.

Suppose that the probe blinked on point A and blinked on point B. Would a "0" indication at F mean the same thing, that 1 or 2 is bad? Not necessarily. Remember that to get a "1" out of an AND gate all inputs must be "1" simultaneously. The probe might blink at A and at B and still not have a "1" on each at the same time. On the other hand, if C and D inputs to the OR gate blink, point G should also cause the light to blink. But, if the logic level at C and logic level at D never go to the zero logic level at the same time, then G could indicate a "1" at all times. Therefore, answer *b* is the correct response in *Question 8*.

Question 9 points out another area where care must be exercised not to jump to false conclusions. If the input from line F to the gate, inside the IC chip, is open note that a logic probe could easily blink at all three points: F, G, and H; and the gate would be bad. Answer *d* is the correct response.

A logic pulser is also a probe available for troubleshooting logic. This device sends pulses into the point attached to the probe. This is useful in toggling gates on or off. It is usually used in conjunction with a logic probe, the probe detecting the output of the gate being switched or toggled.

In *Question 10* the transistor should stay off as long as B is grounded, answer *a*. However, if B is lifted from ground a pulse should be indicated by the logic probe at the collector. Most logic probes will blink whether the input to the probe is low most of the time, or high most of the time.

Logic analyzers have 8, 16, or 32 input lines. The CRT or other display shows the activity on each of these input lines. Some displays can be selected for binary, hex, or octal. If a CRT is used, timing and memory map modes are also available. The answer to *Question 10* is *d*. In any of these modes of operation, it is necessary to know the proper sequence, or pattern of data on the many lines, in order to interpret the results.

A good deal of computer troubleshooting is accomplished without the need for electronics or programming knowledge. This is made possible by relying on diagnostic routines available on most manufacturer's computers, printers, etc. In fact most machines have a self-test incorporated in the 'turn on' procedure. When a trouble is isolated to a subassembly, or PC board, that board, or subassembly, is exchanged and hopefully the machine operates. Most manufacturers have an exchange program for these boards or subassemblies.

Unfortunately, this kind of procedure ties technicians closely to the manufacturer. And what happens when the manufacturer no longer supports the exchange program on a particular unit? Then the technician needs to be able to isolate problems down to the component level in order to be able to repair that particular unit.

Common Computer Equipment Problems

By far the largest group of problems with computer equipment is mechanical, or related to mechanical movement. For example, floppy-disk drives cause a good deal of trouble by becoming misaligned; that is, the record/play-back head becomes misadjusted from wear, vibration, or impact. Printers cause a lot of problems with platen drive, carriage drive, and hammer drive problems. The keyboard may also have keys that stick, or fail to make contact. Keyboards are also susceptible to foreign material problems such as coffee and cola spills.

Another very common mechanical problem is connector problems. Many computers are repaired by removing and reinserting IC chips (socket mounted) and connectors. Special cleaners can be purchased for connectors.

ESD and Safety

Electrostatic Discharge is an important subject. As the density of components on IC chips increases and with the increase in usage of MOSFET chips, static damage is an ever present danger. Computers and other digital equipment should be worked on at a static-free workstation.

Many technicians have been heard to say that they never had problems with static and hence didn't need wrist straps, static pads, nickel-plated bags, or anti-static packing material. The trouble is that it is hard to point to a problem caused by ESD damage. No one knows for sure. But any company that has taken steps to protect components from ESD has seen call-backs reduced, and in the case of manufacturers, have seen reliability increases that are sometimes dramatic.

ADDITIONAL READING

Coffron, James W.: *Practical Troubleshooting Technique for Microprocessor Systems,* Prentice-Hall, 1981.

Inbody, Don: *Principles and Practice of Digital ICs and LEDs,* TAB BOOKS Inc.

Lenk, John D.: *Handbook of Practical Microprocessor Troubleshooting,* Reston Publishing Co., 1979.

Namgostar, M.: *Digital Equipment Troubleshooting,* Reston Publishing Co., 1977.

Osborne, Adam: *An Introduction to Microcomputers, Volume 0 the Beginner's Book,* 2nd Ed., Osborne & Associates, 1979.

Paynter, Robert T.: *Microcomputer Operation, Troubleshooting and Repair,* Prentice-Hall, 1986.

Short, Kenneth L.: *Microprocessor and Programmed Logic,* Prentice-Hall, 1981.

Slater, Michael and Barry Bronsen: *Practical Microprocessors,* Hewlett-Packard, 1979.

Communications Electronics

This chapter covers some fundamental concepts in communications. Communications electronics is a broad field and the technician in this field will gain a wide range of experience and knowledge. This chapter deals only with those communications concepts that are more likely to be needed by every electronics technician.

QUIZ

Q1. A certain amplifier has a gain of 3 dB. If the input is 20 mW the output would be:

a. 60 mW

c. 23 mW

b. 40 mW

d. none of these

Q2. Decibel notation can be used to describe specific voltage values, such as zero dBmV (one millivolt):

a. true

b. false

Q3. If zero dBmV equals one millivolt, then two millivolts would be equal to two dBmV:

a. true

b. false

Q4. If 10,000 microvolts is equal to 20 dBmV, then 20,000 microvolts would be equal to:

a. 10,000 dBmV
b. 20,000 dBmV
c. 2 dBmV
d. 26 dBmV

Q5. When referring to the output level of an amplifier versus the input level, or an antenna's forward signal pick-up versus its rearward signal pick-up, dBs are used to indicate:

a. current gain
b. the ratio between two quantities
c. voltage drops
d. power supply input

Q6. Ordinarily, in master antenna systems, it is easier to calculate the line, splitter, tapoff, and insertion losses by adding, subtracting, multiplying, and dividing the microvolt levels rather than by adding or subtracting one or two digit dB expressions:

a. true
b. false

Q7. A folded dipole antenna has a characteristic impedance near:

a. 73 ohms
b. 300 ohms
c. 600 ohms
d. 150 ohms

Q8. The characteristic impedance of an antenna:

a. can be measured with an ohmmeter
b. is normally 0
c. is normally very very high
d. none of these

Q9. In a certain transmission line many reflections are noted. This could be caused by:

a. an open load
b. a shorted line
c. an open line
d. all of these

Q10. For data to be transmitted over "voice-quality" transmission lines:

    a. a modem will be used
    b. an ultrasonic carrier will be used
    c. 10.7 MHz will be used
    d. none of these

BEL (dB)

In communications many systems use the bel or decibel to measure power gain or loss. The bel was originally defined as the amount of energy change needed in audio power to just *hear* a change. Through experiment it was found that this was logarithmic. This relationship is expressed mathematically:

$$bel = \log_{10} \frac{P_2}{P_1}$$

The decibel is 0.1 bel, hence:

$$dB = 10 \log_{10} \frac{P_2}{P_1}$$

If as in *Question 1* an amplifier has a gain of 3 dB, then:

$$3 \ dB = 10 \log_{10} \frac{P_2}{P_1}$$

$$0.3 = \log_{10} \frac{P_2}{P_1}$$

Look up in a table or use calculator:

$$2 = \frac{P_2}{P_1}$$
$$or \ P_2 = 2 \ P_1$$

And since P_1 in this problem is 20 mW
P_2 = 40 mW (Answer: *Question 1*)

The dB equation is often given for voltage ratios. It is:

$$dB = 20 \log_{10} \frac{V_2}{V_1}$$

It must be remembered that this equation is true only if measurements are made across the same impedances. To illustrate this let's calculate dB for an amplifier with different input and output impedances, with each dB equation (illustrated in Fig. 11-1).

$$dB = 10 \log \frac{P_2}{P_1}$$

$$P_2 = \frac{e_o^2}{R_o}$$

$$= \frac{(8)(8)}{8}$$

$$= 8$$

$$P_1 = \frac{e_{in}^2}{R_{in}}$$

$$= \frac{(2 \text{ mV})^2}{10 \text{ k}}$$

$$= 4 \times 10^{-10} \text{ watts}$$

$$dB = 10 \log \frac{8}{4 \times 10^{-10}}$$

$$= 10 \log 20,000,000,000$$
$$= 10 \times (10 + \log 2)$$
$$= 10(10 + .3)$$
$$= 10 (10.3)$$
$$= 103$$

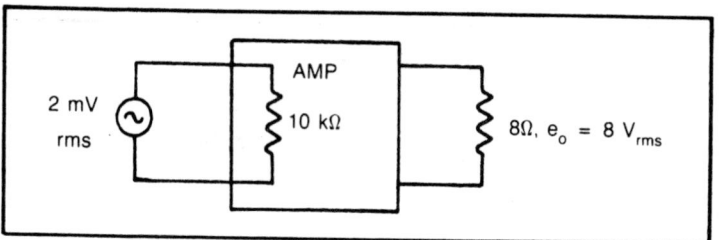

Fig. 11-1. Amplifier with different input and output impedances.

Using the voltage ratio, however, gives an erroneous answer:

$$dB = 20 \log \frac{8}{2 \text{ millivolts}}$$

$$= 20 \log 4000$$
$$= (20)(3 + \log 4)$$
$$= 20 (3.6)$$
$$= 72$$

To further illustrate, let's use the same voltage levels, but change to equal resistances (Fig. 11-2).

$$P_1 = \frac{(2 \text{ mV})^2}{1 \text{ k}}$$

$$= \frac{4 \times 10^{-6}}{1 \times 10^3}$$

$$= 4 \times 10^{-9} \text{ W}$$

$$P_2 = \frac{(8 \text{ V})^2}{1 \text{ k}}$$

$$= 64 \text{ mW}$$

$$dB = 10 \log \left(\frac{64 \text{ mW}}{4 \times 10^{-9} \text{ W}} \right)$$

$$= 10 [\log (16 \times 10^6)]$$
$$= 10 [(6 + \log 16)]$$
$$= (10)(7.2)$$
$$= 72$$

175

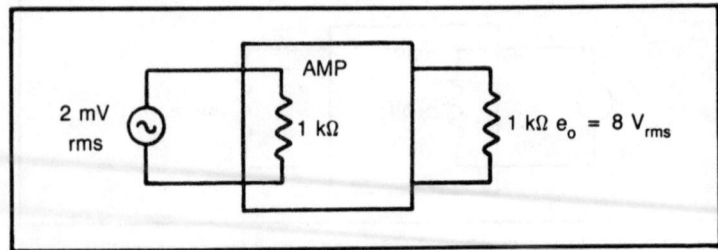

Fig. 11-2. Amplifier with equal input and output impedances.

And using the voltage ratio equation:

$$dB = 20 \log \frac{V_2}{V_1}$$

$$= 20 \log \frac{8 \text{ V}}{2 \text{ mV}}$$

$$= 20 \log (4 \times 10^3)$$
$$= 20 \left[(3) + (.6) \right]$$
$$= 72$$

Hence, it can be illustrated that the voltage equation for dB is only true for equal impedances. Equal impedances often occur in transmission distribution systems. Examples are coaxial cable systems, telephone systems, and antenna distribution systems.

There are few areas of electronics that don't eventually need to use decibels (dBs). Especially in the study of antennas and distribution systems, or in audio technology. Most technicians can learn to easily handle decibels or understand quantities expressed in decibels. The problem is that dBs aren't common usage terms (like inches, pounds, or gallons which we all can readily visualize). It's hard to visualize 6 dBs. How big? How wide? How much? On the other hand, dBs really aren't difficult if a little time is spent getting used to them.

Concepts

If a few basic truths are locked into your mind, all the values and levels used in systems and specifications that use dBs can be understood.

TV distribution systems use zero decibels (0 dB) as 1,000 microvolts (μV). The value should be referred to as zero dBmV in this usage, but isn't always. The answer to *Question 2* is *a*.

When discussing signal strength in TV and MATV systems, then, we can communicate by stating that a 100,000 μV signal is also a 40 dBmV signal. Or, a 500 μV TV signal is a – 6 dBmV signal. So, dBs are used in this way to indicate a "specific voltage level". This is convenient if you are frequently dealing with signals that all relate to one base, or set amount of signal.

Why is 1,000 μV important? In the early design of television sets it was determined that a TV receiver should be manufactured so that it would produce a 'snow-free' picture with an input signal of 1,000 μV, hence zero (0) dBmV of broadcast signal is important. If you remember that a TV set requires 1,000 μV, or zero (0) dBmV, of signal then you already know an important fact needed to understand dBs. When speaking of TV signal levels from an antenna, or in a master antenna TV system (MATV), you can refer to any signal level as it relates to 0 dBmV. A technician who works on antennas for long will know that a – 20 dBmV signal level is going to produce a very snowy picture and a + 20 dBmV signal will not only be ample to supply a noise-free picture, but could easily be split to supply two, three, or four more televisions and all would have snow-free picture quality.

Expressing dBs as a signal level relative to 0 dBmV is used extensively in television-radio work. But dBs are used in comparing human hearing, and in audio work, where 0 dB equals 10^{-16} W/cm², the threshold of hearing and 120 dB is the pain threshold for the human ear.

The traditional use of dBs in electronics is in expressing the "difference" between one signal level and another signal level (gain or loss). An easy way of visualizing this is to compare the amount of signal you would expect from two different antennas—one stronger than the other (see Fig. 11-3).

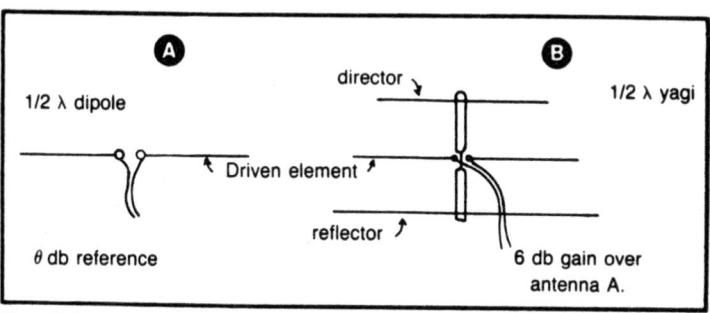

Fig. 11-3. Antenna gain.

One example, antenna A, is a basic 1/2 wave dipole. Other antennas are compared to it. Antenna A, no matter what amount of microvolts are produced at its terminals, is said to have 0 dB. It is the reference for comparing other antennas. It is the standard starting point. Other antennas don't exactly have gain in the sense that they amplify the signal received; but by stating that an antenna has a 6 dB gain, we mean that it will pick up more signal (in this case twice as much) than a simple dipole. We can't ever say that one antenna will have an exact microvolt level of signal at its terminals. That is because the antenna could be sitting directly under a broadcast antenna, thus receiving 'volts' of signal, or, it may be a hundred miles from the broadcast antenna and be lucky to receive 50 μV of signal. However, knowing that an antenna with 6 dB of gain will perform twice as well as a basic 1/2-wave dipole gives us something to compare with, to visualize, and we can understand it. It can be seen from this that the answer to *Question 3* is *b* (false).

A second example would be from an antenna that needs to supply a TV signal to two television sets. To divide the signal a splitter is needed that properly maintains the impedance of the system (75 ohms when using TV coax). Signal splitters basically all have the same voltage loss—that being 3.5 dBs. It can be seen that splitters do not divide a signal in half (that would be a voltage loss of 6 dB). Only about a third of the signal is dropped to each output of a two-way splitter. Knowing that whenever you divide the signal, using a splitter, you will then decrease the signal by 3.5 dBs per line means you can accurately determine what signal you will have at the TV sets.

In the above example the signal was split between two televisions. If the antenna was supplying only – 10 dBmV of signal and the signal was decreased by another 3.5 dB, through the splitter, – 13.5 dBmV would then be left at the TV sets. But, if you had + 6 dBmV supplied by the antenna and the signal was decreased by 3.5 dB, through the splitter, you would still have + 2.5 dBmV at the TV sets. While – 13.5 dBmV would not make a useable picture, and – 10 dBmV would be marginal at best, + 2.5 dBmV would be excellent.

It's important to know that wire losses, splitter losses, and tapoff losses are something predictable. How much signal a TV set needs; what the signal level is coming off an antenna; or, what the signal level is coming out of an amplifier is not needed in order to determine a system's losses. That's good. This makes it quite easy to figure MATV systems, or to determine what you will have after you install an antenna and run it to three or four rooms in a house. By using dBs in signal systems to calculate gain, or loss, the numbers are small—usually only one or two digits (see Fig. 11-4).

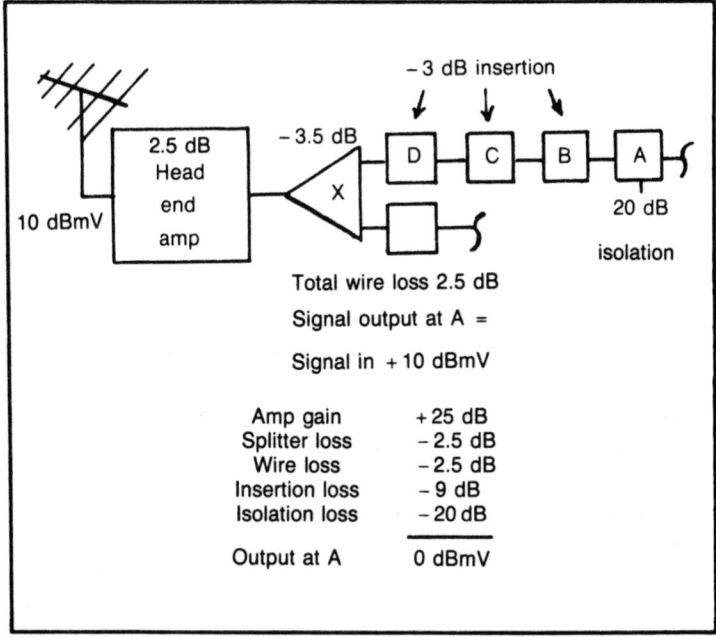

Fig. 11-4. Sample MATV calculations.

DECIBEL MATHEMATICS

Six decibels (6 dBs) is the secret to using decibel mathematics. Remember that. A gain of 6 dBs means whatever signal level you originally had increased to twice as much. A signal level of one volt, increased by 6 dB, will now be two volts. A 200 μV level increased by 6 dBs will become 400 μV. No matter what the original level, a 6 dB gain is twice the original level. In *Question 4* doubling the signal increases the gain by 6 dB, answer *d*.

Conversely, – 6 dB is 1/2 the original. A one volt signal, to begin with, when reduced by 6 dB is now 0.5 volts (or 500 millivolts). Therefore, one volt increased by a 6 dB gain has a 1,000 millivolt change, but a 6 dB loss (– 6 dB) has only a 500 millivolt change.

That's important to recognize. The 200 μV level reduced by 6 dB is only 100 μV.

You can approximate decibel signal levels anywhere in a system by simply halving or doubling, when indicated, voltage levels.

Let's use an example to show how easy this is. Start with five volts of signal. After amplification you now have 25 volts. What amount of gain did you produce within the amplifier? Obviously it is a gain of 5 times the input; however, to use dBs to express that gain let's first double five volts to 10 volts. That is a 6 dBs gain. Now double the 10 volts to 20 volts. That is another 6 dBs of gain. Now we have 12 dBs of gain. Let's double the 20 volts to 40 volts for another 6 dBs of gain. But wait, we wanted only 25 volts, not 40. In review, 20 volts was 12 dBs of gain and 40 volts was 18 dBs of gain. So, 25 volts lies somewhere between 12 and 18 dBs of gain. In antenna work knowing that may be all you need to know in order to solve a problem or to design a system. But we can make a closer approximation to the actual dB gain. We know that 25 volts isn't half way between 20 and 40 volts, half way would be 30 volts. So 25 volts would probably not be a gain of 12 + 3, or 15 dBs of gain. It would be less than 15 dBs of gain. Let's guess that it would be 14 dBs. If you guessed 15 dBs that would be close enough for practically all system calculations you will meet up with. While we can scientifically calculate it to an exact decibel amount, there is little reason to do so. Why? Because another factor is involved in dB loss calculations. Loss in a TV system will be much less for channel two frequencies than for channel 83 frequencies. Wire loss will be over twice as much for channel 83. Therefore, to demand that you be precise in loss calculations accomplishes little. Even so, the fact that you don't have to be exact is not a reason to remain cloudy in using decibels. Think of it as making your job easier and less demanding. However, if you use the formula shown previously you will arrive at the actual dB gain of 13.979.

Decibel Chart

Look at the chart in Table 11-1. Start by first assuring yourself that 0 dBmV is listed as 1,000 μV. It is. Therefore, you know all dB levels shown will pertain to 0 dBmV, the basic starting point for rf signals. That makes it easy. Now you and I could discuss a signal problem or we could design a signal distribution system noting the signal levels at any point. We would both know what each was saying to the other.

Table 11-1. dB Versus Microvolts.

Micro-volts	dBmV	5-Place dBmV	Micro-volts	dBmV	5-Place dBmV
10	−40	−40.00000	1995	6	6.00000
16	−36	−35.91760	2000	6	6.02060
32	−30	−29.89700	3200	10	10.10300
63	−24	−24.01319	4000	12	12.04120
100	−20	−20.00000	8000	18	18.06180
125	−18	−18.06180	10000	20	20.00000
250	−12	−12.04120	16000	24	24.08240
316	−10	−10.00000	32000	30	30.10299
500	−6	−6.02060	63000	36	35.98681
560	−5	−5.03624	64000	36	36.13260
630	−4	−4.01319	100000	40	40.00000
700	−3	−3.09803	127000	42	42.07607
800	−2	−1.93820	250000	48	47.95880
891	−1	−1.00250	320000	50	50.10300
1000	0	0.00000	500000	54	53.97940
1100	1	.82785	1000000	60	60.00000
1300	2	2.27887	2000000	66	66.02060
1400	3	2.92256	4000000	72	72.04120
1600	4	4.08240	8000000	78	78.06180
1800	5	5.10545	10000000	80	80.00000

Analyzing the chart further, note that it only goes negatively to −40 dB. Actually that 10 μV signal is not negative. It is truly a +10 μV signal. Only the dB is negative, when compared with our standard starting point of 0 dBmV, to indicate a decrease in level.

Why stop at −40 dBmV? A 10 μV signal is so small, it is virtually no signal at all. In fact, the FCC rules governing CATV systems require that any stray signal leakage on the cable system be measurable at no more than −40 dBmV. That is just about zero signal so far as a TV antenna or TV set is concerned. You've seen far off TV stations appear faintly on a normally unused channel, one that is barely discernible, usually unable to lock, with so much snow that you cannot recognize objects in the picture, color is nonexistent and the sound is hissing—that is a −40 dBmV signal! Listing anything below that serves no purpose.

On the other end of the scale the chart shows 80 dB, or 10 volts of signal. That's such a giant signal that most TV sets would be 'swamped'. Preamps and line amplifiers ordinarily cannot handle such a large signal input. You may find 35 to 40 dBmVs of signal too much, at least too much for most systems and especially too large a signal for a TV set. Televisions work great on −6 dBmV to +25 dBmV. Anything less is snowy. Anything more and the dreaded adjacent channel interference becomes a problem; however, 80 dBmV is frequently used in large CATV and cable system trunk lines.

If you start at 0 dBmV and increase by 6 dB, doubling the voltage, until you arrive at 36 dBmV you should wind up with 64000 μV. Many dBmV charts will show 63000 μV at this point because 63000 μV is actually closer to 36 dBmV, namely 35.98681 dBmV. Notice in this chart that 64000 μV is slightly over 36 dBmV, 36.13260. The reason for the error is that double the voltage is a little over 6 dB. It is 6.02060. Six dB is actually a voltage gain of 1.995 (note the values in the chart). For practical purposes the small error, introduced by the assumption that 6 dB is equal to a doubling of voltage, is insignificant.

ANTENNAS

Many communications systems use antennas for the distribution of signals, either for transmitting power or receiving power. Some fundamentals of antennas should be understood by all technicians. For example, the antenna has a characteristic impedance. This impedance acts like a load to the transmitter and like a generator impedance to the receiver. Theoretically, the characteristic impedance of a simple dipole, away from all grounds, is about 73 ohms. This impedance cannot be measured with an ohmmeter. At dc the simple dipole is an open circuit. A folded dipole antenna has a characteristic impedance of about 300 ohms (*Question 7* answer *b*). *Question 8* asks about characteristic impedance. Neither a, b, nor c are correct; therefore, answer *d,* is the correct response.

A wavelength of a frequency of electromagnetic radiation as it proceeds through space has a certain length as given by the formula:

$$\lambda = \frac{300}{f}$$

where λ is the wavelength in meters and f is the frequency in megahertz

$$\lambda = \frac{984}{f}$$

if the wavelength is to be measured in feet.

An antenna wavelength is somewhat shorter than the free air

wavelength. For a wire antenna it is about 0.95 of free air wavelength.

Example: CB antenna

$$f \cong 27 \text{ MHz}$$
$$1/4 - \text{ wavelength} = \text{dipole length}$$
$$L = 1/4 \; \lambda$$
$$L = 1/4 \; \frac{984 \; (0.95)}{27}$$
$$L = 8.65 \text{ feet}$$
$$L = \frac{8.65}{12 \text{ in}}$$
$$= 104 \text{ in}$$

TRANSMISSION LINE

Some concepts of transmission lines are important to all fields of electronics. Signals take a finite amount of time to propagate down a transmission line. For short lines this is normally of little concern except that it should be kept in mind for troubleshooting. Also, this feature is often used deliberately. For example, the delay line in many oscilloscopes is a transmission line (a coaxial cable). The delay line in color TV sets is a transmission line.

Transmission lines have a characteristic impedance. This impedance is a function of the inductance of the line, the capacitance between conductors, the resistance of the line, and the frequency applied to the line. Within certain operating ranges, however, given lines have a fairly constant, resistive, characteristic impedance. Since R, L, and C all vary with physical construction of the transmission line, it is logical to expect different characteristic impedances for different lines. Some standard lines are shown here with their characteristic impedances.

If a transmission line is not terminated on both ends with its characteristic impedance, however, standing waves occur on the line, reflections occur in the line and the input to the line may look inductive or capacitive. *Question 9* pertains to this topic. Any of the answers *a, b,* or *c* cause the line not to be properly terminated resulting in reflections. Answer *d* is correct.

Telephone lines are normally twisted-pair lines. These lines have a characteristic impedance like any other lines. Another characteristic of these lines is that frequencies above 3 kHz are

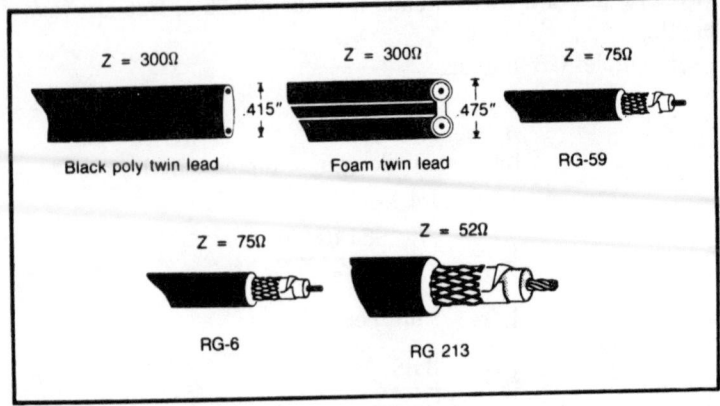

Fig. 11-5. Common transmission-line types.

much attenuated. Because of the limited band-width, these lines are limited in the speed at which binary data can be sent. This means that in order to send data quickly over phone lines, it must be modulated in such a manner that the slow signaling rate contains more information. To do this involves the use of a modulator on the transmitting end and a demodulator on the receiving end. Of course, it is usual for both ends to send and receive. Hence, both ends will need a modulator and both ends will need a demodulator. The *mod*ulator, *dem*odulator is called a modem. *Question 10a* is the correct response.

ADDITIONAL READING

Bose, Keith W.: *Aviation Electronics,* Howard W. Sams Co., 1977.

Carr, Joseph J.: *The TAB Handbook of Radio Communications,* TAB BOOKS Inc., 1984.

Mandl, Matthew.: *Principles of Electronic Communications,* Prentice-Hall, 1973.

Reference Data for Radio Engineers. International Telephone and Telegraph Corp., 1956.

Safety Precautions and Checks

This chapter covers the types of safety questions that will be asked on the exam.

QUIZ

Q1. A shorted balun on a TV set or other communications gear, coupled with a 'hot' chassis, is safe if the equipment uses a polarized line cord:

    a. true
    b. false

Q2. A spark obtained when connecting antenna leads or cables to a receiver antenna post can be caused by:

    a. static electricity collected on the antenna elements
    b. leakage between windings in the receiver power transformer
    c. receiver on/off switch leads being hooked up backwards
    d. antenna leads being reversed

Q3. Which of the following will be *least* likely to present a shock hazard to a repair technician?

a. radio transmitter final output-stage tube-plate connections
b. audio amplifier regulated power supply transformer wires
c. tube-type TV receiver p-c board connections
d. mast-mounted rf signal amplifier circuit

Q4. CRT high-voltage power-supply rectifier tubes can be safely removed, without shock hazard, providing the cathode circuit—CRT pigtail wire circuit—is not brought into close contact:

a. true
b. false

Q5. The CRT high-voltage circuit should be discharged by:

a. shorting to chassis
b. shorting to the cabinet
c. using a high-voltage probe
d. shorting high voltage to collector heatsinks

Q6. To prevent further damage when troubleshooting a receiver that appears to have an internal short:

a. use a fuse less than 100% larger than the recommended size
b. use a dropping resistor in series with the ac line or battery voltage
c. substitute a resettable circuit breaker for the line fuse
d. use an isolation transformer

Q7. Equipment used to monitor medical patients may develop leakage current. To reduce the likelihood of leakage between the patient and the equipment:

a. use equipment with a 3 prong to 2 prong ac adapter
b. ground the patient
c. use only AHA equipment
d. use equipment (containing an isolation transformer) that had a leakage test prior to use

Q8. It ordinarily takes 100-500 mA of 60 Hz ac current arm-to-arm to induce ventricular fibrillation. Lower levels of current can also induce fibrillation if:

a. the person is isolated
b. higher frequencies are induced
c. the person is hypertensive
d. medical equipment (needles, contact probes, etc.) is connected to the person causing a lowering of his/her skin resistance

Q9. Equipment used in dangerous locations such as damp basements, construction sites, outside the home, etc. can *best* be made safer by:

a. operating with one hand only
b. checking resistance between line cord and case
c. cease using if case becomes "hot"
d. using ground fault ac circuits for power

Q10. Which of the following tests can be performed without damage to the component?

a. shorting collector to base on a transistor
b. shorting collector to emitter
c. shorting base to emitter
d. shorting emitter to ground

Q11. CMOS chips, field-effect transistors and other sensitive electronic components can be damaged easily by:

a. operating for long periods of time
b. use near high-voltage supplies
c. long shelf life
d. any type of static discharge

EQUIPMENT SHOCK HAZARDS

One purpose of the polarized ac plug is to assure that the electrical equipment chassis of a "hot chassis" is connected to the low side of the ac power source. By so doing the shock hazard is lessened. An unsafe condition occurs if the balun of a TV set is shorted. The balun, made up of a couple of capacitors and a few turns of wire around a ferrite sleeve, is used as a transformer. Baluns are susceptible to lightning damage. Should the receiver chassis be connected to the hot side of the line, and should that chassis be shorted to the antenna system through the balun, a shock hazard exists. See Fig. 12-1.

While use of polarized line cords lessens the chance of shock hazards of this kind, some ac power outlets have been known to have been wired backwards! Therefore, *Q1* is a false statement. Other equipment (such as an add-on do-it-yourself phonograph) that may be connected to the primary unit may have ac power shorts also. The best rule then is to never completely trust any equipment you are working on. *Always* find the cause of sparks when the antenna cable or leads are connected or when any other equipment is connected.

In addition to the above discussion, power transformers (especially after years of use in a hot environment) may have insulation breakdowns which cause the primary ac input windings to be connected to one or more of the secondary windings. The answer to *Question 2* is *b*. Depending on the resistance of the short and the location, the receiver can become "hot." When this occurs a 50 Vac to 120 Vac level on the chassis is not unusual. This creates a severe shock hazard and must be repaired, or the equipment taken out of use. Measuring the ac levels between power source, ground, and chassis is recommended practice for all electronics technicians.

Transmitter output tubes are high-power circuits using high voltage. Observe extra precautions here. Except in small transistor amplifiers using low dc levels, amplifier power supplies can be designed to produce 100 V to 200 V and more. Present day regulator circuits with their high current driving capability can be hazard-

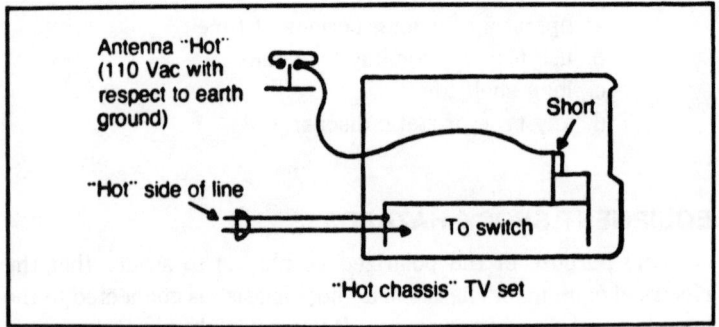

Fig. 12-1. Shorted antenna coil.

ous. Tube type TV and radio circuits often use 100 V to 300 V supplies and may use 110 Vac to power the filament circuits. Few areas of these sets do not pose a serious shock hazard. The rule is to use only one hand in any of these sets with the other hand completely isolated from any part of it.

The mast-mounted rf signal amplifiers used in TV and radio use ac power from the ac line source, but this is dropped through a transformer to about 20 Vac before being supplied through the coax or antenna down-drop to the mast-mounted transistorized signal amplifier. This small source is not much of a hazard. The *best* answer to *Question 3* is *d*, but should the source have a fault, such as a shorted step-down transformer, then this too becomes a shock hazard.

While technicians usually regard 15 V — 25 V power sources as little or no shock hazard, a note here is in order. Some of the most serious accidents involving electrical shorts have come in low level circuits. Automobile radios are an area where technicians have been known to get their rings or watch bands shorted between 6 V or 12 V and the frame. With little resistance between the frame, the battery, and the solid piece of gold, silver, or other conducting metal, the heat generated can cause a severe burn in seconds.

Most of the time the statement in *Question 4* is true. The cathode circuit and CRT pigtail are usually well insulated in order to eliminate arcing and secondarily to protect the technician. However, a percentage of high-voltage-rectifier vacuum tubes and some solid-state diode types will develop shorted elements. Taking off the anode cap and coming in contact with the anode is then the same as touching the cathode CRT pigtail circuit. See Fig. 12-2. It can be a shock hazard. Grounding these circuits before servicing

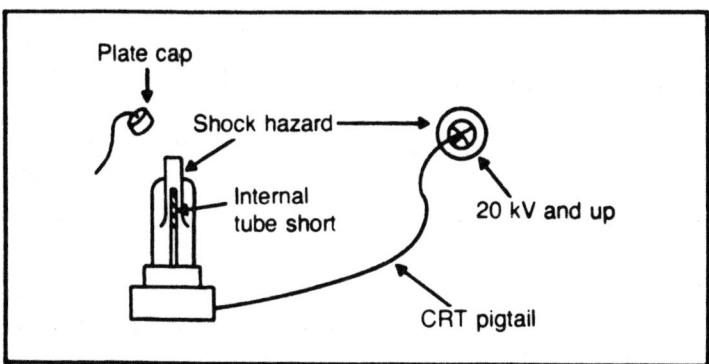

Fig. 12-2. High-voltage dangers.

is the surest method of avoiding shock. And, of course, the set should be turned off.

All video screens use high voltage on the second anode. This may be as high as 40 kVdc. Television sets and computer monitor screens are becoming even more numerous and subject to service. The potential on the high voltage tube (such as 3A3) or solid state tripler or quadrupler can be harmful. Even if the actual current is not harmful in itself, the physical reaction by the technician to a shock can cause harm to himself, or to other equipment. Picture tube circuitry is such that the high voltage may be partially maintained for some time before it can bleed off. In *Question 5* a high-voltage probe can be used to discharge the circuit prior to servicing, but the proper method is to short the pigtail lead to chassis ground. It should *not* be shorted to the cabinet since the cabinet may *not* be directly connected to the chassis and the shock hazard will still exist. It should not be shorted to any heatsinks used to mount transistors as they may be isolated from the chassis and the transistor may be destroyed by the overvoltage.

TROUBLESHOOTING SHORTED POWER PROBLEMS

The technician must learn how to service equipment that has an internal short, one that perhaps blows fuses. Some technicians use a circuit breaker and clip leads with small diameter wire, as in answer *c* of *Question 6*. The circuit breaker protects against any large current and the small wire also acts as a resistance and fuse. This protects the set and may quickly show up the location of the short. While this practice may be acceptable where the equipment being serviced is familiar, a better method for all kinds of equipment is to insert a large-wattage dropping resistor in series with one leg of the ac power line. The more severe the short, the greater the drop across the resistor, limiting the current and thus the damage that might be caused to the equipment. A 50-ohm 10-watt resistor will work on sets that are designed to operate up to 1 amp of 110 Vac power. Most technicians use a variac to troubleshoot shorts, gradually increasing the ac power input while monitoring the unit for the short and for the input current in order to keep it reasonable.

MEDICAL ELECTRONICS SAFETY

Using an isolation transformer between equipment and patients eliminates some leakage possibilities. Obviously, ground fault ac circuits and remote sensors isolated with optical couplers are good protection devices. Many technicians use isolation transformers to power their shop workbenches and equipment in a like manner in order to eliminate such hazardous potentials. Never defeat the 3-prong plug with an adaptor in medical environments. The answer to *Question 7* is *d*.

In medical monitoring equipment, probes may be placed on the skin or actually in the body. The resistance of the body of contact points is reduced. Therefore much smaller levels of current are needed to cause severe patient harm. The answer to *Question 8* is *d*.

SAFETY ENVIRONMENT

Question 9 is about equipment used in dangerous locations. Ground fault interrupters open the line-voltage supply with the slightest amount of leakage current caused by: defective tools and equipment, stripped insulation on ac service lines, or other causes. Technicians who are routinely located in shops or field locations with wooden floors and benches, rugs and plastic floor coverings, become complacent regarding shock hazards. Other environments (out-of-doors and in locations where wetness occurs) can place the technicians and others in lethal positions. Extra care should always be used in these areas.

Transistors are difficult to service. *Question 10* addresses this difficulty. A momentary short of the test lead between collector and emitter or between collector and base will destroy the transistor. A simple trouble can be made into a compound one if parts are ruined by carelessness. The only sure method of turning transistors on and off safely is by carefully shorting the base to the emitter. This removes the forward bias and turns off the transistor. Caution should be used in direct-coupled stages with this method.

Static is a constant problem with sensitive CMOS chips. Merely walking a few steps on a nylon carpet can build up too many volts of static electricity on a technician. Should he/she then touch the chip or transistor leads and cause the static to discharge through the chip in the wrong way the part will be destroyed as the static blows a hole in the very thin insulation between component sections. The answer to *Question 11* is therefore *d*.

NATIONAL ELECTRICAL CODE

Technicians also need to keep track of safe installation practices, when installing equipment in customers homes. Safety procedures, contained in equipment manuals, should be followed

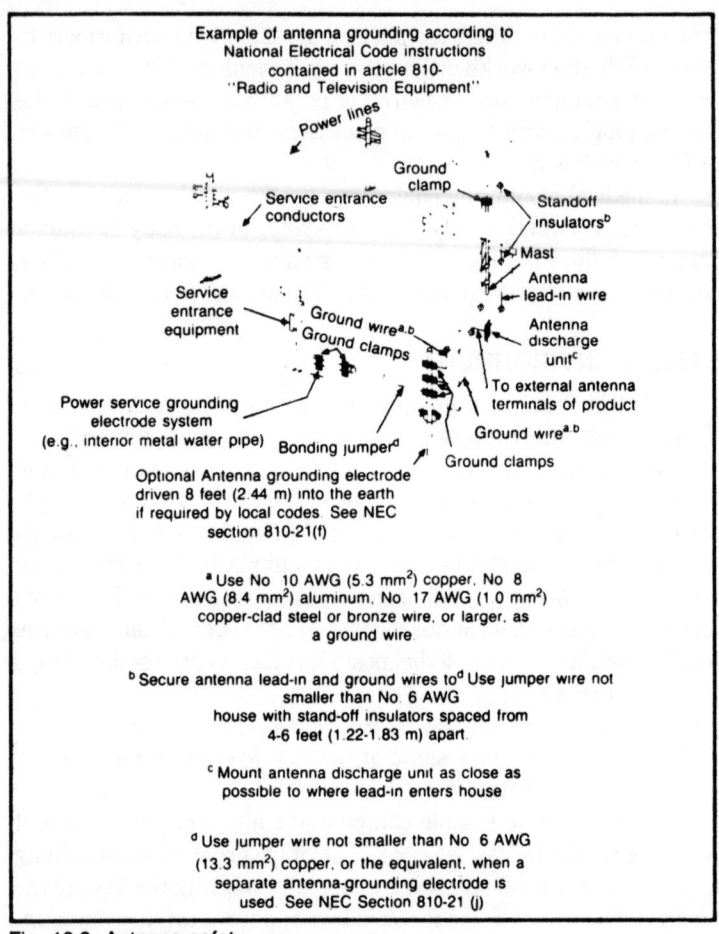

Fig. 12-3. Antenna safety.

on all installations. In addition, the National Electrical Code should be followed as well as all local codes governing the installation of electrical equipment and appliances. A portion of the code covers antenna installation, see Fig. 12-3.

ADDITIONAL READING

Lacy, Edward A.: *The Handbook of Electronic Safety Procedures,* TAB BOOKS Inc., 1983.

Lenk, John D.: *Handbook of Practical Microcomputer Troubleshooting,* Reston Publication Co., Inc., 1979.

Summers, Wilford J.: ed. *The National Electrical Code Handbook,* National Fire Protection Association, 1978.

C E T
ASSOCIATE
13

Consumer Electronics Basics

This chapter covers the basics of consumer electronic devices.

Q1. A carbon microphone is similar in operation to a/an:

a. phonograph cartridge   c. variable capacitor
b. electromagnetic speaker   d. variable resistor

Q2. Loudspeaker impedance is:

a. the resistance measured on the 1-ohm scale of a VTVM
b. important for matching purposes
c. the impedance in ohms measured at 10 kHz
d. the average impedance over the 16-20 kHz audio range

Q3. Phonograph cartridges can be expected to produce what level of output?

a. 1 V for ceramic; 5-10 mV for magnetic
b. 100 mV for ceramic; 50 mV for magnetic

c. 5 V for ceramic; 100 mV for magnetic
d. both types produce equal levels of output

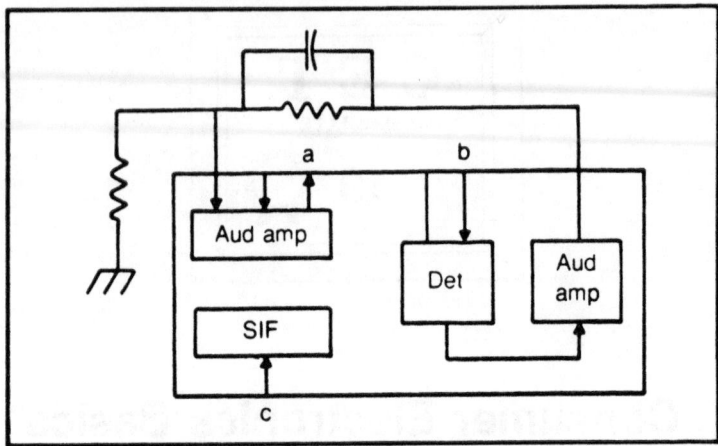

Fig. 13-1. Audio chip for Q4.

Q4. In Fig. 13-1 the power amplifier or speaker circuit would probably be connected to which pin on the TV's audio chip?

a. a   c. c
b. b   d. neither a, b, nor c

Q5. The transistors in Fig. 13-2 are used for audio output.

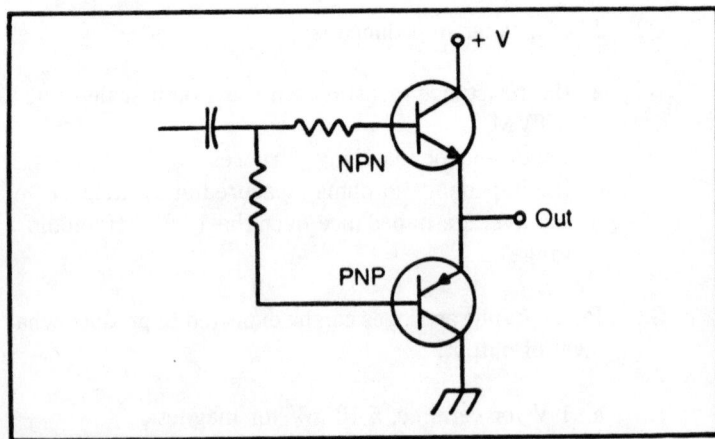

Fig. 13-2. Audio output circuit for Q5.

Using alternate forms of otherwise identical transistors in this fashion eliminates the output transformer and produces a purer audio signal. What is this type of circuit called?

a. class C amplifier   c. Darlington pair
b. complementary   d. differential

Q6. Rf signals are often measured in microvolts. With an input to a stage of 300 microvolts, and a voltage gain of 6, the output voltage of the stage would be:

a. 900 microvolts   c. 1.8 V
b. 9 mV   d. 1.8 mV

Q7. Match the following commonly used i-f frequencies to their product or circuit:

a. 455 kHz   1. television sound i-f frequency
b. 10.7 MHz   2. TV video i-f
c. 45.75 MHz   3. FM radio
d. 4.5 MHz   4. AM radio
e. 19 kHz   5. FM stereo pilot
f. 67 kHz   6. SCA (subsidiary communications
                   authorization)

Q8. Match the waveforms in Fig. 13-3 to the descriptions below:

a. TV signal   c. FM radio signal
b. AM radio signal   d. audio waveform

Q9. Match the frequency transmission bands to the frequencies listed:

a. 1 MHz   1. FM band
b. 4 GHz   2. TV band
c. 54 MHz   3. AM broadcast band
d. 96 MHz   4. satellite receiver band

Q10. When confronted with a television, radio, or other type of home entertainment product which when turned on

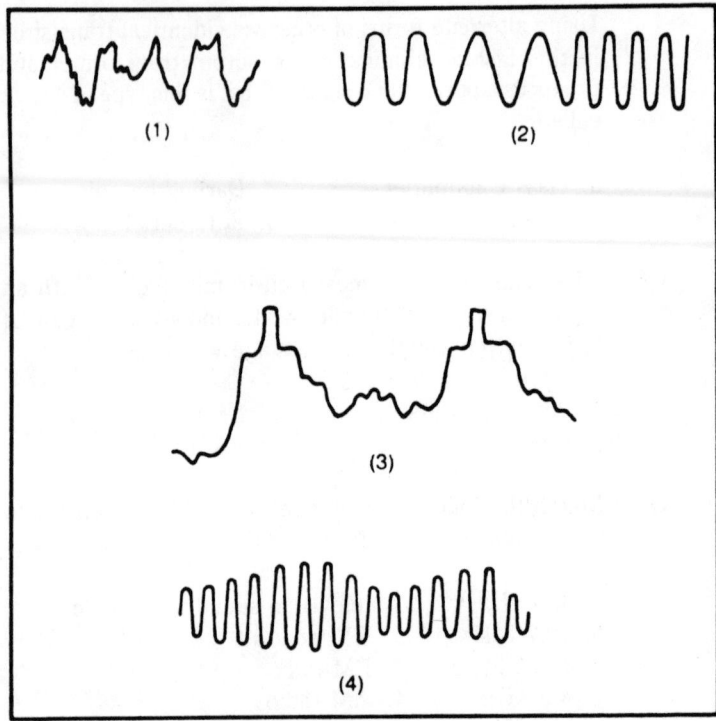

Fig. 13-3. Waveforms for matching in Q8.

has a dial light, but otherwise is 'dead', a good step in finding the trouble is to:

a. check the on/off switch
b. check the power supply voltages
c. use a signal tracer at the audio output transistors
d. substitute a speaker

Q11. When confronted with a TV set that has sound, but has a snowy and ghostly picture, a good first step in troubleshooting is to:

a. check the power supply voltages
b. check the power supply voltages to the tuner
c. check the automatic frequency control circuit
d. check the antenna system

Q12. When confronted with an AM-FM cassette player which

performs OK on cassette but has no AM or FM, to find the trouble a good first step is to check the:

a. power supply voltages
b. audio output and speaker circuit
c. external antenna connections
d. tuner and i-f sections

Q13. Video tape recorders, 8-track and cassette players, and recorders with "wow" or speed variation problems are most likely to have problems with:

a. drive wheels and belt slippage
b. speed control p-c board electronics
c. intermittent switches
d. varying power supply voltages

Q14. The polar pattern of Fig. 13-4 is most likely that of a:

a. dipole antenna   c. Yagi
b. rabbit ear antenna   d. Rhombic

Q15. The wavelength of a broadcast frequency of 1000 kHz is:

a. 98.4 feet   c. 9.84 feet
b. 984 feet   d. about 1 foot

Q16. In the installation of a TV antenna, it is proper to tape twin-lead to the antenna mast:

a. true
b. false

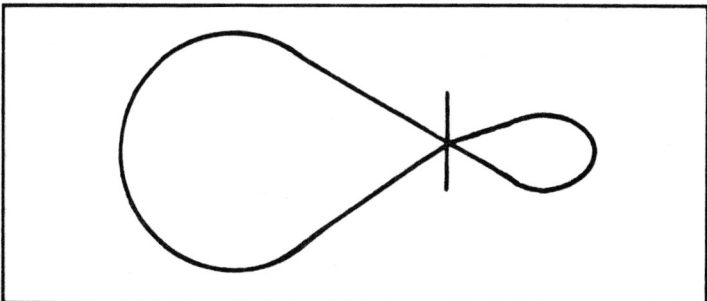
Fig. 13-4. Antenna polar pattern for Q14.

AUDIO

The carbon mike is constructed of granules of carbon that are slightly compressed by sound variations. As the sound compressions vary the pressure on the granules, the resistance of the block of granules changes in a manner similar to that of a resistor being varied. The answer to *Question 1* is *d*. A phono cartridge could be made similarly but none are as it is more practical to use crystals or magnetic coils for good reproduction of record groove modulations. Microphones may also be constructed using variable capacitance.

Question 2 is a question on speaker impedance. Speaker impedance is important in matching output stages to the speaker or speakers (answer *b*) for maximum power transfer efficiency. The speaker impedance, however, is a very complex quantity. It varies with frequency and with the environment of the speaker. The impedance rating on a speaker is defined as the minimum impedance on the high frequency side beyond the speaker's resonant frequency. See A on the sketch in Fig. 13-5.

Phonograph cartridges in use today are of two basic types; a low-level magnetic type and a ceramic crystal type. The ceramic replaces earlier crystal (quartz) versions which had inferior frequency response and were most susceptible to mechanical damage. The ceramic cartridge produces a high level output (some reach a volt or more). This eliminates the need for a separate preamplifier. The moving coil, or moving armature type magnetic cartridges have a very low output (5-10 mV) but can be made to more faithfully follow the grooves and reproduce the stereo information. The best answer in *Question 3* is *a*.

Audio circuitry is often found to have very few components other than the integrated circuitry of a single chip. Figure 13-1 needs some additional circuitry to work, including: a crystal resonator to assist the detector circuitry at b, a 4.5 MHz input transformer at c, and output power amplifier at a. However, similar chips are made

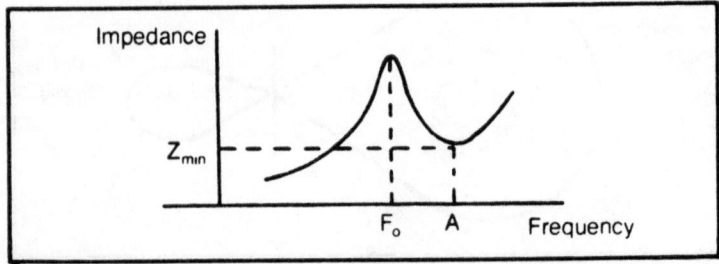

Fig. 13-5. Speaker impedance vs. frequency.

to power the speaker directly from *a*, which is the only possible location for a speaker from the information given in *Question 4*.

In *Question 5*, the complementary transistors (Fig. 13-2) are often sold in pairs for audio output circuits, for TV vertical deflection circuitry, and for other applications. Since the circuit is quite common, it should be familiar to all technicians. The top (NPN) transistor increases in conduction during the positive half of the sine wave but decreases during the negative half. The bottom transistor turns ON harder during the negative half. The two amplifiers are basically emitter followers driving the low impedance speakers. The correct answer to this question is *b*.

RADIO AND TV

Voltage gain is the subject of *Question 6*. The voltage gain, A_v, is a number found by calculating the ratio of output volts divided by input volts. If the gain is 6, as in this case, the output will be 6 times the input. Since the input was given as 300 microvolts, the output will be:

$$300 \ \mu V \ (6) = 1800 \ \mu V$$
$$= 1.8 \ mV \ \text{answer to } Question \ 6$$

Gain is also expressed in dB. This subject is covered in Chapter 11.

Each of the *Question 7* frequencies are common and have been in use for over 20 years. The SCA frequency is the only one that is not regularly encountered by consumer product technicians. The others should be easily recognizable. In the same manner and for the same reasons each of the *Question 8* waveforms should be immediately identified by their appearance as displayed on an oscilloscope. To produce these patterns the oscilloscope's horizontal frequency will have to be changed and/or a demodulator probe used prior to insertion of the signals into the oscilloscope.

As in *Q7* and *Q8*, the frequency locations in *Question 9* should become second nature to you, whether they are in kHz, MHz, or GHz form. Because earth satellite use is relatively new, the present day use of the 4 GHz range may change as the service matures. At the present time 12 GHz is also being used for satellite transmissions.

TROUBLESHOOTING

The on/off switch in *Question 10*, is okay if the dial light is capable of being turned on. Substitution of a speaker or signal tracing in the output stage would be "guessing" at the trouble rather than attacking the most probable cause by checking the power supply voltages first.

Checking the tuner in *Question 11* might not be a bad idea, but from the symptoms given, the tuner is working, at least partially, otherwise the correct sound and some video information would not be getting through. So checking the antenna system first would be the most logical step. If that fails to correct the problem investigation of the tuner might be in order.

If the tape is playing in *Question 12* then power supply voltages are okay. In today's radios, built-in AM and FM antennas will allow at least some local stations to be received, even if the external antenna is disconnected or damaged; therefore, checking the radio section (the tuner and i-f) would be more logical.

Question 13 has more than one correct answer since many of the recent VTR's and video disc players do, in fact, use electronically controlled drive-speed regulation. However, mechanical drives, idler wheels, and belts continue to be the cause of *most* "wow", or speed variation problems.

WAVE PROPAGATION

Technicians need to know the basic polar patterns of antennas. The Yagi has several director elements in front of the driven element, and reflectors on the rear portion. These elements give the Yagi a higher front than rear reception as in Fig. 13-4 pattern of *Question 14*. Rabbit ear, dipole, or Rhombic antennas do not have reflectors or directors and thus have the same front and back reception capabilities. The dipole and rabbit ear would have an equally lobed figure-8 pattern. The Rhombic has a four-leaf-clover pattern.

The formula for wavelength is:

$$\lambda \text{ ft} = \frac{984,000}{\text{freq in kHz}}$$

The wavelength of the 1000 kHz in *Question 15* is therefore 984 feet, answer *b*.

A common transmission line for use in antenna installations is flat twin-lead. One reason is that it is low in losses. It is also 300 Ω, which matches a folded dipole antenna; therefore, a matching transformer is not needed at the antenna.

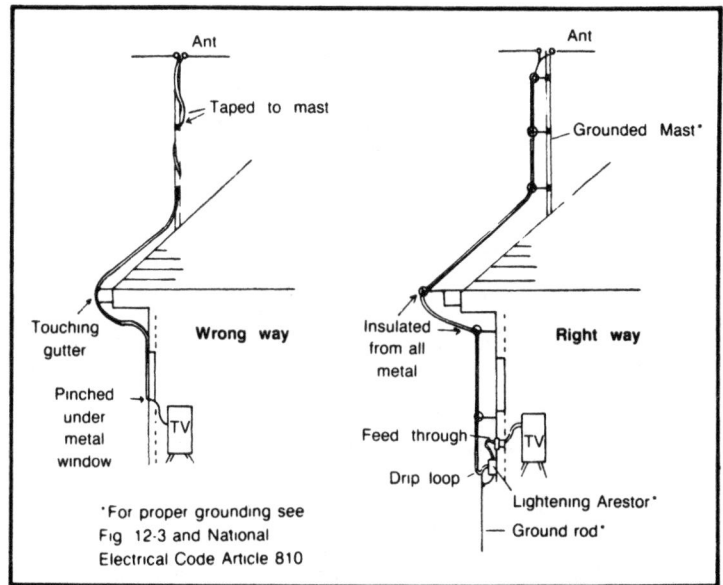

Fig. 13-6. Antenna installation with twin-lead.

The disadvantage of flat line is that it must be kept away from metal objects in order to stay 300 Ω at all points. See Fig. 13-6.

If the line crosses a gutter, as shown in the "wrong way" example of Fig. 13-6, the impedance will change at that point causing reflections and standing waves on the transmission lines. Taping the lead-in to the mast is, of course, not a good practice. The answer to *Question 16* is *b*, false.

ADDITIONAL READING

Goodman, Robert L.: *How to Troubleshoot & Repair Electronic Circuits*, TAB BOOKS Inc., 1982.

Grob, Bernard.: *Basic Television*, McGraw-Hill Book Co., 1964.

Hartman, Bernard.: *Fundamentals of Television*, Charles E. Merrill Publishing Co., 1975.

Herrick, Clyde N.: *Audio Systems*, Reston Publishing Co., 1974.

Herrick, Clyde N.: *Color Television*, Reston Publishing Co., 1973.

Prentiss, Stan.: *Color Television Theory and Troubleshooting*, Reston Publishing Co., 1979.

Tremaine, Howard M.: *Audio Cyclopedia*, Howard W. Sams, 1973.

C E T

ASSOCIATE

14

Block Diagrams

and Troubleshooting

This section of the book is devoted to block diagrams and to troubleshooting concepts.

QUIZ

Q1. In the functional block diagram of Fig. 14-1, block A is most likely a/an:

a. mixer
b. power supply

c. video amplifier
d. EKG isolator

Q2. In the block diagram of Fig. 14-2 (a voltage regulator), the arrow was omitted from the line at **A**. It should be drawn:

a. into the error detector
b. out of the error detector

Q3. If the overall gain of the amplifier group in Fig. 14-3 is 40 dB, B should have a gain of:

a. 10/36 dB
b. 104 dB loss

c. 16 dB
d. none of these

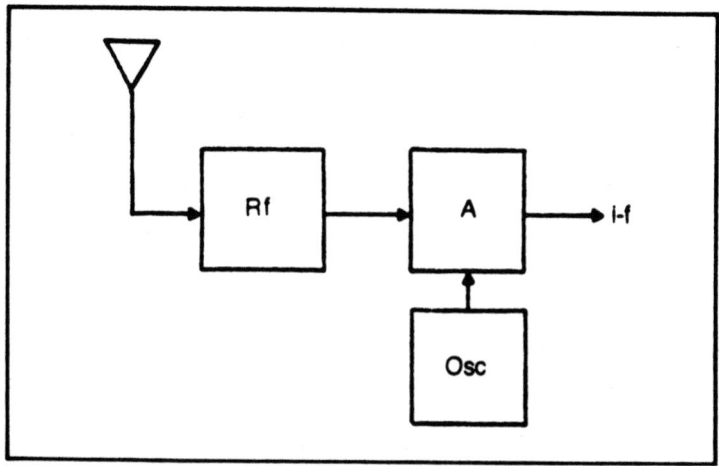

Fig. 14-1. Functional block diagram for Q1.

Figure 14-4 is used in questions Q4 to Q7.

Q4. This circuit is most likely a/an:

    a. power supply regulator   c. class A amplifier
    b. mixer   d. oscillator

Q5. Suppose the xtal opens up. You would expect to measure what voltage at either collector?

    a. about V_{CC} c. about $V_{CC}/2$
    b. about zero volts   d. about $3/4\ V_{CC}$

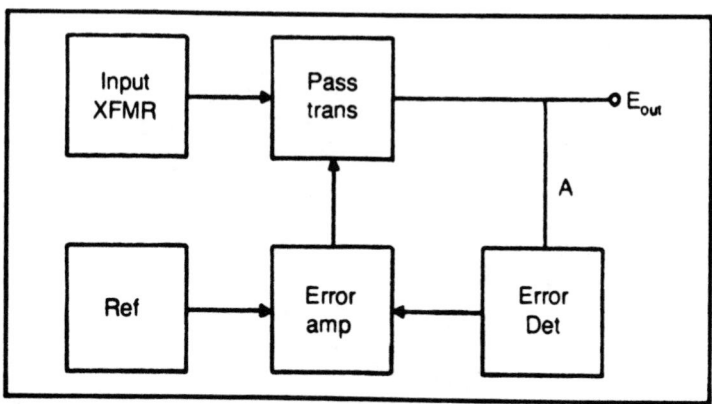

Fig. 14-2. Voltage regulator block diagram for Q2.

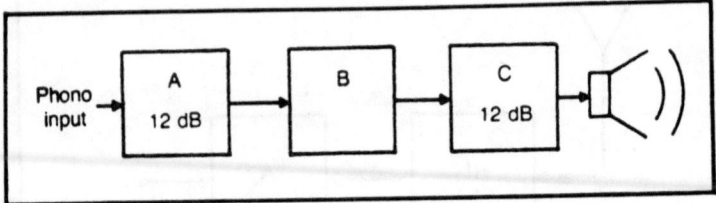

Fig. 14-3. 40 dB amplifier for Q3.

Q6. If this circuit was inoperative (no output signal) and you measured $+V_{CC}$ at the base of Q1, the problem could be:

a. Q1, shorted collector to emitter
b. Q2, open collector
c. Q1, collector resistor open
d. Q1, base open

Q7. If the resistor in the base of Q2 opened up, the collector voltage of Q2 would:

a. increase   c. remain the same
b. decrease

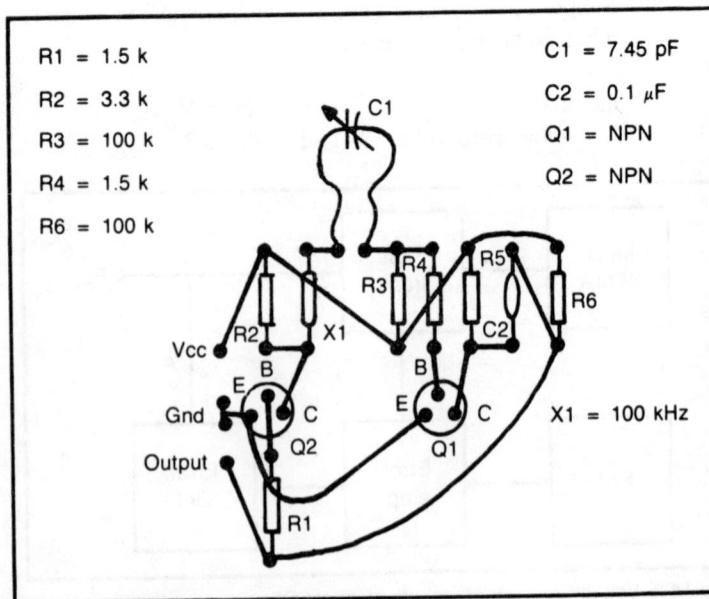

Fig. 14-4. Printed circuit for Q4 through Q7.

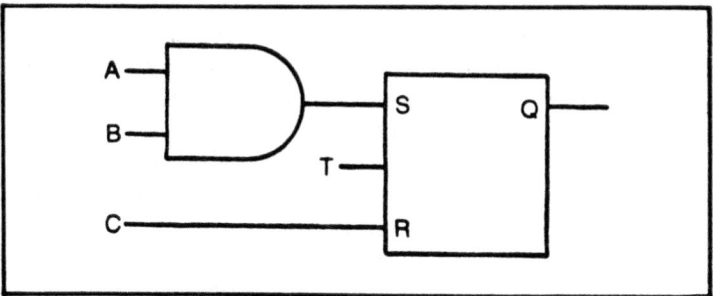

Fig. 14-5. Logic circuit for Q8.

Q8. The output of the logic circuit in Fig. 14-5 at Q is always a logic one. The problem could be:

   a. C is always "0"
   b. T is missing
   c. A and B are both "0"
   d. a and b are both possibilities

Q9. In the switching circuit of Fig. 14-6 with SW1 open, the base voltage measures −10 volts, because:

   a. the base or the emitter could be open
   b. the collector is shorted to the emitter
   c. the transistor is OK
   d. none of these answers is correct

BLOCK DIAGRAMS

Block diagrams are used for many things in electronics. One of the more useful block diagrams is the functional block diagram.

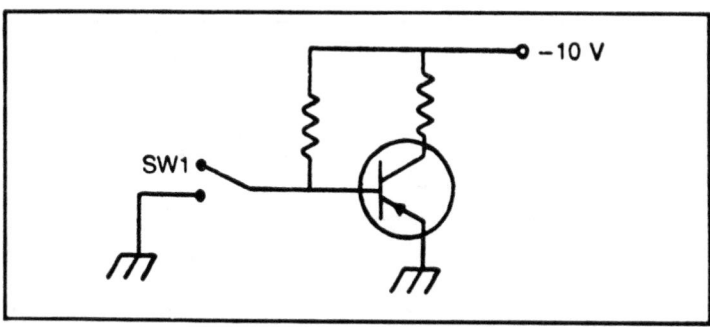

Fig. 14-6. Switch circuit for Q9.

A functional block diagram separates a piece of equipment into functions and shows the flow of signals between functions. These functional block diagrams may be very simple or very complex depending on the details that need to be portrayed. Blocks sometimes have shapes to indicate their function, as in a logic block diagram. Here is a simple one of a TV set (Fig. 14-7). The speaker and the picture tube are diagrammatic reminders of their physical shapes. Note also that arrows are usually used to indicate signal direction.

The input of a heterodyne-type receiver is depicted in *Question 1*. Many types of equipment use a similar type of "front-end", including avionics receivers, broadcast receivers of all types (including TV receivers) and many others. A small signal is developed in an antenna and fed to a radio-frequency amplifier. The block labeled rf represents this function (Fig. 14-1). An oscillator (Osc in this drawing) feeds a signal to block A. The output of the rf amplifier also goes to A which is the mixer. In this example you can see that functions are more detailed than in the Fig. 14-7 example. If still more details are desired, they could be placed on the block diagram or the diagram could even be expanded further.

The block diagram of *Question 2* (Fig. 14-2) is almost detailed enough to be a circuit, but not quite. It is the block diagram of a voltage regulator. The signal at A is a variation in output voltage. The error detector senses this change and passes it on to the error amplifier. Therefore, the arrow at A should point into the error detector.

Frequency spectrum, gain, types of active components, and so forth are details that may be included on a block diagram. *Question 3* is a troubleshooting question. A piece of information is missing and you are to figure out the missing piece. Expect this type of troubleshooting question. In this case, the gain of the B stage is missing. Since gains given in dB add:

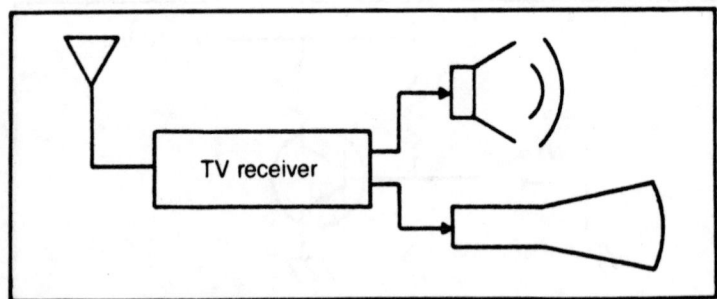

Fig. 14-7. TV block diagram.

$$A \text{ dB} + B \text{ dB} + C \text{ dB} = 40 \text{ dB}$$
$$12 \text{ dB} + B \text{ dB} + 12 \text{ dB} = 40 \text{ dB}$$
$$B = 16 \text{ dB}$$

CIRCUIT TROUBLESHOOTING

The industry expects beginning technicians to be able to troubleshoot without the aid of a schematic. You will undoubtedly have occasions when creating a schematic from the unit you are attempting to troubleshoot, is the most efficient way to repair the unit. You will find in the certification exam, therefore, questions like Q4 through Q7. When you do, it will probably be most beneficial to draw the schematic. Here is the schematic for the drawing in *Q4* to *Q7* (Fig. 14-8). Since there is no input but there is an output, and since there is cross-coupling between the stages, the circuit is an oscillator.

In all probability, the crystal opening up would cause the oscillator to cease operation. With no oscillations, what will the transistor do? That is really the question asked in *Question 5.* Since the base-emitter junctions of both transistors are forward biased, the transistors will probably saturate. But let's find out. The base current for each one is $(V_{CC} - 0.6) \div 101.5$ k. Let's just pick a voltage of 10 volts for V_{CC}. Then I_B for either transistor is 9.4/101.5 k, or 0.093 mA. If the current gain of the transistor is 100 (a reasonable assumption) the collector current would like to be 9.3 mA. But 9.3 times 3.3 k ohms gives more voltage drop across the collector resistor than is available, namely 31 volts. Hence, the transistor will be saturated with a reasonable current gain and the collector voltages will both be nearly zero volts.

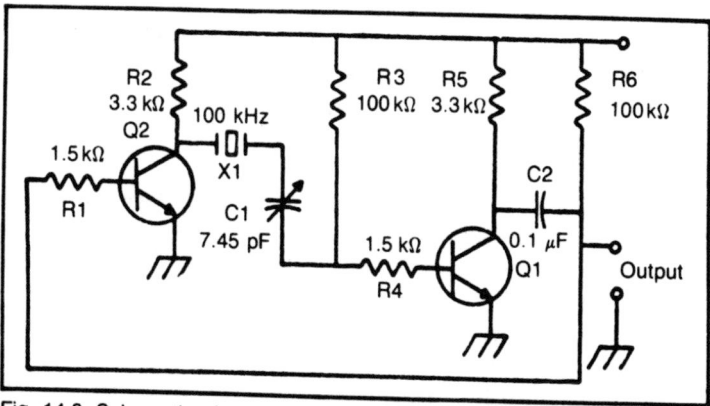

Fig. 14-8. Schematic of printed circuit of Fig. 14-4.

In *Question 6* a voltage measurement is given as V_{CC} at the base of Q1. The only way V_{CC} can be measured at the base is if no current is flowing through the resistors (R3 and R4). With no current flow the voltage drop across the resistors is zero; therefore, the base would be at V_{CC}. If the base is open, there would be no current flow, hence, answer *d* is the best of the choices given.

The next question (*Question 7*) turns a similar situation around and asks for a result, namely if the base resistor of Q2 is open what happens to the collector voltage. With the base resistor open the transistor cannot conduct since it cannot be biased on. Therefore, the collector resistor will not drop any voltage so the collector will be at V_{CC}.

You may also find logic troubleshooting problems such as *Question 8*. Q8 states that the output, Q of the flip-flop in Fig. 14-5 always stays at a logic one. If you missed this you might want to review Chapter 9 sections on flip-flops. The correct answer is *d*. The reset input, being always a "0," might cause Q to stay at "1" or if a trigger does not occur, it might stay at logic "1."

Also, there are questions on troubleshooting switching circuits from a circuitry standpoint. *Question 9* is such a question. This question is almost identical to Q7 except it is a switching circuit. The same reasoning applies. If current flows in the base circuit the voltage must be one diode drop away from ground. In order to be a voltage of V_{CC} the base or emitter must be open.

SUMMARY

These sample questions should give you an idea of the type of questions asked in troubleshooting. Trouble symptoms are described and results are asked for. Normal operational conditions are also used for questions. Abnormal voltages are given and symptoms, or results of other voltage measurements, are used for questions.

ADDITIONAL READING

Buchsbaum, Walter H.: *Tested Electronics Troubleshooting Methods*, Prentice-Hall, 1974.

Coffron, James W.: *Practical Troubleshooting Techniques for Microprocessor Systems*, Prentice-Hall 1981.

Goodman, Robert L.: *Practical Troubleshooting with Modern Electronic Test Instruments*, TAB BOOKS Inc., 1979.

Herrick, Clyde N.: *Electronic Troubleshooting; A Manual for Engineers and Technicians*, Reston Publishing Co., 1974.

C E T

ASSOCIATE

15

Antenna and Wave-Propagation Theory and Signal Distribution

Here's a quiz on the above topics.

QUIZ

Q1. In antenna systems, 0 dBmV is:

    a. total lack of signal
    b. less than 1 volt of peak-to-peak signal
    c. 1000 microvolts or 1 millivolt signal level
    d. insignificant noise level within the desired signal

Q2. The wavelength for a 27 MHz signal will be:

    a. about 4 feet   c. nine feet
    b. slightly over 36 feet   d. 18 feet

Q3. In Fig. 15-1, if you design for 0 dBmV at the A tap then you should have (for this example assume each line loss at 0 dB and each tap has 4 dB loss from input to tap and 2 dB insertion loss from input to output):

    a. −4 dBm at D output   c. 2 dBmV at B output
    b. 0 dBmV at B input   d. +10 dBmV at D input

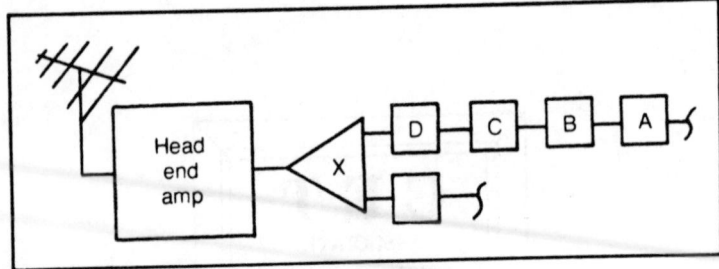

Fig. 15-1. Antenna distribution system for problem in Q3.

Q4. In Fig. 15-1 what is the function of "X"?

a. a balun
b. a splitter
c. an op amp
d. an OR gate

Q5. Coax cable has greater losses at which frequencies?

a. TV channels 2-13
b. TV channel 83
c. TV channel 14
d. at FM frequencies

Q6. In Fig. 15-2, A, B, and C, which drawing best depicts a coax cable's loss elements as they appear to a UHF signal?

a. A
b. B
c. C

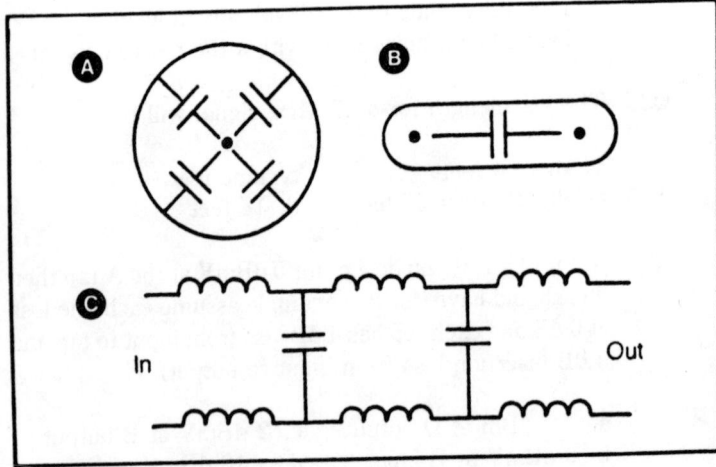

Fig. 15-2. Three transmission lines.

Q7. By observing the three drawings in Fig. 15-2 you would expect coax (compared to flat line) to have:

a. more capacitance per foot
b. more resistance per foot
c. less loss per foot

Q8. The impedance of a TV transmission line depends on several factors. Which one of the following is *not* one of those factors?

a. diameter
b. distance between conductors
c. dielectric or insulator material
d. length of wire

Q9. A smaller diameter conductor, used in a transmission line, will cause a greater signal loss:

a. true   b. false

Q10. The frequency used in a transmission line affects the signal loss, per 100 feet:

a. true   b. false

Q11. Which coaxial cable listed best matches the 75 Ω of a simple dipole antenna?

a. RG 58C   c. RG 213
b. RG 59B

Q12. Which of the following transmission lines is nearer to 0.4 inches in diameter?

a. RG 213   c. RG 6
b. RG 59

Q13. Parasitic antenna elements are:

a. undesirable
b. the driven or directly connected elements of an antenna
c. the directors and reflectors

Q14. An AM transmitter operating at 1 MHz is modulated with a 60 Hz tone or sinewave. What sidebands are produced?

a. no sidebands are produced with a pure sine wave
b. 1,000,060 Hz and 999,940 Hz
c. 1,000,030 and 999,970 Hz

Q15. FM broadcasting stations may have a deviation from their assigned frequency of:

a. 20 kHz   c. 75 kHz
b. 40 kHz   d. 150 kHz

Q16. TV station sound transmitters may deviate how many kHz? (FM Deviation)

a. 20 kHz   c. 40 kHz
b. 25 kHz   d. 75 kHz

Q17. Which antenna in Fig. 15-3 is a simple dipole?

a. A   c. C
b. B

Q18. If transmission lines are not terminated in their characteristic impedance:

a. standing waves will exist
b. the line will tend to be flat
c. an attenuator must be used
d. reflected waves will be reduced

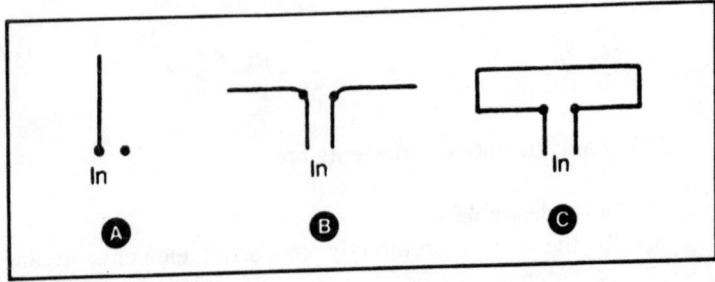

Fig. 15-3. Antennas for Q13.

Q19. If two identical antennas are combined to increase signal strength, what gain might be realized over a single antenna?

 a. no gain, but signal-to-noise-ratio is increased
 b. a signal voltage gain of 100% or 6 dB
 c. 10 dB
 d. 1 dB

Q20. Coax cable is used in MATV systems because:

 a. it is shielded and less affected by electrical wires, metal and the like
 b. it has higher gain
 c. it matches the ordinary 75-ohm antennas
 d. lightning arrestors are not needed

Q21. The antenna element acts similar to a tuned electronic circuit, having inductive reactance, capacitive reactance, and resistance:

 a. true   b. false

Q22. A very short antenna, say 1 inch long, will respond to higher frequencies than a longer antenna, say 10 inches long:

 a. true   b. false

dB REVISITED

When referring to the voltage level of an antenna system, a gain of 100% (doubling the voltage) represents a +6 dB gain. Reducing the voltage level by one-half, or 50%, means a loss of 6 dB, or a −6 dB gain. When referring to the power or milliwatt levels of a signal the ratios are only one-half as great. Doubling the power is a 3 dB gain. The formulas are covered in Chapter 11.

For convenience in the field of rf signal distribution a quantity of 1 mV or 1000 μ volts is defined as 0 dBmV, answer *c* in *Question 1*. As 0 dBmV is amplified with a voltage gain of 2 (or 6 dB) the output can be calculated by adding the gain in dB to the signal level in dBmV. In this case 6 dBmV (2 mV).

WAVELENGTH REVISITED

The formula for wavelength:

$$\text{in feet} \quad \lambda = \frac{984.000}{\text{f in kHz}}$$

$$\text{in meters} \quad \lambda = \frac{300,000}{\text{f in kHz}}$$

$$\text{in inches} \quad \lambda = \frac{11,000}{\text{f in MHz}}$$

The formula for determining wavelength is useful to technicians in determining which antenna in a multi-antenna array is used for each purpose—low VHF, CB, High VHF, FM, UHF, and so forth. The problem is that few antennas are a wavelength long. Many are one-half or one-fourth wavelength. So one must become familiar with the antennas used in their area of work. Communications antennas (CB and FM) reduce the physical length of the antenna by using an inductance in the antenna base. Capacitance in series reduces the electrical length. Calculating to 27 MHz gives a wavelength slightly over 36 feet, and b, Q2.

MATV SYSTEM

Because of the many varieties of products used in MATV work, the effect of the distributed signals is not always easily calculated unless you have the specifications for each product. However some things are known. Each tap of a distribution system will have a certain amount of isolation (or loss) between input and tap. The tap introduces a loss in the leg in which it is inserted (insertion loss). Each two-way splitter will reduce the original signal level by 3.5 dB to each leg. The splitter is X in Fig. 15-1; therefore, the answer to *Question 4* is *b*.

In the Fig. 15-1 system the head-in amplifier builds up the signal received from the antenna. How much it should be designed to amplify is determined by 2 factors: the signal input and the needs of the distribution system. Fortunately, there is a beginning point. No tap should have less than 0 dBmV or 1 millivolt of signal at the user tap. With that beginning point we then need 0 dBmV from the output tap at A and 4 dB for the loss between input and tap. To overcome its inherent loss B needs 2 dB. Insertion loss is 2 dB at C. Therefore, at D we must have at least 8 dBmV output or 10 dBmV input. The answer to *Question 3* is *d*. If the "X" splitter were perfect we would need 20 dBmV, plus some cushion for losses in the splitter (which are really there). Also there are losses in the actual coax cable wiring. So perhaps a 23 dBmV level would be satisfactory.

Looking now from the antenna to the amp, we need a signal out of the amp of at least 14 millivolts (23 dBmV). So, measuring the antenna signal with an rf signal strength meter using the weakest desired frequency we can calculate the gain needed by the amp.

If the antenna is sending a 14 mV signal to the amp, we then need no amplification and can get by with a 0 dB amp gain. That rarely is the case, though. A 14 mV weakest-signal level is rather high. If we had a 1 mV signal the amp would have to have a 23 dB gain. If the weakest channel is only 20 μV, then the amp must have a gain of 57 dB or more. (dB = 20 log 14000 μV)/20 μV.

Considerations involved in signal distribution systems, in addition to the above are: traps, couplers, matching transformers, transmission line losses, tap isolation, termination stubs, and stacking of antennas. These all must be understood by the technician dealing in signal distribution systems.

In Fig. 15-1 "X" is a splitter. Its purpose is to divide the signal into two separate legs, such as would be required for a motel video system in a building that has two wings of rooms, or a cable TV system supplying 2 different sides of the street. Splitters have insertion losses of 2 to 5 dB. They should have good isolation between the 2 (or more) legs so that undesirable conditions in one leg do not affect the other. Isolation should be at least 20 dB.

TRANSMISSION LINES

Coax cable losses vary directly with frequency. The formula for attenuation in coax line in dB per foot is:

$$a = \frac{4.6 \sqrt{f} \, (D + d)}{(D) (d) \left(\log \frac{D}{d}\right)} \times 10^{-6}$$

a = attenuation in dB per foot
f = freq. in MHz
D is inside diameter of the outer conductor in inches
d is outside diameter of the inner conductor in inches

215

What this says in understandable terms is:

- RG 8 coax has an attenuation at 1 MHz of 0.16 dB per 100 feet.
- RG 59 coax has an attenuation at 1 MHz of 1.1 dB per 100 feet. (RG 59 is smaller in diameter than RG 8).
- At 400 MHz RG 8 has an attenuation of 4.5 dB per 100 feet.
- At 400 MHz RG 59 has an attenuation of 8.5 dB per 100 feet.
- RG 59 has a loss at 100 MHz of 3.8 dB per 100 feet.

Putting this into comparative terms for better understanding, the 100 feet of RG 59 coax would lose only about 12% of the 1 MHz signal voltage in a 100 foot run. But at 400 MHz (low end of the UHF band) it would lose 8.5 dB or about 2/3 of the original signal. At TV channel 83 (885 - 889 MHz) the loss is nearly 12 dB, reducing the 1 mV signal to 0.25, or 1/4. TV-channel 83 or *b* is the highest frequency choice given in *Question 5*.

In *Question 6*, Fig. 15-2C shows series inductors and capacitor shunts. That is the effect coax cable has on rf signals. As you can see from the attenuation formula, the diameter of the cable has a great deal to do with how much attenuation is in the cable. Generally, the larger the diameter the less attenuation. For instance, RG 8 with a diameter of 0.4 inches, has an attenuation at 1 GHz of 8.5 dB, RG 59 at 1 GHz having a 16 dB loss.

Figure 15-2A shows several (4) theoretical capacitors between the outer shield of coax and the center conductor. The capacitor effect is equal to an infinite number of capacitors around the cable and up and down its length. You would therefore expect more capacitance per foot in coax than in twin lead. Answer *a* is correct in *Question 7*.

The impedance of coaxial cable is given by the formula:

$$Z_o = 138 \log \frac{D}{d} \times \frac{1}{\sqrt{k}}$$

Where D is the inside diameter of the outer conductor, d is the outside diameter of the inner conductor, k is the dielectric constant.

From this formula it can be seen that the characteristic impedance of coax is certainly dependent upon diameter, dielectric, and distance between conductors. The only answer in *Question 8* not affecting the impedance is the length, answer *d*.

Smaller wire used in coax will increase the resistance of the wire thereby increasing the loss in the coax. Answer *a* is correct for *Question 9*.

Table 15-1 illustrates several characteristics of various common coaxial cables. Notice that for the higher frequencies the attenuation in each cable is higher. This means that the answer to *Question 10* is *a*, true. It can also be seen in the table that RG 59B has a characteristic impedance of 73 ohms, which closely matches a simple dipole impedance. Answer *b* in *Question 11*. Also the diameter of RG 213 is the closest diameter to 0.4 inches, answer *a* in *Question 12*.

ANTENNAS REVISITED

Parasitic antenna elements are the directors, reflectors, and resonators that "ride along" on the antenna array boom. They are not directly connected to the dipole or folded dipole active elements to which the transmission line or cable is connected. Answer *c* is correct for *Question 13*.

The directors are in front of the active element at a right angle to the direction of the station transmitter. They become progressively shorter away from the active elements. This technique tends to broaden the bandwidth and reemphasize the signal directly in front of the antenna and to deemphasize signals from other directions (such as the same signal being delayed and bouncing off of a barn roof at perhaps 20° or 30°. Reflectors are progressively larger behind the active elements (see Fig. 15-4). They reflect signals away arriving from the rear direction and reflect forward, or towards the driven element, signals coming from the desired direction.

Table 15-1. Coaxial Cable Data for Commonly Used Coaxial Cable.

Type RG#	Imp Ohms	Outer diam(")	Cap/ ft(pf)	Attenuation/100' @ 10 mHz	Attenuation/100' @ 400 mHz	Uses
6A	76	.332	20	.78	6.5	Video signals
58C	50	.195	29	1.6	14	Test leads
59B	73	.242	21	1.1	8.5	TV lead in
174	50	.10	30	–	19	Instrumentation
213	52	.405	29.5	.55	4.5	General purpose

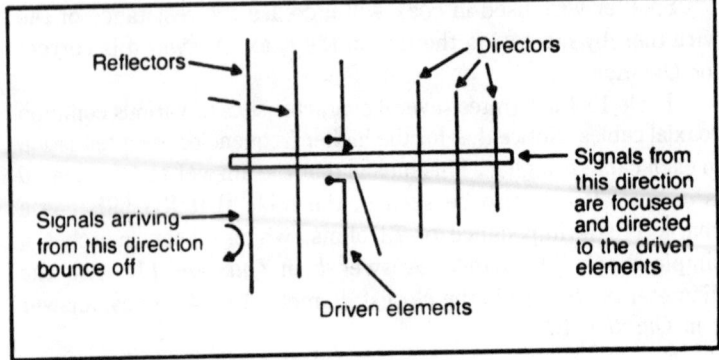

Fig. 15-4. Pictorial diagram of an antenna.

MODULATION

When two or more waveforms are combined they form combinations of the frequencies. The best known occurrence of this phenomenon is in the mixer stage of a superheterodyne radio. In it the incoming rf signal is combined with the radio's local oscillator frequency. The oscillator frequency is 455 kHz higher than the incoming rf signal in an AM radio. The output of the mixer stage will have original signals (the rf and oscillator signal), plus the sum, and the difference signals. A band-pass filter eliminates the undesired frequencies and passes only the difference frequencies.

When an AM transmitter is modulated with a voice signal from the announcer's microphone, the audio variations also add and subtract from the CW transmitter frequency. These effects on the original transmitter frequency create numerous sideband frequencies depending on the frequencies of the audio modulation. A 60 Hz sine wave would produce only two sidebands.

In the transmitter, the frequencies in Fig. 15-5 are produced, (answer *b* in *Question 14*). One of the original two frequencies is not reproduced in the output of the transmitter. That is the modulating tone (60 Hz here). It is bypassed to ground in the output due to the impedance of the output circuit being near 0 at audio frequencies.

The permissible frequency deviation for FM broadcasting

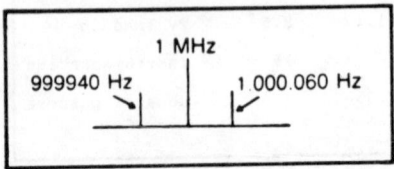

Fig. 15-5. Side-bands produced by a 60 Hz sine wave.

stations is set by the FCC and is 75 kHz. The purpose of this rather generous broadcast band is the desire to allow full fidelity broadcasting to the public. The answer to *Question 15* is *c*, or 75 kHz.

The TV frequency spectrum is crowded due to the broad band of information (6 MHz) needed by each station. Even with suppressed sideband transmission the room for the sound portion of the TV band had to be less than 75 kHz; therefore 25 kHz was the compromise chosen. The answer to *Question 16* is *b*.

In *Question 17*, Fig. 15-3A is an omnidirectional antenna. Figure 15-3B shows the common or simple dipole and Fig. 15-3C shows the folded dipole. It should be apparent that A and B would check infinity with an ohmmeter across the terminals. The folded dipole would check zero resistance.

Transmission line length is important. If the transmission line and the antenna are properly sized to the exact quarter, half, or full wavelength, the voltage and current from the transmitter, or to the receiver, will be equal at all points. If the lengths are not correct, some of the signal will be reflected back causing standing waves and loss of signal. These show up as multiple ghosts on TV receivers and loss of power in radio reception. If lines are not properly terminated by their characteristic impedance, reflections will also occur, causing standing waves as in *Question 18*.

Adding an identical antenna as in *Question 19* will double the signal received. In deep fringe areas stacking antennas is necessary in order to intercept the weak signals. When adding antennas it is necessary to double the number of antennas in order to double the signal level. One additional antenna will double the signal over a single antenna. Two more will double that signal. Four more will double that signal. Adding one identical antenna gives a 6 dB gain, adding two more results in a 12 dB gain over a single one, and stacking 8 together gives an 18 dB gain. Obviously, you encounter a physical problem with so many sections in the array. You would need stronger mounts, guying, cross beams, and base. Also the cost would be high. So ordinarily the number of antennas combined is limited. A better solution to a weak signal problem is usually a boom mounted wide-band signal amplifier.

Many people working in TV in the 60s and 70s were convinced that coaxial cable delivered a higher signal level than twin lead. Some felt that reason for this was that coax, being shielded, kept the signal inside. Therefore little was lost from the antenna to the receiver. *Questions 5, 6,* and *7* explain coax characteristics which show that coax has higher losses than open wire or twin lead. *Question 20* asks why coax is preferred in most applications. If the signal strength is sufficient, or if an amplifier is successfully used to build a strong signal at the antenna, the losses in coax are unimportant. Instead, the benefits of coax become important. They are:

■ Since the outer shield is grounded, rain and ice, and weather-caused oxidation collections have no effect. They do have an effect on twin lead.

■ Coax can be attached directly to the mast, run over gutters, through aluminum siding and across duct pipes and iron beams with no effect on its signal. Twin lead or open wire must be held away from these items with standoff insulators.

■ Coax and its associated hardware lasts longer and is less likely to be damaged.

■ Coax must be used in apartments and motel systems in order to eliminate pickup of "forward ghosts". The antenna system will produce a delay in the signal as it travels from antenna through amplifiers, splitters, etc. If direct signal pickup is allowed at the receiver, in addition to the delayed cable signal, two images will be present, the original amplified signal and the stray signal picked up direct by any unshielded wires near the receiver.

ANTENNA RESONANCE

Antenna resonance is a difficult concept. Working the formulas and figuring wavelength for a certain frequency signal is one thing, but getting the 'feel' of what is really going on is difficult.

In the following example we will use as a reference the TV channel 10 frequency. That carrier is 198 megahertz.

The formula for wavelength is:

$$\lambda = \frac{984\,(0.95)^*}{f \text{ in MHz}}$$

*The formula must be modified for formulas on the earth because of earth's conductive plane. In space the wavelength would be the same as free air wavelength.

Substituting the frequency of channel 10:

$$\lambda = \frac{984 \ (0.95)}{198} = 4.72$$

We could use an antenna 4.72 feet long and achieve good results but what is actually used in practice is a *half-wave* antenna. A 1/2-wave antenna works just as well, costs less, and is less bulky. The reason a 1/2-wave antenna works as well is that a maximum voltage level, or node, and a minimum level can be induced on the 1/2-wave antenna just as easily as on a full-wave antenna.

1/2 wavelength for channel 10 then is:

2.36 feet or about 28 inches long.

The basic antenna from which most TV antennas evolved is shown in Fig. 15-6. It is called a 1/2-wave dipole antenna.

In Fig. 15-7, note the voltage levels (or nodes) are maximum at both ends of the antenna rods when they are minimum at the center feed connections. One-fourth wavelength later (or earlier) the voltage levels are minimum at the ends and maximum at the center. The channel 10 signal waveforms from the broadcast station *resonates* the electrical particles in the rods. Just like the wind blowing past a length of metal tubing sometimes makes it "hum", vibrating it mechanically at its mechanical resonant frequency. The *electronic resonant frequency* is not exactly the same thing, but it can be visualized in the same manner. As to how the simple rods deliver an actual electrical voltage impulse of several hundred microvolts at the terminals, think of the channel 10 broadcast signal causing an inductive influence on the electrons in the metal of the rods. This causes a difference of potential from one point on the rods to another, from one end to the other. The antenna acts like

Fig. 15-6. Simple dipole.

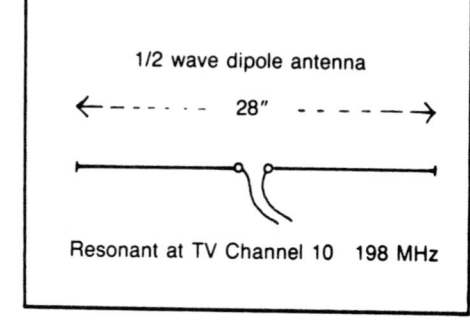

1/2 wave dipole antenna

←------ 28″ ------→

Resonant at TV Channel 10   198 MHz

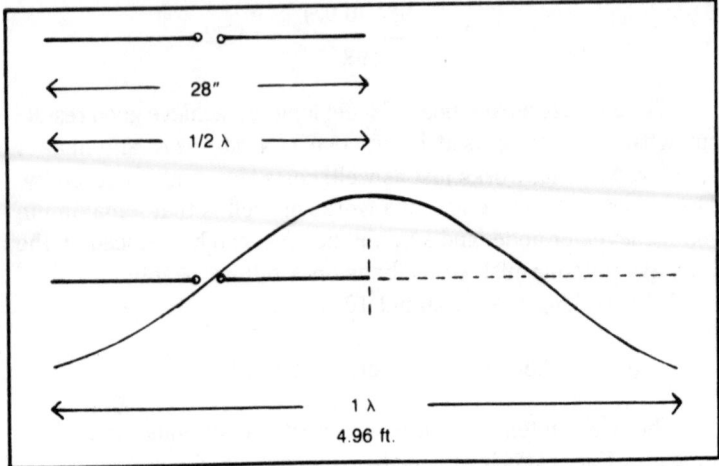

Fig. 15-7. Voltage distribution.

a tuned tank, resonating (or ringing) at the channel 10 frequency. *Question 21* is therefore true, answer *a*.

In Fig. 15-7 notice how a full wavelength is exactly twice the length of the antenna rods and that a 1/2 wavelength acts the same as a full wavelength. Note in Fig. 15-8 how the voltage levels change in time as a cycle passes. To try to understand this better, think of the transmitter at channel 10 as the primary of a transformer, and the receiving antenna as the secondary. See Fig. 15-9.

The channel 10 broadcast antenna causes an inductive influence on the electrons in the metal of the rods—a difference in potential

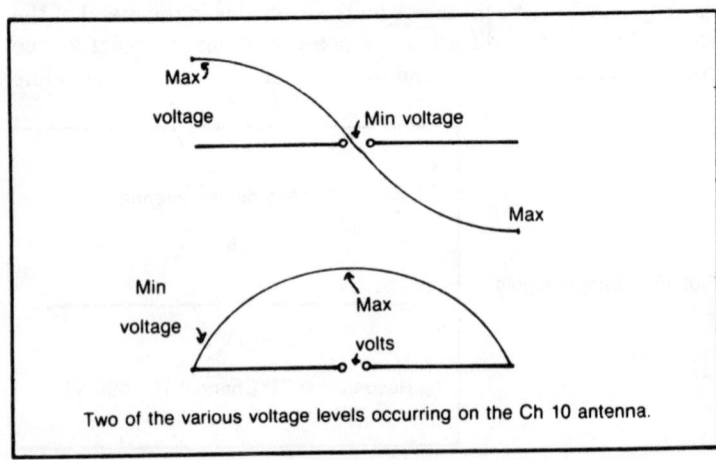

Two of the various voltage levels occurring on the Ch 10 antenna.

Fig. 15-8. Voltage at different instants in time.

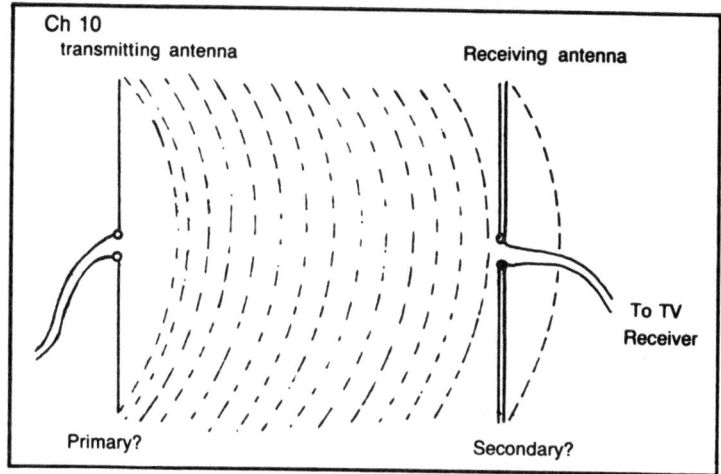

Fig. 15-9. Transformer analogy.

from one point in the rods to another—from one end to the other.

Now that you see what happens to the channel 10 antenna when the exact right size signal waveform hits it, let's look at what happens to the same antenna rod when a higher frequency waveform hits it. In Fig. 15-10 you see the same channel 10 antenna rod, but now let's see what happens when a much higher frequency, channel 30, passes it. Channel 30 is at 567 MHz. Using your formula calculate the 1/2 wavelength for channel 30. It is about 10 inches.

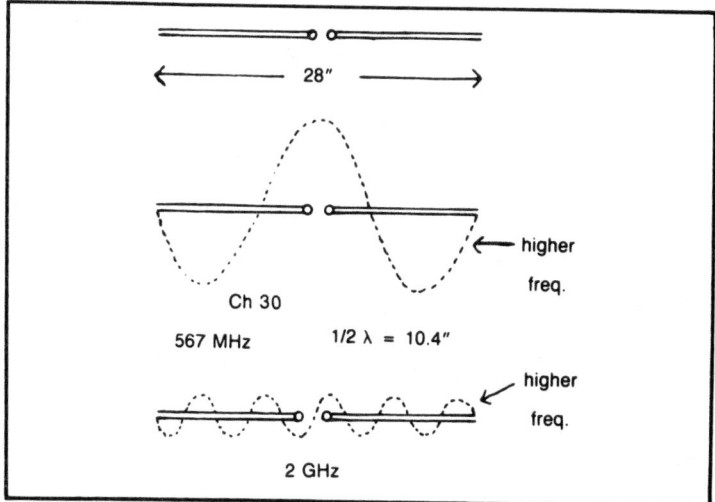

Fig. 15-10. Channel 10 antenna at higher frequencies.

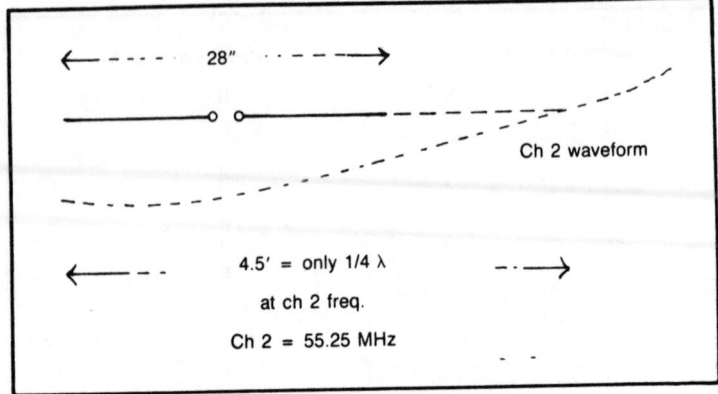

Fig. 15-11. Channel 10 antenna at lower frequencies.

Note in Fig. 15-10 that the higher wavelength doesn't 'fit'. As the cycles progress, you never have a full wavelength exactly fitting the rods and over 3 1/2 wavelengths can ramble around the rod. The confusion gets worse with a much higher frequency of 2 Gigahertz. Now many nodes are rambling across the rod and never is there much difference of potential between one end and the center connections. The antenna is not resonant at the channel 30, or 2 GHz frequencies. If any signal is picked up, it will be much lower in amplitude than the resonant frequency.

Using the same channel 10 antenna, look what happens with a lower frequency, or longer waveform. In Fig. 15-11 Channel 2 has a 1/2 wavelength of 9 feet. Even 1/4 wavelength is too long to fit the 28 inch rods and you can see there can be practically no difference between the rod ends and the center feed connectors. Again, there will be very little, if any, signal produced by the antenna at this non-resonant frequency.

By now it should be clear that the answer *a* is correct for *Question 22*.

ADDITIONAL READING

Hicks, Davis E.: *CB Radio Antenna Guidebook,* Howard W. Sams, 1965.

Finco MATV Greenline Planning Manual. The Finney Co., 1968.

Graf, Rudolf F.: *Electronic Databook—3rd Edition,* TAB BOOKS Inc., 1983.

Reference Data CATV Systems. Jerrold Co., 1970.

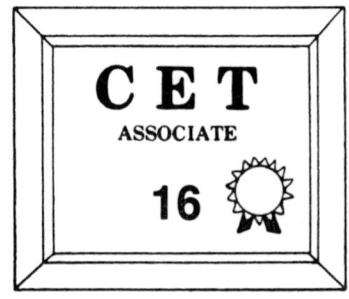

Journeyman Options

The purpose of including this chapter in an associate study guide is to show beginning technicians a little of what is expected in a particular field of study. If a technician finds a particular group of questions interesting, easy, or otherwise appealing, he might want to consider a career or further study in that area. The inclusion is also intended to give a small sampling of the type of questions contained in a specific certification option as opposed to the broadbased associate option.

QUIZ

Industrial Option

Q1. In Fig. 16-1 the bulb will light as long as SW1 is making contact and will not light when SW1 is not making contact:

    a. true   b. false

Q2. When the voltage at A is equal to the voltage at B the light is out:

    a. true   b. false

Q3. The purpose of the CR1-A relay contacts is to keep the

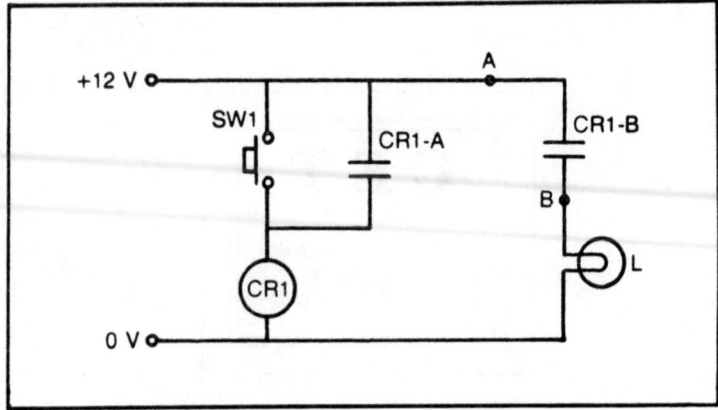

Fig. 16-1. Industrial electronic circuit for Q1, Q2, and Q3.

relay ON after the SW1 switch is released:

a. true   b. false

Q4.   Match the following industrial component symbols:

a.      1. control valve

b.   F   2. triac

c.   3. generator

d.   (G)   4. photodiode

e.   5. thermal cut-out circuit
                            breaker

f.   6. fuse

226

Q5. Which of the following contains a charged capacitor capable of injuring the test technician?

   a. ECG machine   c. echoencephalograph
   b. defibrillator

Q6. The green wire in a common 117 V wall socket wiring system is:

   a. ground   c. 117 Vac
   b. neutral   d. extra for 220 V applications

Q7. Match the following:

   g. 0.05-100 Hz   1. brain wave recorder
   h. EEG machine   2. maximum leakage current
   i. renal   3. kidney
   j. 10 microamps   4. electrosurgery
   k. tachycardia   5. ECG frequency range
   l. 500 W rf   6. fast heartrate

Q8. LIS in hospital electrical systems stands for:

   a. Line Isolation System
   b. Local Identification Setup
   c. Local Interruptable Service
   d. Low Interference Systems

Computer Option

Q9. The truth table in Fig. 16-2 represents the logic decisions for:

   a. AND gate   c. OR gate
   b. NAND gate   d. exclusive OR gate

Fig. 16-2. Truth table for Q9.

A	B	C
0	0	0
1	0	0
0	1	0
1	1	1

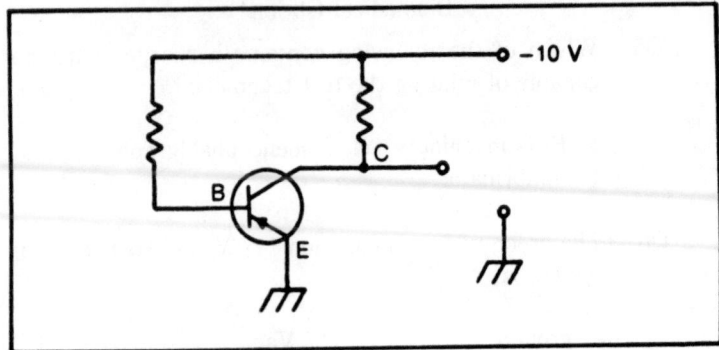

Fig. 16-3. Transistor circuit for Q11.

Q10. The NOT gate is the same as:

a. an inverter   c. a diode
b. a NOR gate   d. an open circuit

Q11. Which transistor lead in Fig. 16-3 will have the highest current when the transistor is conducting?

a. E   c. C
b. B

Q12. The value of the decimal number 5 can be represented in binary by a 4-bit equivalent. What is it?

a. 0110   c. 0101
b. 0111   d. 1010

Communications Option

Q13. The input power to the final amplifier in Fig. 16-4 is:

a. 0.12 watts   c. 4 watts
b. 8 watts   d. 24 watts

Q14. If the final amp stage is 75% efficient, the output power will be 3 watts.

a. true   b. false

Q15. If Q1 in Fig. 16-4 were operating class B, collector current

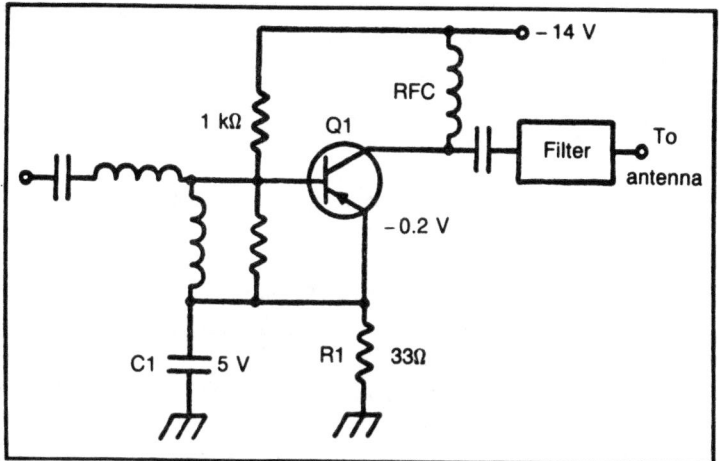

Fig. 16-4. Communication electronic circuit for Q13, Q14, and Q15.

would occur about 25% to 35% of an input cycle.

    a. true   b. false

Q16. PWM stands for:

    a. Power With Modulation
    b. Pulse Width Modulation
    c. Press When Modulating

Q17. The Clarke belt satellites are about 22,000,000 miles above the equator:

    a. true   b. false

Q18. The average power output of a satellite C-band transponder is:

    a. 1/2 watt   c. 50 watts
    b. 5 watts   d. 500 watts

Q19. The frequency band for C-band TVRO downlink transponders is:

    a. 3700 to 4200 MHz   c. 60 to 80 MHz
    b. 11.7 to 12.2 GHz   d. 0.950 to 1.450 GHz

Q20. The band of frequencies allotted to C-band or k-band sat-ellite transmission is how wide?

a. 24 MHz   c. 500 MHz
b. 240 MHz   d. 50 GHz

Q21. The parabolic (or other) dish surface of a TVRO system serves in a similar manner as:

a. a reflector on a U/V TV antenna
b. the driven elements on a TV antenna
c. an rf amplifier
d. a waveguide in a radar transceiver

Q22. TVRO receivers are basically radios which receive, detect, and modulate video and audio and send it out to a TV receiver. The type of signals received from the satellites are:

a. AM video, FM audio
b. FM video and FM audio
c. AM video and AM audio
d. a special dithering process is used that is neither AM nor FM

Q23. Critical adjustments that are made in aiming a TVRO dish, on a polar mount, are:

a. elevation, azimuth, and declination
b. elevation, focus, and latitude
c. focus, elevation, and geo-synchronous orbit
d. elevation, declination, and North-South alignment

QUIZ ANALYSIS

You will note that the quiz covered only four of the available journeyman options. The four covered were Industrial, Biomedical, Computer, and Communications. These questions will give you a sample of the material in those options, which is somewhat unique to those areas of electronics. The remaining options, Radio-TV, Audio Hi-Fi, MATV, and VTR, have been touched on throughout the other chapters in this book. Today it is difficult for technicians to be experts in each specialty area of the profession. To be speedy in repair work a TV technician, for instance, needs years of experience. They not only must know basic electronics well, but the products and new circuits call for constant study and refamiliarization. In addition, the unusual phenomena, difficult parts procurement, customer conflicts and the need for knowledge of business truths all present such a volume of mental requirements that few have any time remaining in which to pursue study of other option areas. Many technicians have a great desire to get into communications electronics, or computer electronics but they realize that more time is already needed for further study of their own electronic products. It's the same with computer technicians: many find that the proliferation of products and the innovations in circuit and component design make it difficult just to keep up with the single product series to which they are assigned. Little time is left to become involved with other areas of electronics, even as a hobby.

Technicians are encouraged, as professionals, to do their best to become familiar with the other option areas. With only knowledge of a single product line, the opportunities for employment elsewhere diminish. A factory man who runs only one production machine for years likewise has no chance to change companies or positions within that company. Technicians can become experts on one brand of computer or radio and then find that they are complete strangers to rf work, industrial controls, communications, signal distribution, VTR, wireless telephones, or other brands of computers or radios.

With this in mind, the ETAI certification program encourages broader understanding of the various electronics specialties. That is one reason the highest certification level is the Masters Program. The ETAI Master Certification program requires the ability to pass each option of the exam program. Master technicians are able, without great amounts of refamiliarization, to shift from a position in one option area to another, in their same place of employment, or at another firm. They are also able to better direct service operations in companies that are involved in several different kinds of electronics products.

ETAI also has a Senior Certification program. It encourages presently certified technicians with eight or more years experience to become certified as a Senior CET, or to become recertified if already a CET. The object here is to verify that a technician has become an expert in his/her field. The test requires an 85 percent score to pass at the Senior level.

In this chapter, questions give some insight into the type of questions you may find later when you take the journeyman portion of the certification exam. Of course, as an Associate you will be continuing your studies in the specialty you have chosen. Hopefully, you will also find great value in having knowledge of the other phases of electronics.

INDUSTRIAL ELECTRONICS

The SW1 switch in *Question 1* makes contact, which causes the relay contacts to close—both CR1-A and CR1-B. So long as CR1-A is closed it will keep current flowing through CR1 and thus keep the contacts closed. Once the circuit is opened, by removing the 12 V (perhaps by turning off an on/off switch) the relay de-energizes, the contacts open up and the light goes off. Part of the difficulty with industrial electronics is that unless you work with it regularly you may not recognize some of the symbology and notations. Note the relay contacts look like capacitors in other symbology and the relay does not show the "coil of wire" symbol familiar to other areas of electronics.

In *Question 2* (Fig. 16-1), when A and B are equal voltages the CR1-B contacts must be closed and the lamp is lit unless the 12 V supply is missing. Assuming the 12 V is as shown, with the contacts open, A will be + 12 V with respect to 0 V reference. B will be at the potential of the minus side of the 12 V supply or 0 V.

Question 3 explains the purpose of the CR1-A contacts. This allows SW1 to be a momentary, low-power contact switch, rather than a toggle or rotary mechanical switch. In high-power circuits, SW1 could be a smaller control-panel button switch while the relay could be located elsewhere closer to the main power and the activated device, perhaps a light bulb or motor.

The symbol in *Question 4 a* is that of a thermal cutout type of circuit breaker. This is one of several fuse/breaker types found in industrial electric/electronic drawings. The ordinary current overload circuit breaker is often presented as in Fig. 16-5.

Fig. 16-5. Industrial symbol for current-overload circuit-breaker.

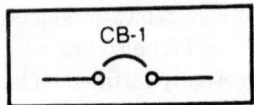

The thermal cutout depicted in *a* of *Q4* shows the added heating element symbol, which confirms that it is heat that causes the circuit breaker to open. The symbol in *Q4 b* is a fuse. In industrial work this style of fuse is a carry-over from the physical appearance of the cartridge fuses so common in electrical work. Two other symbols are also in common use today for fuses (Fig. 16-6) F1 is normally a glass-enclosed wire while F2 is a fusible resistor, usually wire-wound.

The symbol in *Q4 c* is a control valve such as is used in the process-control industry to change the flow of steam, air, or fluids. Today such devices are directly controlled by computers which sample many important locations in manufacturing processes. Petroleum refining, insulation manufacturing, paper making and many others use control devices. Pressures, levels and temperatures are monitored and compared in these systems. Transducers like *c* are then caused to open or close in exact amounts necessary to optimize the operation for maximum efficiency and safety.

The symbol for a generator is shown in *Q4 d*. Since alternators, starters and motors are similar in appearance the G is used to positively identify that the device is a generator.

Q4 e is a Triac. A single SCR can be used in a dc circuit for many purposes. An SCR used in an ac circuit cuts off 1/2 of the waveform, as in Fig. 16-7b. A Triac behaves like back-to-back SCRs connected as in Fig. 16-8. Triacs and SCRs can be used in heavy current circuits while being controlled by a gate signal much smaller than the controlled current.

Item *f* is the symbol for a photodiode in *Q4*. The photodiode must have a trigger. This comes as an outside light source. Arrows pointing *in* indicate a semiconductor device that is activated by light. Arrows pointing *out* indicate the device produces light.

BIOMEDICAL ELECTRONICS

Defibrillators produce a large voltage shock, which is used to stop fibrillation in the human heart. If the heart does not restart by itself attempts must be made to restart it. A capacitor is used to build up the charge prior to medical personnel releasing the

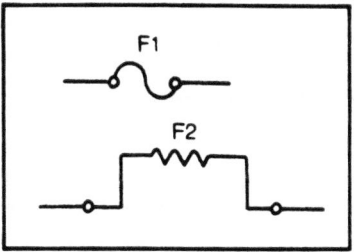

Fig. 16-6. Two symbols for a fuse.

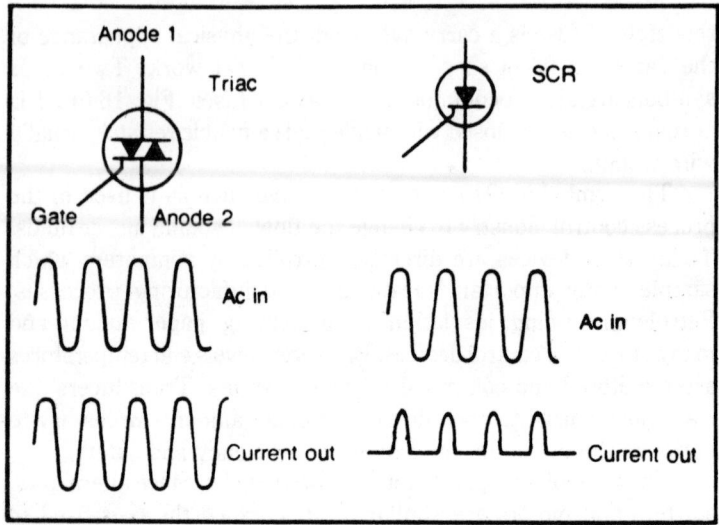

Fig. 16-7. Thyristors.

charge across the patient's chest. ECGs or electrocardiographs receive a signal from the body corresponding to heart beats. The print out of these signals is called an electrocardiogram. Echoencephalographs use acoustical signals in a radar-like manner to show conditions in the brain tissue. The answer to *Question 5* is *b*.

Building wiring codes call for the high side of an ac line to use the black wire. The low or neutral side uses the white wire and the conduit or other grounds are connected to the green third wire

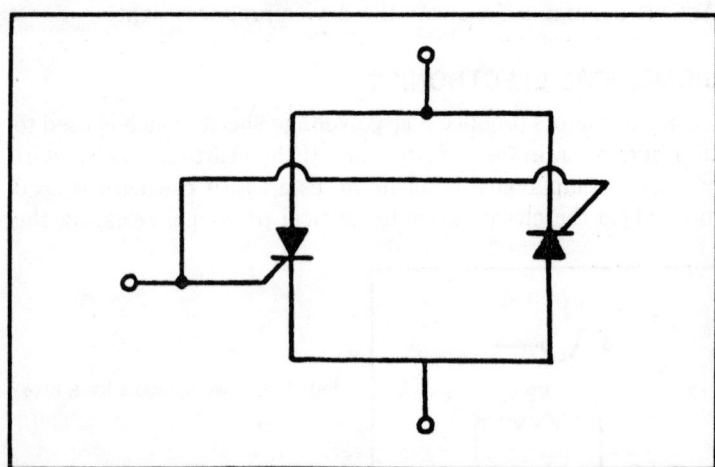

Fig. 16-8. SCR equivalent for a triac.

as in *Question 6*. Some cables do not use a green wire. Instead they have a single bare copper wire to join all the outlet and conduit grounds. Properly wired equipment, when plugged into a properly wired wall socket will have exposed metal tied to the green or ground wire.

An Electrocardiograph needs to reproduce very low frequencies—the heart beat rate. So the 0.05 to 100 Hz band must be reproducible. In *Question 7*, then, item *g* matches answer 5.

An EEG (electroencephalograph) is a recording of the neural activity of the brain, brain waves. Item *h* matches answer 1. Renal is the term used to refer to kidneys. So item *i* matches answer 3.

Ten microamps is the level of leakage current set as a maximum for medical equipment. While that is quite small, it must be realized that medical equipment may be inserted under the skin and therefore the patient is many times more susceptible to shock than he would be with the skin acting as a partial insulator. Tachycardia is the term given to heart speed that is faster than normal.

In electrosurgery 500 to 600 watts of rf may be used. The method is to ground the patient using a large metal plate, thus distributing the skin contact over a large area of the body. That is one electrode of the series circuit. The other electrode is the actual surgical probe. Since the probe has a very small contact point, the current density is great at the probe tip and rf surgery cutting can take place. The large surface where the body is contacted to the plate causes very low current density and thus no harm to the patient in that area by the series current.

The initials LIS stand for Line Isolation System in *Question 8*. Some hospital rooms are connected to the power line through a 1:1 isolation transformer such as you might be using on your electronics service bench. In addition to isolation from the ac power line, the system is hooked to alarms which sound if any neutral or ground wire fault occurs.

COMPUTER ELECTRONICS

The truth table in *Question 9* is used to show how the gate will react to various combinations of logic levels at the two (or more) inputs. You should become familiar with truth tables for all of the gates. Since some gates have more than two inputs, you might now work out your own truth table for a 3-input AND gate and then similar tables for the other gates until you are easily working with truth tables.

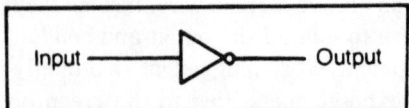

Fig. 16-9. Inverter.

Question 10 concerns the NOT gate. Figure 16-9 shows the NOT gate symbol. A NOT gate merely inverts the signal. If it has + 5 volts on the input, then the output is 0 V, and vice versa.

In *Question 11* the emitter current is a combination of the collector and the base currents. Therefore I_E must be the largest current. Often we ignore the base current in quick calculations, as it is small in relation to the collector current.

In a 4-bit binary numbering system as in *Question 12*, the far right digit is the least significant. The next from the right is the 2's digit, the second from the left is the 4's and the leftmost is the 8's digit.

$$
\begin{aligned}
0000 &= 0 \\
0001 &= 1 \\
0010 &= 2 \\
0011 &= 3 \\
0100 &= 4 \\
0101 &= 5
\end{aligned}
$$

(Answer *c* in *Q12*)

COMMUNICATIONS ELECTRONICS

The input power is the power being consumed by the circuit. The power in this case is the − 14 volts being supplied to the collector and base circuits in Fig. 16-4 times all the current through the emitter resistor. This is 0.2 V/.33 ohms. The current is then known (0.6 amps). If P = E ×I then 14 ×.6 = 8.4 watts for the correct answer to *Question 13*.

Question 14 is false. Of course, if you figured question 13 wrong, you will also get this wrong. The wattage out is only 75% of the input power in this case, or 6.3 watts.

Class B operation is conduction in the tube or transistor for 1/2 of the input cycle. Class A is conduction during the entire cycle. Class C has been used in transmitters as it is more efficient. Class C operates only on the peaks of the cycles—perhaps on 25 percent of each cycle—allowing the development of the entire cycle in the output inductance and antenna circuits. *Question 15* is therefore false.

236

Pulse width modulation in *Question 16* is one of many types of modulation used to carry intelligent information in radio transmissions. There are over two dozen forms of radio emissions, such as CW for continuous wave, FM for frequency modulation and so forth. Each has been assigned designations such as A0 for a steady, unmodulated carrier, A1 for ON/OFF CW telegraphy, A3 for AM, etc. PWM has a designation of P3e. Communications technicians should have a knowledge of the various types of modulation and their designations.

TVRO ELECTRONICS

TVRO technology burst on the scene and quickly became the 'ultimate' form of communications in the late 70's. Unlike broadcast radio and TV, as we have known it since the early half of the century, satellites can reach practically every location in the world. Reception is not hampered by 'line of sight' problems, ghosts, or interfering E-layer skip. Tiny signals are transmitted in such a way that near perfect reception is possible. The cost for all the necessary electronics and hardware can be the same as the cost of a common U/V antenna and tower installation. Yet, satellite reception provides over 100 different channel choices, with the promise of more to come. In addition, crystal clear broadcast radio stations from thousands of miles across the continent are available.

Technicians install this communications equipment and provide service. Just about every type of electronics background is helpful. Satellite electronics involve robotics in positioning the dish from satellite to satellite and in setting the angle of the tiny antenna in the feed horn. Computer memory and programming is used to store channel frequencies, stereo channel mode and frequencies, antenna polarity, and satellite positions, and to automatically tune mechanical and electronic adjustments. Antenna, video, TV, MATV, and audio experiences are assets in servicing TVRO.

The Clarke belt (see Fig. 16-10) where satellites can maintain geo-synchronous is 22,247 miles above the equator. This means that *Question 17* is false, answer *b*. The satellites use solar cells to power as many as 24 transponders. They use hydrazine thrusters to maintain their correct position and attitude in the belt. They are expected to have fuel and solar cell capability for 10 or more years of service. They travel from West to East at about 8,000 miles per hour, which allows them to appear stationary with respect to the surface of the earth. With only five to ten watts of power, per tran-

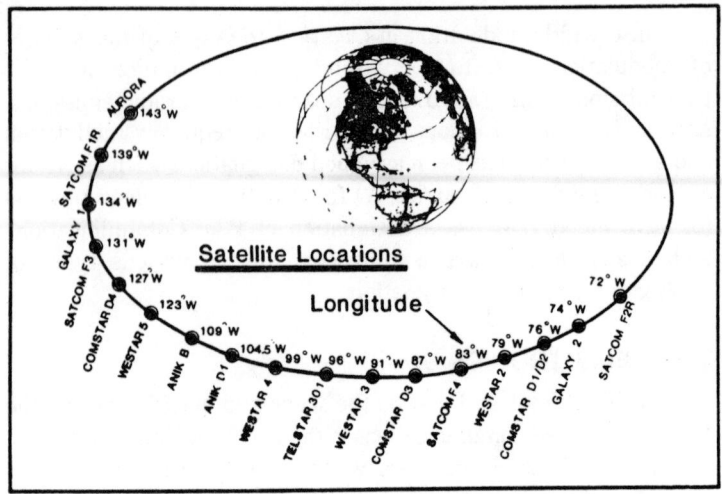

Fig. 16-10. The Clarke belt.

sponder, little signal would appear at any ground location if the transponder antenna radiated in every direction, or in a 360 degree horizontal plane like earthbound TV stations. The satellites beam their signals in tight cylinders, or cones, to specific land areas (primarily to North America in the early 80's). By concentrating the transmitter power thusly, a five- to ten-watt transmitter produces the same signal in its 'footprint' as if it were an ordinary 500-watt radio station. This is described as effective radiated power. Some transponders beam to the U.S. mainland, then have two smaller and tighter beams aimed at Alaska and Hawaii. The Moreles satellite is aimed at Mexico. Intelsats satellites beam signals to Europe and Africa.

Transponders for C band receive uplink signals at 5.295 to 6.425 GHz (X band). They convert this frequency and retransmit it to earth at 3.7 GHz to 4.2 GHz (C-band). The answer to *Question 19* is *a*. There is also a Ku band (part of the k band of 10.9 to 36 GHz). Most C band transponders have 12 vertically polarized transponders which are 36 MHz wide. In addition to the 36 MHz they have a 2 MHz guard band (40 MHz total). With 20 MHz left over, this makes for a 500 MHz band of frequencies used for all 24 channels. Answer *c* for *Question 20*. (In addition to the 12 vertically polarized channels there are also 12 horizontally polarized channels). By using opposite polarity and shifting V or H channels 20 MHz higher or lower in frequency, the 24 channels are used in the same spectrum as the original 12 vertical channels and no channel interference is experienced. Channel one frequency is 3700 to 3740 GHz, channel 24 is 4160 to 4200 GHz (with guardbands). See Fig. 16-11.

The metal reflector of the dish system acts like the reflector elements on an ordinary U/V TV antenna, bouncing the signal back into a three inch hole at the focal point, into a feed horn. Answer *a, Question 21.* Inside the feed horn is either a small rotatable antenna, about one inch long, or in dual polarity systems, the signal is channelled directly to a pickup probe at the entrances of the two 90-degree-mounted low-noise amplifiers. Whether the first active electronic unit is called LNA, LNB, LNSB, LNF, or other abbreviation its function is to amplify the tiny signals in the same manner as a radio amplifies AM, FM, or TV signals.

Early TVRO receivers used a separate converter (called a downconverter) to lower the 3.7 to 4.2 GHz signals to 70 MHz. Seventy MHz (about the frequency of broadcast TV's channel 3) is easily transported over ordinary RG 59 coax for a distance of over 100 feet. The signal is fed into the TVRO receiver, which demodulates one channel at a time from its FM format, deemphasizes it and converts the video and audio through a modulator to a signal identical to that sent to TV sets from ordinary broadcast TV (FM audio and AM video). The answer to *Question 22* is *b.*

Modern receivers use a 'block' system of conversion. In this method, the signal is first amplified in the LNA (Low-Noise Amplifier) section, then the entire 24 channels are converted from the 3.70 to 4.2 GHz range to (most commonly) 950 to 1450 MHz.

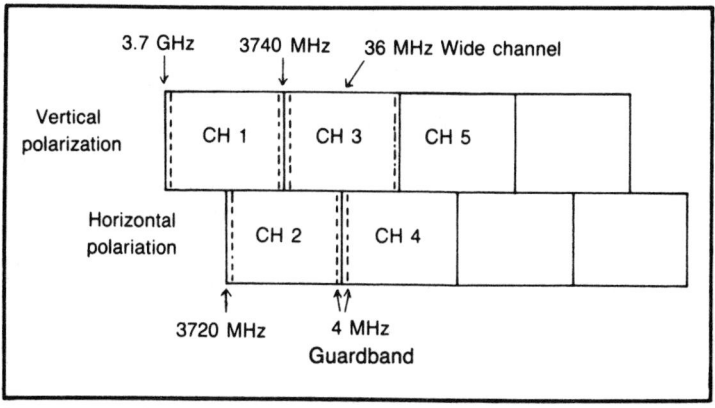

Fig. 16-11. Horizontal and vertical polarization and channel displacement by 20 MHz.

In the receiver, the 24 channels are converted one at a time to 70 MHz. The FM modulated 70 MHz is then demodulated as baseband video and stereo audio, or remodulated to either channel 3 or channel 4 rf for TV reception.

Early earth stations used angle-iron mounts for the dish which could be rotated East and West, or, up and down. These two adjustments were called azimuth and elevation and eventually this type of mount was named the AZ-EL. With only one or two satellites of interest, the AZ-EL worked fine. However, with a number of satellite choices there was a need to move along the entire Clarke belt to view different programming. The polar mount was developed. It used only one motor (or hand crank) driving a telescoping push shaft to move the dish on a pivot across the entire belt of satellites available in North America. This method made it simple

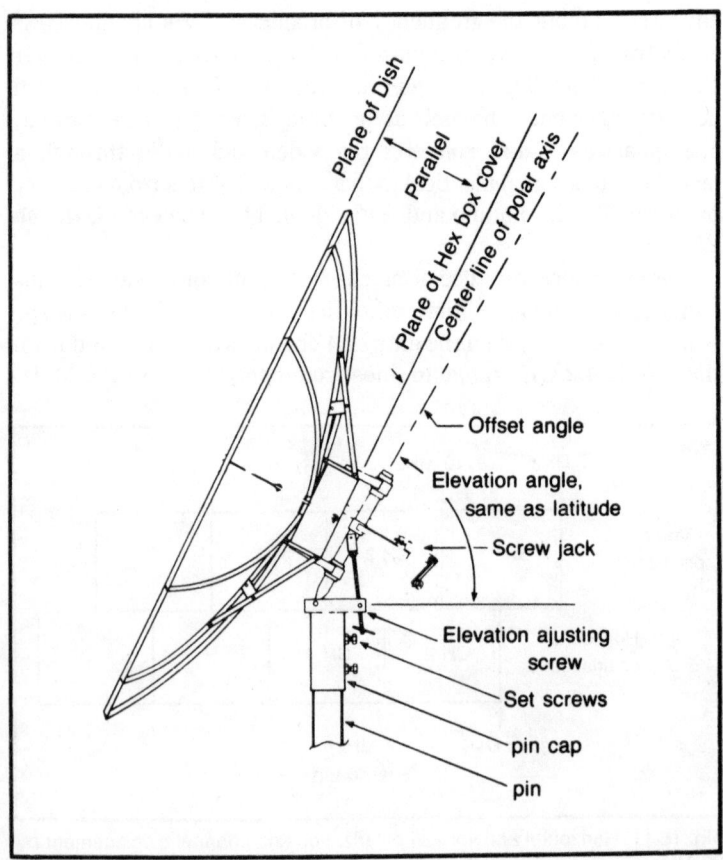

Fig. 16-12. Dish terminology.

to use a numerical control sensor to accurately program satellite positions for easy location like Fig. 16-12.

The early mount movement was accomplished with a hand crank (screw jack). It was replaced with a manually-operated East-West motor-drive. That evolved into an East-West drive with an LED position readout. This made it simple to return to the exact same satellite position previously noted. Then programmable positioners, that required only the inputting of a two digit satellite abbreviation to move to a different satellite, were made. Today, many receivers also contain all the positioner electronics and are computer controlled. They have the ability to remember separate stereo formats and frequencies; polarity and satellite positions; and can prevent unauthorized channel or satellite reception. More than one receiver can be utilized while aimed at a single satellite, with either receiver able to select any of the 24 available channels, or video or audio presentations.

Technicians must be expert in aiming the dish. There is no room for errors of even 1 percent. A 1 percent error in the perpendicularity of the pole on which the dish is sitting, or in the declination angle, or in elevation will result in no reception. A misadjusted focal point between dish and feed horn opening will cause unwanted sidelobe reception and reduced signal or snowy, sparkly video. Any obstructions to a clear view of the sky will reduce the signal. Water particles are a problem, the signal at 4 GHz acts much like light. Moisture causes a diffusion, perhaps even a cancelling action. Tiny sap-filled branches will cause many dBs of signal loss. Even tree branches, out of boresight but close by, will cause a cancelling action making a 10-foot dish perform like an eight-foot dish.

In Fig. 16-13 you can see that if your dish were located at the equator, you could merely rotate it from East to West with the face of the dish horizontal to the ground. You could then aim at each satellite. But, on either side of the equator the offset angle becomes important. If the dish is moved down from horizontal to an angle equal to the latitude of that location, the dish would be aimed parallel to a line from the center of the earth through the equator and it would miss intersecting the satellites directly above the equator. So a declination offset adjustment must be added to the dish face in addition to the elevation angle. In Fig. 16-13 see the dotted line without declination offset and then with declination offset to give the solid line to the satellite, also see Fig. 16-12 again.

Because dishes are rarely manufactured to exact tolerances,

241

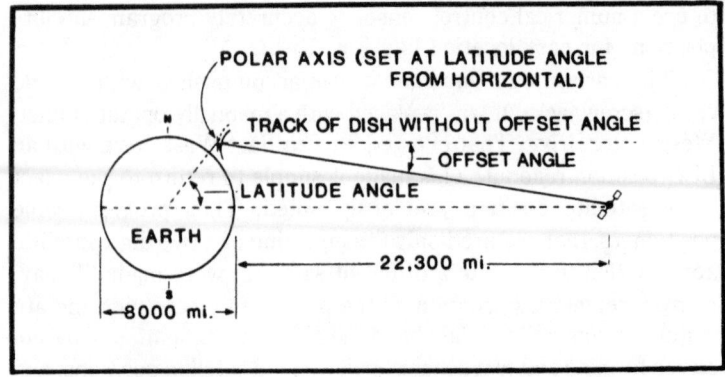

Fig. 16-13. Dish aiming.

setting elevation to the precise angle, declination to its precise offset, and having a pole perfectly perpendicular seldom gives a perfect picture. Additional 'jogging' of elevation is needed. Sometimes the pole and dish mount fit sloppily and need shims. Elevation must be peaked using a signal strength meter or carefully watching the picture. If focus isn't exact it must be reset. If all these are correct but the polar bar on which the dish mount pivots isn't pointing exactly North (to the North Star) only a few satellites will be received. Some technicians make the adjustments using a TV or signal meter right at the dish. Others use walkie-talkies between the receiver/TV and the dish. Answer *d* is correct in *Question 23*.

About 10 percent of the installations are in the path of terrestrial interference caused by microwave telephone frequencies which come from AT&T and other terrestrial communications companies. Test equipment and filters to lessen the problem are available and may range from simple built-in 60 or 80 MHz receiver filters, to outboard units, waveguide-tunable cavity type traps. Mesh fencing may sometimes be needed to shield the dish from microwave interference.

ADDITIONAL READING

Bose, Keith W.: *Aviation Electronics*, Howard W. Sams, 1977.

Buchsbaum, Walter H.: *Buchsbaum's Complete Handbook of Practical Electronic Reference Data*, Prentice-Hall, 1978.

Buckstein, Edward J.: *Electronics for Medical Personnel*, Howard W. Sams, 1972.

Buckstein, Edward J.: *Introduction to Medical Electronics*,

Howard W. Sams, 1973.

Carr, Joseph J.: *CET License Handbook*, TAB BOOKS, Inc., 1974.

DeMarre, Dean A. and David Michaels: *Bioelectronics Measurements*, Prentice-Hall, 1983.

Gottlieb, Irving M.: *Power Supplies, Switching Regulators, Inverters and Converters*, TAB BOOKS Inc., 1984.

Kanter, Elliott S.: *Servicing Electrocardiograph*, Howard W. Sams, 1975.

Kanter, Elliott S.: *Servicing Biomedical Equipment*, Howard W. Sams, 1974.

Mahoney, Timothy J.: *Industrial Solid-State Electronics Devices and Systems*, Prentice-Hall, 1979.

Pearman, Richard A.: *Power Electronics*, Reston Publishing Co., Inc., 1980.

Pearman, Richard A.: *Power Electronics Solid State Motor Control*, Reston Publishing Co., Inc., 1980.

Spooner, Robert B., Ph.D.: ed. *Hospital Instrumentation Care and Servicing for Critical Care Units*, Instrument Society of America, 1977.

Answer Key

Chapter 1

1. a	3. c	5. b	7. a	9. b
2. a	4. a	6. c	8. b	10. c

Chapter 2

1. a	6. b	11. b	16 a. AB	f. 0
2. b	7. a	12. a	b. X	17. c
3. c	8. a	13. d	c. $\underline{G+H}$ K	18. d
4. d	9. a	14. d	d. $\overline{A}$ + BC	19. a
5. b	10. c	15. b	e. 1	

Chapter 3

1. c	10. a = x	b. *157,000 Ohms*
2. c	b = z	c. *157 Ohms*
3. c	c = y	14. b
4. a	11. b	15. b
5. b	12. a. *318 Ohms*	16. a
6. a	b. *318,741 Ohms*	17. c
7. b	c. *0.003 Ohms*	18. b
8. b	d. *31,847 Ohms*	19. b
9. a	13. a. *3,140,000 Ohms*	20. c

Chapter 4

1. c	3. b	5. b	7. c	9. d
2. a	4. d	6. c	8. a	10. a

| 11. b | 13. b | 15. a | 17. b |
| 12. a | 14. c | 16. d | 18. b |

Chapter 5
| 1. d | 3. d | 5. b | 7. a | 9. c |
| 2. d | 4. a | 6. a | 8. a | 10. b |

Chapter 6
1. d	5. a	9. b	13. b	17. d
2. c	6. d	10. b	14. c	18. b
3. a	7. b	11. a	15. b	
4. a	8. d	12. c	16. a	

Chapter 7
1. a	6. d	11. a	3-q
2. d	7. b	12. d	4-o
3. d	8. a	13. b	5-n
4. d	9. b	14. 1-p	6-r
5. b	10. c	2-m	7-s

Chapter 8
1. a	5. d	9. c	13. a
2. d	6. b	10. b	14. c
3. a	7. b	11. d	
4. a	8. a	12. d	

Chapter 9
1. b	5. b	9. b	13. a
2. a	6. d	10. c	14. d
3. a	7. b	11. c	
4. a	8. a	12. a	

Chapter 10
| 1. d | 3. a | 5. c | 7. b | 9. a |
| 2. b | 4. c | 6. b | 8. d | 10. d |

Chapter 11
| 1. b | 3. b | 5. b | 7. a | 9. d |
| 2. a | 4. d | 6. b | 8. d | 10. a |

Chapter 12
| 1. b | 3. d | 5. a | 7. d | 9. d | 11. d |
| 2. b | 4. b | 6. b | 8. d | 10. c | |

Chapter 13
| 1. d | 7. a-4 | 8. a-3 | c-2 | 14. c |
| 2. b | b-3 | b-4 | d-1 | 15. b |

3. a	c-2	c-2	10. b	16. b
4. a	d-1	d-1	11. d	
5. b	e-5	9. a-3	12. d	
6. d	f-6	b-4	13. a	

Chapter 14

1. a 4. d 7. a
2. a 5. b 8. d
3. c 6. d 9. a

Chapter 15

1. c 5. b 9. a 13. c 17. b 21. a
2. b 6. c 10. a 14. b 18. a 22. a
3. d 7. a 11. b 15. c 19. b
4. b 8. d 12. a 16. b 20. a

Chapter 16

1. b   d-3   h-1   9. a   15. b   21. a
2. b   e-2   i-3   10. a 16. b   22. b
3. a   f-4   j-2   11. a 17. b   23. d
4. a-5 5. b   k-6   12. c 18. b
   b-6 6. a   l-4   13. b 19. a
   c-1 7. g-5 8. a   14. b 20. c

Appendix

The following is a listing of certification administrators. Administrators, like other people, move from time to time and forget to put our ETA, International test office on the list of places to send a forwarding address. If a listed administrator fails to respond to your request, please check with the Director of Certification whose office is listed below. Also, if no administrator is listed near your location please let the director know of your interest and he will make every effort to locate an official to administer an exam for you.

> ETA, I Director of Certification
> PO Box 1258
> ISU Station
> Ames, Iowa 50011
> (515) 294-5060

The Defense Activities Non-Traditional Education Support group makes ETAI tests available to military personnel by agreement with ETAI. Military personnel interested in certification should contact their DANTES test officer to make arrangements for taking the exams. DANTES test officers that have requested exams are listed in this appendix.

BELGIUM
DANTES
Samuel J. Alderete, TCO
Army Ed. Cntr.
NSSG (US)
Chievres
APO, NY 09088

ENGLAND
DANTES
D.J. Riley, Jr. MSgt., USAF
NCOIC Ed. Svcs.
7274 ABG/DPE
Bedfordshire
APO, NY 09193

Banu S. Churchill, TCO
20 CSG/DPE
Oxfordshire
APO, NY 09194-5000

Shirley J. Johnson
Ed. Svcs. Officer
Dept. of the Air Force
Hdqs. 513th Combat Support
Group (USAFE)
Suffolk
APO, NY 09127

CANADA
Heikki Thoen, CET
7475 Sherbrooke St. W.
Montreal, Quebec H4B 1S4

Ken Arner
Radio TV & Comp. Elect.
Northern Inst. of Tech.
Box 3003
Prince Albert, Saskatchewan
S6V 6G1

Gordon H. Bjornson, CET
c/o Bjornson Electronics, Ltd.
1564 Agnew Ave.
Victoria, British Columbia
V8N 5M5
604-477-4830

Ray Pierce, CET
1-1202-300 Regina St. N.
Waterloo, Ontario N2J 3B8
745-7128

GERMANY
DANTES
Dorothy Pulliam
Army Ed. Cntr.
Katterbach/Heliport
Ansbach
APO, NY 09326

Charles A. Adimaro, GS-12
Community Education Dir.
Army Ed. Cntr.
US Milcom Activity
Aschaffenburg APO, NY
09162

L.A. Chartier
Dept. of the Army
US Military Comm. Activity,
Augsburg
Sheridan Army Ed. Cntr.
APO, NY 09178-0505

John Lenahan, TCO GS-11,
DAC
Army Ed. Cntr.
Bad Kreuznach
APO, NY 09111

John McLaney
US Army, Berlin
G3 Ed. Branch
Army Ed. Cntr.
Andrews Barrack, APO, NY
09742-5003

Maureen Nesta
Test Control Officer
Army Ed. & Trng.
Giessen Depot
APO, NY 09169

Karen Rische, TCO
Army Ed. Cntr.
Grafenwoehr
APO, NY 09114

Levoy Achenbach
Army Ed. Cntr.
Kleber Kaserne
c/o 189th PSC
Kaiserslautern
APO, NY 09227-3799

Ruth Freiseis, TCO
Army Ed. Cntr.
Neureut, Kaserne
Karlsruhe
APO, NY 09164

Mary L. Blackwell, GS-9
Guidance Counselor
Army Ed. Cntr.
3rd BN., 84th FA
Artillery **Kaserne**
APO, NY 09176

Steven White
Army Ed. Cntr.
Landstuhl Post, Box 37
APO, NY 09180

Nancy L. Ray
Dept. of the Army
Mainz Military Comm.
Finthen Ed. Cntr.
Finthen Army Airfield
APO, NY 09185

Bernadette A. Hassfeld, TCO
Army Ed. Cntr.
Sullivan Barracks
Mannheim
APO, NY 09086-3877

Philip Jones or John Marinos
DANTES Test Examiner
Army Ed. Cntr.
Wiley Barracks, **New Ulm**
APO, NY 09035

Kurt E. Modest
Box 5512
Ramstein
APO, NY 09012

Cindy Montgomery
Rhein Main AFB Ed. Cntr.
435 CSG/DPE
APO, NY 09057

Beth Jackson
Testing Administrator
52 CSG/DPE (USAFE)
Spangdahlem AB
APO, NY 09123

John Devlin
Wiesbaden Ed. Cntr.
AETV-WSB-EDC
APO, NY 09457

John H. Peet
DAC, GS-12
Army Ed. Cntr.
Wilaflecken
APO, NY 09026

Commander
Army Ed. Cntr.
USMCA-WORMS
Worms
APO, NY 09058

Lawrence Grosser
Guidance Counselor
Ed. Serv. Branch
Dept. of the Air Force
Hdqrs. 26th Combat Support
Grp. (USAFE)
Zweibrucken
APO, NY 09860

GREECE
DANTES

Jeffrey Z. Wilbur, GS-12
7206 AB GP/DPE
Athens
APO, NY 09223

Stephen B. Kimble
DANTES TCO
Dept. of the Air Force
Hdqs 7276 Air Base Group
(USAFE)
Crete
APO, NY 09291

Susan Kakavas
US Naval Comm. Sta.
Ed. & Trng. Office
Nea Makri
FPO, NY 09525

GUAM
DANTES

Mary N. Johnson
Navy Campus Office
Box 142, NCWP
FPO SF, CA 96630

HAITI
Temporary

Julio Racine, Director
Ecole Professionnelle Sainte
Trinite
Margaret Woodbury Strong
PO Box 857
Port-au-Prince, Haiti

ITALY
DANTES

Isobel Clay or Joanne
Franceschina
8th Support Group
Army Ed. Cntr.
Leghorn
APO, NY 09019

Jim L. Tabor, Capt. USAF
DANTES TCO
Dept. of the Air Force
2181 Communications Squadron
(AFCC)
Box 101
Naples
FPO, NY 09520

A.M. Quattrone
DANTES TCO
Ed. Cntr.
Naples
FPO, NY 09524

Harry Austin, GS-12
Army Ed. Cntr.
HQ 22 ASG & USMCAV
Attn: TCO
Vicenza
APO, NY 09221

JAPAN
DANTES

Masaaki Hirayama
DANTES TCO
US Marine Corps
Joint Education Office
US Marine Corps Air Sta.
Iwakuni
FPO Seattle, WA 987764-5001

Barbara Walton
DANTES TEST Cont. Officer
Dept. of the Navy
Naval Ed. Trng. & Support
Cntr.
Navy Campus Office
US Fleet Activities
Yokosuka
FPO Seattle, WA 98733

KOREA
DANTES

Joseph A. Aul
Army Ed. Cntr.
West Camp Casey
2nd AG Co., 2nd Infantry Div.
Tongdachon-Ni
APO, San Francisco, CA
96224-0310

Laddie Broz, DAC GS-11
Army Education Center
Hqs. 23rd Support Group
Pyongtaek
APO SF, CA 96271-0164

Alpha O. Scott, SSgt. USAF
NCOIC/ESO REP
Education Services Office
6170 CSS/DPE
Suwin
APO, San Francisco, CA 96461

OKINAWA
DANTES

Joseph Butler, GM-13
18 CSW/DPE
Kadena
APO, SF 96239-5000

PANAMA
DANTES

Commander
193rd Infantry Brigade
Attn: Education Center
APO Miami, FL
34004-5000

PHILIPPINES
DANTES

Harry King
Test Control Officer
3CSG/DPE
Luzon
APO SF, CA 96274

SAUDI ARABIA
DANTES

Diana Jensen
US Embassy
Education Counselor
US/S
Riyadh
APO, NY 09038

SCOTLAND
DANTES

James Onderdonk
Navy Campus
US Naval Support Activity
Hoyloch
FPO, NY 09514-0008

SPAIN
DANTES

Margot Espinosa
Ed. Specialist
Navy Campus for Achievement
US Naval Sta., Box 2
Rota
FPO, NY 09540

TURKEY
DANTES

Commander
528th USAAG
Attn: AESE-AT-ED
Istanbul
APO, NY 09380

Ozgul Onen, Civ.
DANTES
Dept. of the Air Force
HDQ 7241st & ABG (USAFE)
Izmir
APO, NY 09224

Education Center
Attn: TCO
USAFS-SINOP
Sinop
APO, NY 09133

UNITED STATES of AMERICA
ALABAMA

Baby L. Hall, SET
P.O. Box 209
Deatsville, AL 36022
826-4325

Kenneth M. Hornsby, CET
304B John Street
Tallassee, AL 36078

Harold L. Coomes
Electronics Instructor
John M. Patterson State
  Technical College
3920 Troy Highway
Montgomery, AL 36116
205-288-1080

DANTES

Paula Johnson
Education Service Officer
AMSMI-TT-E
Bldg 32-22
Redstone Arsenal, AL
35898-5192

ALASKA
DANTES

Elizabeth Tucker
Navy Campus Advisor
Box 5215 NAVSTA
Adak
FPO Seattle, WA 987791
907-592-8135

Kathy Bonner
Army Ed. Cntr.
Attn: Tesring Section
Bldg. 659
Ft. Greely
APO Seattle, WA 98733

Sarah J. Shores
Comm. Officer
USCG LORSTA **Port Clarance**
VIA: Nome, AK 997762-9993

ARIZONA

Dr. Goodwin Petersen, CET
148 Sierra Grande
Sierra Vista, AZ 85635

DANTES

Joan Paredes GS-09
Ed. Services Office
836 MSSQ/DPE
Davis-Monthan Air Force Base,
AZ 85707-5000

Richard Davis
Dept. Of Air Force
Headquarters 832 D Combat
Support Group (TAC)
Luke AFB, AZ 85309

Harold R. Hall, GS-11, TCO
US Army Education Center
Headquarters Fort Huachuca
ATTN: CCH-PCA-PSE
Fort Huachuca, AZ 85613

TCO Daniel Leone
82 ABG/DPE(AF)
Williams AFB, AZ
85240-5615

ARKANSAS

Gayle Clover, CET
R.R. #1, Box 323 A
Conway, AR 72032
501-565-0983

CALIFORNIA

Bob Derby
DeVry Institute
12801 Crossroads Pkwy. S.
City of Industry, CA 91744
213-699-9927

C.P. Johnson
Long Beach City College
4901 E. Carson St.
Long Beach, CA 90808

Clifford Hansen, CET
Westgate TV-Stereo Serv.
Center
Hamilton Square
841 West Hamilton Avenue
Campbell, CA 95008
379-7670

Daniel C. Harley, CET
United Western Electronics
21775 Hwy. 18, Bldg. B4
Apple Valley, CA 92307
619-247-9512

Earven F. Horton, CET
21845 Mission Boulevard
Hayward, CA 94541
415-537-2628

Walter Nelson, CET
859 1/2 W. Ave. 1
Lancaster, CA 93534

Robert Paynter, CET
Academy of Business College
2007 0 Street
Sacramento, CA 95814

Earl Snyder
21008 South Rd.
Apple Valley, CA 92307
619-247-8620

DANTES

John Adkins, Sr.
Test Cont. Officer
93 CSG/DPE
Castle AFB, CA 95342

Glen Blezak
Commander, National Training
Center
Attn: AFZJ-PTT-E(ITEC)
Fort Irwin, CA 92310-5000

Lloyd Bumpas
Training Officer
Naval Comm. Sta.
Stockton, CA 95203

J. Cruz
NCFA Office
Bldg. 25
Naval Air Sta.
Moffett Field, CA 94035

Dennis R. Hale
Senior Education Spec.
NAS Lemoore
Trng. Bldg. A, Wing Z, Rm. 218
NAS Lemoore, CA 93245

Michael Koester
22 Combat Support Group/DPE
Education Center #0536
March AFB, CA 92518

Carlos Marletto, Jr.
Navy Campus
Naval Sta. Bldg. #8, Rm 212
Long Beach, CA 90822
213-547-6173

R.A. Miller
Joint Ed. Cent.
MCAS El Toro
Santa Ana, CA 92709-5010

Hal Novic
DANTES TCO
Naval Air Sta.
Point Magu, CA 93042

Leah Ritchie
Education Specialist
CBC Navy Campus Office
Port Hueneme, CA 93043

Francis Rohrer
Naval Ed. & Trng. Support
Cent.
Navy Campus Area, Pacific NW
Bldg. 18
Naval Air Sta.
Alameda, CA 94501-5025

Joan Schleicher
63 ABG/DPE
Norton AFB, CA 92409

George Teague, Jr. GS-12
Dept. of Air Force
323 ABG/DPE
Mather AFB, CA 96555-5000

Valerie Woods
Education Center
ATFL-TP-P
DLI/FLC
Presidio of Monterey, CA
93940

Army Education Center (ACES)
AFZW-CA-ED Attn: Test Hall
Fort Ord, CA 93941-5610

TCO Navy Campus Office
PO Box 24
Bldg. 610, Naval Air Sta.
North Island
San Diego, CA 92135

COLORADO

Fred Bantin, CET
Technical Division
AIMS Community College
P.O. Box 69
Greeley, CO 80632
303-426-7267

Alan B. Greager, CET
P.O. Box 38
Nucla, CO 81424
303-864-7358

David Reynolds, CET
Lake Arbor
8221 Newland Circle
Arvada, CO 80003

CONNECTICUT

Pat Carangelo, CET
584 Gilbert Avenue
Hamden, CT 06514
203-248-2854

Albert Marcarelli, CET
Connecticut School of
Electronics
586 Boulevard
New Haven, CT 06519
203-624-2121

DISTRICT OF COLUMBIA

Pentagon Education Center
Rm. 3C147, Pentagon
Washington, DC 20310-6400

FLORIDA

John Bracher, CET
2268 Atlantic Boulevard
Jacksonville, FL 32207

Jim Clower, CET
1515 Morningside Dr.
Mt. Dora, FL 32757
904-343-1141

Charles Couch, Jr., CET
1305 N.E. 7th Ter.
Gainesville, FL 32601
904-376-3580

B.H. Flowers
RCA International Service Co.
POB 4308 Antigua
Patrick AFB, FL 32925

Edward Guary, CET
1110 N.E. 4th Avenue
Ft. Lauderdale, FL 33304
305-463-2998

Dennis L. Miles
Pinellas Vocational Technical Institute
6100-154th Ave. No.
Clearwater, FL 33520
813-535-4590

Theodore Riener, CET
9840 S.W. 23rd Terrace
Miami, FL 33165
305-226-5519

United Electronics Institute
James Russell, CET
Louis Saunders, CET
Henry Stephens, CET
1802 N. Trask
Tampa, FL 33607

Thomas Zelenski
9623 8th Ave.
Orlando, FL 32824

DANTES

Andrew Bayes
Head, Program Development
DANTES
Pensacola, FL 32509-7400

Vicki L. Dunn, GS-9
Alt. Test Control Officer
Education Svcs. Office
56 CSG/DPE (TAC)
MacDill AFB, FL 33608-5000

Jean Fleming
Senior Ed. Specialist
Department of the Navy
Naval Ed. & Trng. Support
Cntr.
Navy Campus Field Office
Bldg. 26, Box 157
US Naval Air Sta., Cecil Fld.
Jacksonville, FL 32215

Frank Paradiso, GS-11
DANTES Test Control Officer
Dept. of the Navy
Navy Campus Education
  Center
Bldg. 2089
Naval Training Center
Orlando, FL 32813

Frederick Voight
Navy Campus Bldg. 506
NTTC Corry Sta.
Pensacola, FL 32551

Commanding Officer
USCG Loran Sta.
PO Box 387
Malone, FL 32445

GEORGIA

William Bowman, CET
Walker Technical School
Box 185
Bicentennial Lane
Rock Springs, GA 30739
404-764-1016

Frank Boyd
3511 Rushing Rd.
Augusta, GA 30906
404-796-6900, Ext. 295

Harry Buswell, CET
Chemistry Dept.
Georgia Tech
Atlanta, GA 30332
404-894-4017

Roy Chastain, CET
NGA Tech-Voc School
Electronics Department
Burton Road
Clarkesville, GA 30523
754-3131

Richard L. Harris
Rt. 1, Box 174
Trion, GA 30753
404-764-1016

Robert Jewett, CET
1803 McDowell Street
Augusta, GA 30904
404-736-6065

Hershall Lawhorn, CET
1013 Main Street
Perry, GA 31069

Dorman McDonald, CET
3411 Norwich Street
Burnswick, GA 31520
265-5181

Pat Reilly, CET
Augusta Tech
3116 Deans Bridge Rd.
Augusta, GA 30906
404-796-4979, Ext. 286

Edward Thurman, Sr. CET
Rt. 4, Box 2217
LaFayette, GA 30728
404-764-1016

DANTES

Brenda G. Allen
Test Control Officer
2853 ABG/DPE
Bldg. 905, Rm. 157
Robins AFB, GA 31098

Gloria Chandler
Education Division
Attn: ATZH-DTE
Ft. Gordon, GA 30905-5070

Herbert Cooke GS-11
Navy Campus Ed. Cntr.
Bldg. 1030
Naval Submarine Base
Kings Bay, GA 31547

William E. Hodges, TCO
Army Education Center
Hq 24th Inf Div (Mech) & Ft.
Ft. Stewart
Fort Stewart, GA 31314-5144

HAWAII
DANTES

Christine Hoban
DANTES TCO
P.O. Box 61 Naval Station
Pearl Harbor, HI 96860

Education Center
ATTN: H. Oshiro
15th Air Base Wing
Hickam AFB, HI 96853

Harold D. Saurer
Navy Campus Ed. Spec.
NAVCAMS EASTPAC
Bldg. 63
Wahiawa, HI 96786

IDAHO

Jack Bennett, CET
1602 North 4th
Coeur D'Alene, ID 83814
208-664-5177

Glen Brusse, CET
970 Lusk St.
Boise, ID 83706
208-344-8376

Vernon Honey
10 Canyon Dr.
Middleton, ID 83644
585-3728

Paul R. Jansson, CET
600 East Columbia
Meridian, ID 83642
208-888-7377

Melvin Quale, CET
1730 Kimberly Road
Twin Falls, ID 83301
208-733-4910

Francis True, CET
1516 Addison Avenue, E.
Twin Falls, ID 83301

ILLINOIS

Dick Bridgeman, CET
DeVry Inst.
566 Norman Rd.
Bolingbrook, IL 60439
321-953-1300 Ext. 280

Eddie Lane, CET
1501 Honeysuckle
Champaign, IL 61820
312-356-6996

Norman Miller, CET
Kaskaskia College
P.O. Box 1266
Centralia, IL 62801
618-533-4111

Robert J. Petzing, CET
AVC Electronics
1411 Washington Road
Washington, IL 61571
309-444-2033

Don Thorne, CET
4357 N. Milwaukee St.
Chicago, IL 60641

DANTES

Ms. Jane Ellsworth
Army Education Center
Building 2
Fort Sheridan, IL 60037

INDIANA

Gene Adair, CET
IV Tech
4475 Central Ave.
Columbus, IN 47203

O. C. Brown, CET
413 Mockingbird Dr.
Jeffersonville, IN 47130
282-7787

Ed Bussick, CET
2325 Chester
Richmond, IN 47374

Ed Carroll, CET
115 E. Sumner Ave.
Indianapolis, IN 46227

Robert E. Drake, CET
2320 Evergreen
Bloomington, IN 47401
812-332-6453

Richard L. Glass, Sr. CET
R.R. 3, Box 564
604 N. Jackson
Greencastle, IN 46135
317-653-3849

Ralph Greer, CET
Indiana Voc. Tech. School
1534 W. Sample St.
South Bend, IN 46619
219-289-7001-Ext. 245

Grover Harvey, CET
R.R. #8, Box 11
Greenfield, IN 46140

Leon Howland, CET
4624 E. 10th St.
Indianapolis, IN 46201
317-357-4575

Charles Willliam Lenhart, CET
R.R. #1, Box 61
Hanover, IN 47243
812-866-4980

Larry Lowey, CET
Indiana Voc. Tec. College
7377 S. Dixie Bee Road
Terre Haute, IN 47802
812-299-1121

Thomas Peck, CET
Brewsters TV
1401 Convert Ave.
Evansville, IN 47714
477-7630

Elbert Powers, CET
139 N. Griffith Boulevard
Griffith, IN 46319
923-1550

Dick Schultz, CET
3741 S. Meridan
Indianapolis, IN 46217
317-545-2231

Leonard Smith
Electronics Department
Connersville Area Vocational
School
815 Oak St.
Connersville, IN 47331

Jim Steele, MaCET
2325 Chester Blvd.
Richmond, IN 47374

Charles Workman, CET
P.O. Box 156
Versailles, IN 47042
812-689-5253

IOWA

Donald Anker, CET
Fisher Controls
Marshalltown, IA 50158
515-754-3982

John Arbuckle
Electronics Instructor
Des Moines Area Comm.
College
2006 Ankeny Blvd.
Ankeny, IA 50021
515-964-6277

Ronald H. Brehmer, CET
North Iowa Tech. Coll.
Highway 18 West
Sheldon, IA 51201
712-324-2587

Ron Crow, MaCET
ERI Electronics Shop
131K Coover Hall
Iowa State University
Ames, IA 50011
515-294-5060

Del Menke, CET
3526 Fair Avenue
Davenport, IA 52806
319-386-1154
North Iowa Area Comm. Coll.
Cliff Salmons, CET
Bernard Bookland
500 College Dr.
Mason City, IA 50401

Doug Watson
Kirkwood Comm. Coll.
6301 Kirkwood Blvd. SW
P.O. Box 2068
Cedar Rapids, IA 52406
319-398-5695

KENTUCKY

Ed Burton
Tom Devine
1025 Amsterdam Rd.
Covington, KY 41011

DANTES

R.D. Black
Continuing Ed. Office Branch
USAARMC and Ft. Knox
Bldg. 1174
Ft. Knox, KY 40121-5000

LOUISIANA

Gary M. Raymond, CET
6330 Pratt Drive
New Orleans, LA 70122
947-9120

DANTES

Roy Kinney
Dept. of the Air Force
2 CSG/DPE
Barksdale AFB, LA 71110

MARYLAND

Jesse B. Leach, Jr., CET
231 N. Hammonds Ferry Road
Linthicum, MD 21090
301-789-8668

David Windisch
6218 Mossway
Baltimore, MD 21212
301-668-2676

Stephen Wursta, CET
607 Crestwood Lane
California, MD 20619
301-863-9046

MASSACHUSETTS

Ted Soboscienski, CET
26 Carriage House Path
Ashland, MA 01721

DANTES

Ens. Graham
Educational Service Officer
USCGC Hamilton (WHEC-715)
427 Commercial St.
Boston, MA 02109

D.L. Parr
Commanding Officer
USCGC Chase (WHEC-718)
427 Commercial St.
Boston, MA 02109

J.S. Puntino
Commanding Officer
USCG Loran Station
Nantucket Island
Siasconset, MA 02564

259

Brooke E. Winter
Lieutenant Junior Grade
U.S. Coast Guard
Commanding Officer
USCG Loran Station
Nantucket, MA 02554

Lt. Paul Wolf
US Coast Guard Group
Woods Hole, MA 02543

MICHIGAN

Bob Bellers, CET
4800 E. Huron River Dr.
Ann Arbor, MI 48106
313-973-3316

John Brittan
Lake Michigan College
2755 E. Napier
Benton Harbor, MI 49022

Bruce Miller, CET
Mott College
Flint, MI 48503
313-LE8-1631-Ext. 221

Robert A. Del Raso, CET
4334 Byron Cntr.
Wyoming, MI 49509
616-538-3170

Jesse Ramey, CET
932 Eugenia
Mason, MI 48854
517-676-5271

Walter Reilly, CET
901 Cleveland St.
Lansing, MI 48906
517-489-5325

DANTES

David G. Britten
DANTES Test Cont. Off.
Michigan Army National Guard
Recruiting and Retention Office
2500 S. Washington Ave.
Lansing, MI 48913

Dennis Hickethier
Test Cont. Officer
US Army Ed. Cntr.
(AMSTA-XYB)
US Army TACOMSA-SANG
Selfridge ANGB, MI
48045-5016

Howard W. Spencer
Base Ed. Cntr.
379 CSG/DPE
Wurtsmith AFB, MI
48045-5016

MINNESOTA

John Baldwin, CET
Faribault Voc. Tech. School
1225 SW 3rd St.
Fairbault, MN 55021
332-2423

Stanley Blankenship, SrCET
RR 1, Box 367A
Pine Island, MN 55963
507-356-4293

Robert Brandell, CET
Hennepin Technical Center,
North
9000 North 77th Avenue
Brooklyn Park, MN 55429
421-1397

Jean Captain, SrCET
825-41st Ave. NE
Columbia Heights, MN 55421
612-781-4881

Gene Juelich, CET
Rainy River Comm. Coll.
International Falls, MN
56649

Vincent Lynch, CET
1900 8th Avenue, N.W.
Austin, MN 55912
507-433-7691

Ray S. Pearson, CET
329 W. Faribault Street
Duluth, MN 55803
724-1798

MISSISSIPPI

Robert Arnett, CET
Holmes Junior College
Goodman, MS 39079
601-472-2314

Ted Bogart
Chairman Engineer
Southern Station
USM Box 5172
Hattiesburg, MS 39401

DANTES

Thomas M. Erhardt
Norman Allen
Naval Ed. & Tra. Sup. Ctr. (Atl.)
Navy Campus Field Office
Bldg. 60, Rm. 103
Construction Battalion Ctr.
Gulfport, MS 39501

Glenn F. Ryan, TCO
Tammy Miles
Education Services Branch
Test Control Officer
3380 ABG/DPE
Keesler AFB, MS 39534-5000

MISSOURI

George DeLisle, MaCET
603 NE 73rd Terrace
Gladston, MO 64118

James R. Long, CET
MTS 9623 Charles Rock Rd.
Overland, MO 63114

Vincent J. Lutz, CET, EHF
1546 Sells Avenue
St. Louis, MO 63147
314-381-9944

Terry Stivers
Bailey Tech School
3750 Lindell Blvd.
St. Louis, MO 63108
533-8700 Ext. 331

DANTES

Jim Street
Test Control Officer
Truman Ed. Cntr.
Bldg 499
Ft. Leonard Wood, MO
65473

NEBRASKA

Jim Dutcher, CET
Greely, NE 68842
308-428-3115

Gordon P. Koch, CET
Mid-Plains Voc. Tech. School
I 80 and Highway 83
North Platte, NE 69101
308-532-8740, Ext. 43

Bill Kucera, CET
Central Comm. Coll.
Platte Campus
PO Box 1027
Columbus, NE 68601
402-564-7132

George Savage, MCET
Box 39
Doniphan, NE 68832
402-845-2298

John D. Snyder, CET
3221 S. 45th Street
Omaha, NE 68106
402-397-3000

Bud Sullivan, CET
2620 South 13th
Lincoln, NE 68502
402-476-9037

Eugene L. Young, CET
Central Tech. Comm. College
Box 1024
Hastings, NE 68901
402-463-9811-Ext. 352

NEW HAMPSHIRE

Albert Cloutier, CET
369 Islington St.
Portsmouth, NH 03801
436-9011

DANTES

Albert B. Arrighi, DAFC
Education Center
509 CSG/DPE
Pease AFB, NH 03803-5000

NEW JERSEY

Neil Towey, CET
DeVry Tech. Inst.
479 Green St.
Woodbridge, NJ 07095

Harold Connelly, CET
Cittone Institute
1697 Oak Tree Rd.
Edison, NJ 08820

DANTES

DANTES Test Control Officer
Army Education Cntr
Bldg. 551, Room 23
(Miss Nelson)
Fort Monmouth, NJ 07703

Dept. of Transportation
U.S. Coast Guard
Commander
USCG Group Sandy Hook
Highlands, NJ 07732

NEW MEXICO

DANTES

Jane Shipp, GM-13
Education Services Officer
Dept. of the Air Force
HDQ 1606th Air Base Wing
(MAC)
Kirtland AFB, NM 87117

Leslie Spears
Isabel Campbell
Test Control Officers
Army Education Center
Bldg 464
White Sands Missle Range,
NM
88002-5034

NEW YORK

Charles E. Bechtold
Tompkins Comm. Coll.
170 North St.
Dryden, NY 13053

Michael Brent & Paul Sand
Technical Career Inst.
320 W. 31st St.
New York, NY 10001
212-594-4000-Ext. 280

Richard Hedrick
Harry B. Ward Occupational
Cntr.
970 N. Griffing Ave.
Riverhead, NY 11901

Ralph Herke
Occupation Schools
1833 Dalton Rd.
Lima, NY 14485

James Jumpa
Charles G. May Occupation
Cntr.
Lackawanna Ave.
Mt. Morris, NY 14510

DANTES

J.D. Bagle, Lt. JG
US Coast Guard
DANTES TCO
Coast Guard Air Sta.
Floyd Bennett Field
Brooklyn, NY 11234

Dennis Durand
Commander(PS)
Third Coast Guard Dist.
Governor's Island, NY 10004
Attn: ESO

F.J. Leavitt or Shirley Honsaker
DANTES TCO
416 CSG/DPE
Griffiss AFB, Rome, NY
13441

Lt. J.M. McGuirk
US Coast Guard
830 3rd Ave.
Brooklyn, NY 11232

N. CAROLINA

Wilson Allsbrook, CET
Mitchell Comm. School
West Broad Street
Statesville, NC 28677
704-873-2243

Ricky W. Bean, CET
700 South Fifth Street, EXT
Albermarle, NC 28001
704-982-0980

Ralph Hartley, CET
R.R. #10, Box 901
Hickory, NC 28601
327-6576

Ted Morton, CET
P.O. Box 306
Granite Quarry, NC 28072
704-279-2386

Thomas L. Ruth, CET
1511 Pierson Drive
Charlotte, NC 28205
535-1531

Dorman (Bud) Tatum
944 Davie Avenue
Statesville, NC 28677
704-872-0865

DANTES

John Waters
Base Education Office
Camp Lejeune, NC 28542

**NORTH DAKOTA
DANTES**

Suzanne W. Hunt
321 CGS/DPE
Grand Forks, ND 58205

OHIO

Hal Frutschy, CET
921 29th, NE
Canton, OH 44714

DANTES

DANTES TCO
2750 ABW-DPE
Wright-Patterson AFB, OH
4433-5000

OKLAHOMA

Richard Bartelme, CET
NE Area Vo-Tech
PO Box 825
Pryor, OK 74362
918-825-5555

DANTES

Sue Murphy
Base Ed. Office
2854 ABG/DPE
Tinker AFB, OK 73145

Dept. of the Army
HQ USAFACFS
AZTR-TD(Test Examiner)
Ft. Sill, OK 73503-5000

OREGON

William D.C. Burnett, CET
P.O. Box 451
Lakeside, OR 97449

F.L. Goddard, CET
Box 713
Burns, OR 97720

Al Stratton, Admin
TU & Radio License
4th Flr, La Saor & Ind. Bldg.
Salem, OR 97310

DANTES

Commander
Coast Guard Group Astoria
2185 SE Airport Rd.
Warrenton, OR 97146-9693
Attn: Lt. JG Kirk (Training)

PENNSYLVANIA

Robert Amell, CET
National Ed. Cntr.
5650 Derry St.
Harrisburg, PA 17111
717-564-4112

Stanley Golowski, CET
3614 Orchard Court
St. Lawrence, PA 19606

John Guinan, CET
2178 Joshua Road
Lafayette Hill, PA 19444
215-828-1711

William Hessmiller, CET
1116 Prescott Ave
Dunmore, PA 18512
717-343-7282

Boyd E. Lehman
Admin. Asst. of Adult Ed.
Greater Johnstown Voc.
Tech. Sch.
445 Schoolhouse Rd.
Johnstown, PA 15904-2998

Ronald Lettieri, MET
433 East Drinker Street
Dunmore, PA 18512
717-961-0219

Michael Roscoe
Mercer Co. Area Voc.
Tech. Sch.
PO Box 152, Route 58
Mercer, PA 16137

DANTES

George Zins
Ed. Specialist
Dept. of the Navy
Navy Campus
Naval Station
Philadelphia, PA 19112

PUERTO RICO

Robert Mareno, CET
East 5th 9th St.
Urb Dos Rios
Baymon, PR 00619

S. CAROLINA

William J. Rivers, CET
1451 Bonner Avenue
Columbia, SC 29204

DANTES

T.C. Cary, Jr.
Navy Campus Education
   Center
Bldg. RTC 1, Naval Base
Charleston, SC 29408-9998

SOUTH DAKOTA

Clark Adams, SrCET
409 2nd St. NE
Watertown, SD 57201

DANTES

Ralph S. Miller, DAFC
Test Control Officer
44 CSG/DPE
Ellsworth AFB, SD 57706

TENNESSEE

Donald Bartholomew, CET
P.O. Box 646
Gibson, TN 38338

Larry Haggard, CET
P.O. Box 512
Shelbyville, TN 37160
893-4241

TEXAS

James Berry, CET
Inst. of Elec. Science
Texas A&M University
F.E. Drawer K
College Station, TX 77843
713-779-3880 Ext. 244

Roger Book, CET
Star Route 1, Box 450
Spring Branch, TX 78070
512-885-4476

Alvin Coleman, CET
900 Panola Ct.
Longview, TX 75608
214-737-5314

Dr. Marshall Dean
El Paso Comm. Coll.
Dept. of Electronics
Transmountain Campus
El Paso, TX 79904

D.C. Larson, CET
1308 Aldrich
Houston, TX 77055
713-686-6545

Clay Laster, Instr.
Electronics Dept.
San Antonio Coll.
1300 San Pedro Ave.
San Antonio, TX 78284
512-733-2881

Darris D. Linder, CET
340 South 12th Street
Slaton, TX 79364
806-828-5662

James Richardson
16100 Space Center Blvd #1201
Houston, TX 70062
713-280-8126

David Van Winkle, CET
North Harris Co. Coll.
2700 WW Thorne Dr.
Houston, TX 77073

Ron Witcher
Central Texas College
Highway 190 West
Kileen, TX 76541

DANTES

John Crabb
East Ed. Cntr.
Bldg. 212
Ft. Hood, TX 76544

Dept. of the Navy
Naval Ed. & Test Center
Navy Campus Field Office
250 Bldg. Rm. 114 Code ETS 23
US Naval Air Sta.
Corpus Christi, TX 78419

R.G. Ybarra
Navy Campus Bldg. 1781
Naval Air Station
Kingsville, TX 78363

VIRGINIA

Marion N. Ames, SrCET
725 Bishop Dr.
Virginia Beach, VA 23455
804-499-6111

Curtis E. Anderson, Jr., CET
4814 Conduit Road
Colonial Heights, VA 23834
804-526-3551

Asa Andrews
887 Arnett Dr.
Newport News, VA 23602

Walter R. Cooke, CET
957 North King Street
Hampton, VA 23669
804-723-7578

Donald Crow
7641 Holmes Run Dr.
Falls Church, VA 22046

Jerry Hartley, CET
220 Chesterfield Road
Lynchburg, VA 24502
804-239-4692

John McPherson, CET
P.O. Box 1347
Grafton, VA 23692
804-898-5072

Chuck Mitchell
Kee Business College
803 Diligence
Newport News, VA 23606

Carl B. Rae, Jr., CET
P.O. Box 791
Emporia, VA 23847
804-634-4611

Leon Smith, CET
Blue Ridge Community Coll.
P.O. Box 80
Weyers Cave, VA 24486
243-2461-Ext. 276

James Tetters, CET
2937 East Malden Avenue
Norfolk, VA 23518

DANTES

Roger Alexander
Chief Educ. Serv.
Dept. of the Air Force
Headquarters 1st Combat
Support Group (TAC)
Langley AFB, VA 23665

Kanela M. Gault
Army Ed. Cntr.
Bldg. 1708
Ft. Eustis, VA 23604-5214

William J. Neugebauer
Test Control Officer
Fort Meyer Ed. Cntr.
Bldg. 219
Ft. Meyer, VA 22211-5050

Maria Paulucci
Charles Hobb
Test Control Officers
Navy Campus Afloat Office
Naval Education & Training
Support Center, Atlantic
Bldg. Z-86, Naval Station
Norfolk, VA 23511-6197

Michael R. Rucker
Test Control Officer
Box 999, Naval Sta.
Camp Allen
Norfolk, VA 23511-6798

Carol Thompson
Dept. of the Navy
Naval Ed. & Trng.
Navy Campus Field Office
Bldg. 325
US Naval Air Sta., Oceana
Virginia Beach, VA 23460

WASHINGTON

Robert Eley, CET
125 26th, N.W.
East Wenatchee, WA 98801
509-662-1651

Alfred L. Izatt, CET
2315 Queets
Hoquiam, WA 98550

Herbert Spille, CET
333 N. Elm
Colville, WA 99114
509-684-2461

Dean Thompson
3850 N.E. 95th
Seattle, WA 98115
522-5429

DANTES

Commanding Officer
USCG Support Center
1519 Alaskan Way S.
Seattle, WA 98134
Attn: Lt. JG J.L. Dodds

L. Hanson
David Roberts
Education Technicians
Navy Campus Office
Bldg. 502
Puget Sound Naval Shipyard
Bremerton, WA 93814

N.E. Wicker
Educational Services Officer
U.S. Coast Guard
Port Angeles, WA 98362

WISCONSIN

Duane Busby, CET
2027 Sherman Avenue
Madison, WI 53704

Jacob Klein, CET
3419 Polzer Drive
Wausaw, WI 54401
715-845-6552

Larry Mattioli, CET
Fox Valley Tech Inst.
1825 North Bluemound Drive
Appleton, WI 54913
414-735-5787

Robert H. White, CET
520 Greendale Rd.
Sheboygan, WI 53081
458-7255

WYOMING

Marlin E. Engle, CET
5018 Alcova South
Box 11
Casper, WY 82601

Index

Edited by David Gauthier